FRITZ LEIBER AND
H. P. LOVECRAFT:
WRITERS OF THE DARK

FRITZ LEIBER AND H. P. LOVECRAFT: WRITERS OF THE DARK

Edited by Ben J. S. Szumskyj and S. T. Joshi

WILDSIDE PRESS
HOLICONG, PA • 2003

Fritz Leiber and H. P. Lovecraft:
Writers of the Dark

Published by:

Wildside Press
P.O. Box 301
Holicong, NJ 18928-0301
www.wildsidepress.com

FIRST WILDSIDE PRESS EDITION: 2003

Contents

INTRODUCTION

While Howard Phillips Lovecraft was closing the final chapter of his writing career, Fritz Reuter Leiber was only beginning to open his own. The year was 1936 and Jonquil Leiber, Fritz's first wife, sent a letter on her own initiative to Lovecraft, knowing that her husband had been an avid admirer of his work, ever since his first reading of "The Colour out of Space" and hoping that Lovecraft's presence in Fritz's slow-paced writing career might be the source of inspiration he so dearly needed. Lovecraft replied promptly on November 2 of that year, the seed of an invigorating correspondence, which lasted till Lovecraft's passing.

Through their fruitful letters, Lovecraft directed constructive criticism toward his newly acquired protégé and helped Leiber with his poetry cycle, "Demons of the Upper Air" (Lovecraft at one time considered poetry his primary talent), fiction ("Adept's Gambit"), and general matters of style and research. Leiber stated that Lovecraft was "the chiefest influence on my literary development after Shakespeare," and his early stages of writing fiction (often considered to be between the years 1936 and 1949) support this statement. However, this "Lovecraftian Period" should not be considered analogous to that of Lovecraft's "Dunsanian" period of 1919–21. Lovecraft's influence will not stand out upon first reading; it is only by intentionally looking for this influence that one finds Lovecraft's presence, major or minor as it may be. The influence can be seen by the choice of words, style, mood, and elements weaved in between Leiber's originality.

One series of stories under the spotlight of Lovecraftian influence are the tales of the Fafhrd and the Gray Mouser saga. It is generally known that Leiber forwarded the first draft of the story "Adept's Gambit" to Lovecraft for comment; this draft no longer exists, but Lovecraft's exhaustive letter in which he remarks on it (December 19, 1936) testifies that he found the tale full of promise. This letter shows that Leiber in fact made several minor references to Lovecraft's pseudomythology in the preliminary draft (e.g., Nyarlathotep and Yog-Sothoth); but in the published version these were omitted. Leiber no doubt felt that the tale should stand alone as an original piece, based entirely on his own imagination. It has been recently noted that "The Sunken Land" may be a rewrite of Lovecraft's "The Call of Cthulhu." "Adept's Gambit" itself betrays the influence of that story, even without recourse to explicit references. Consider the following scene:

> And Fafhrd could not speak. His shoulder muscles were contracted as if the weight of the sea were already pressing them down. His mind was

engulfed and oppressed by the ominous presence of sunken Simorgya. Memories of the legends. Thoughts of the black centuries during which sea life had slowly crept and wiggled and swum through the mazes of rooms and corridors until it had a lair in every crack and cranny and Simorgya was one with the mysteries of the ocean. In a deep grotto that opened on the corridor he made out a thick table of stone, with a great stone chair behind it; and though he could not be sure, he thought he distinguished an octopus shape slouched there in a travesty of a human occupant, tentacles coiling the chair, unblinking eyes staring glistening.

Only late in life did Leiber produce an explicit pastiche of the "Cthulhu Mythos"—"The Terror from the Depths." In a letter dated May 24, 1975, Leiber wrote to D. and C. Brown: "In April I wrote THE TERROR FROM THE DEPTHS (22,000), a Lovecraftian novella of the Cthulhu-Mythos sort I once swore myself I'd never write, for [Edward Paul Berglund's] THE DISCIPLES OF CTHULHU…"

Personally, I find this story (along side Leiber's other Mythos tale, "To Arkham and the Stars," which was "written to honor Lovecraft") both worthy and acceptable pieces of fiction, whatever one's view on the Mythos may be. The "Cthulhu Mythos" stories can be examined as follows. If, when if the Lovecraftian element within is extracted, it is able to stand alone as a solid and original story, then it can be considered a creditable work of fiction. That is, if you were to take "Arkham" or "Cthulhu" out of these tales and replace them with a newly created, historical or mythological place and deity, it is a story that does not need the Lovecraftian element within for it to survive. The "Cthulhu Mythos" in general is a flawed genre of pastichism, and a given tale of this type can only be identified as notable if it is able to work without the Lovecraftian additions or if it is able to capture and adopt the moods, style, sense, feeling, and elements Lovecraft mastered so perfectly. Unfortunately, many authors do not meet such criteria; those who do are usually the writers who knew Lovecraft personally through correspondence (i.e., Robert E. Howard, Robert Bloch, Fritz Leiber, and so on). Leiber's two "Cthulhu Mythos" tales can also be described as "fictional memorials." Leiber honoured Lovecraft by writing these stories; and in doing so, he wrote tales that expressed his debt to Lovecraft's arrival in his writing career. In this way, Leiber was saying both thank you and goodbye to a dear friend. If you read "The Terror from the Depths" closely enough, you will clearly realise that Leiber is honouring both Lovecraft (Cthulhu) and Shakespeare (through the father figure) in the story.

Another tale by Leiber (unfortunately not included in this collection) is the novella *The Dealings of Daniel Kesserich*. Although several sources of Lovecraftian inspiration are present in this tale, it is not to be considered a "Lovecraftian" story, as it is more of a novella that incorporates Lovecraft's style and trademark concepts in the midst of Leiber's original and dominant creativity, much like the bulk of the stories written in his "Lovecraftian" period. *The Dealings of Daniel Kesserich* is a story involving science in its most esoteric and unexplainable form. Daniel Kesserich, a God-like scientist who, with his friend, George Kramer, breaks the barriers of the space-time continuum and performs an act that ensures that George's wife Mary is not killed on that fateful day, but at a cost that may be too high, even for love. Weird metaphysical tones and a stroke of the Biblical are ever present within this novella, as well as the slightest echo of Lovecraft's presence.

Onto Leiber's nonfiction. Here you will find some of the best essays ever written on Lovecraft as a writer and as a thinker. Unlike many of Lovecraft's correspondents, Leiber understood and was on the same wavelength as Lovecraft, although he himself has stated that he was not an "altogether uncritical admirer of Lovecraft." His essays projected the hard facts and truth about Lovecraft and gave the reading public insight only a person who knew the man personally could give.

The correspondence between H. P. Lovecraft and Fritz R. Leiber was one of the most insightful in the field of weird literature. Where Leiber gained a mentor, Lovecraft gained a friend, for the two shared the unique ability to master three genres: fantasy, horror, and science fiction. I hope this collection is a door into a world which the two journeyed through profusely and affected one another, in their own special ways. It is one of the most important times in Leiber's life and will hopefully help pave that road to a deserved path of literary and critical analysis.

—BEN J. S. SZUMSKYJ
Melville, Western Australia

H. P. LOVECRAFT: LETTERS TO FRITZ AND JONQUIL LEIBER

[1]   To Jonquil Leiber

66 College St.
Providence, R.I.,
Nov. 2, 1936.

My dear Mrs. Leiber:—

Your enquiry of Oct. 14, after some extremely devious wanderings, has reached me at last; & I must hasten to say how gratified I am to hear of the kind opinion of my fictional efforts held by you & your husband. My pleasure is the greater because of the admiration & appreciation with which I have always regarded the work of your father-in-law. In the earlier years of the century I saw him many times in Mr. Robert Mantell's companies—in parts like Horatio, Iago, Mercutio, Bassanio, Edmund, & Faulconbridge—& delighted in his happy blending of classic traditionalism with the more refined & modulated technique of the present. His Faulconbridge was to me especially unforgettable, and I can still recall across the gulf of years his magnificent rendering of those stirring climactic lines (always prime favourites of mine):

> "This ENGLAND never did—nor never shall—
> Lie at the proud foot of a conqueror,
> But when it first did help to wound itself.
> Now these her princes are come home again,
> Come the three corners of the world in arms,
> And we shall shock them. Nought shall make us rue,
> If ENGLAND to itself do rest but true!"

For a quarter of a century I have associated Mr. Leiber Sr. with these lines, & these lines with Mr. Leiber. It surely pleases me profoundly to know that he has a son & namesake to carry on his tradition, & to find that that son regards my own fantastic attempts with a charitable eye!

. . . .

[Sincerely yours,
H. P. Lovecraft]

[2]   To Fritz Leiber, Jr.

Nov. 9, 1936

My dear Mr. Leiber:

. . . . . Needless to say, your closely analytical remarks on my fiction gratify me immensely—doubly so because your singling out of specific points indicates that I have in certain cases more or less done what I was trying to do. It is vastly encouraging when anyone recognises as clearly as you do the *special direction* of my attempts—the wish to capture some phase of the mystery & terror clinging round the eternal presence & pressure of *the outside* . . . . The mentally & materially inaccessible gulfs of boundless space whose alien worlds & alien laws & values can never be known to us, &

amidst which our earth & solar system & galaxy & conceivable cosmos may form the most negligible, un-typical, transient, & diseased speck. I am tempted to quote from an old article of mine on Supernatural Horror in Literature—where I define my idea of what a weird story must be if it is to form any sort of a serious aesthetic attempt:

"The true weird tale has something more than secret murder, bloody bones, or a sheeted form clanking chains according to rule. A certain atmosphere of breathless and unexplainable dread of outer, unknown forces must be present; and there must be a hint, expressed with a seriousness and portentousness becoming its subject, of that most terrible conception of the human brain—a malign and particular suspension or defeat of those fixed laws of nature which are our only safeguard against the assaults of chaos and the daemons of unplumbed space."

I wish there were a really first-rate writer able & willing to do what I keep on stumblingly attempting—and I am always looking hopefully for the appearance of such. What I miss in Machen, James, Dunsany, de la Mare, Shiel, & even Blackwood & Poe, is a sense of the *cosmic*. Dunsany—though he seldom adopts the darker & more serious approach—is the most cosmic of them all, but he gets only a little way. Another lack which I constantly feel is that of *realism* or *convincing seriousness*. That is, the average weird author is essentially superficial & frivolous in his purpose. He wishes merely to entertain, instead of to reflect potently & artistically those deep-seated human instincts & moods which create & centre around the persistent illusion of violated natural law. Again let me quote from one of my articles—this time a more recent one.

"Atmosphere, not action, is the thing to cultivate in the wonder story. We cannot put stress on the bare *events*, since the unnatural extravagance of these events makes them sound hollow and absurd when thrown into too high relief. Such events, even when theoretically possible or conceivable in the future (as those of a science-fiction tale), have no counterpart or basis in existing life and human experience, hence can never form the groundwork of an adult tale. All that a marvel story can ever be, in a serious way, is a *vivid picture of a certain type of human mood*. The moment it tries to be anything else it becomes cheap, puerile, and unconvincing. Therefore a fantastic author should see that his prime emphasis goes into subtle suggestion—the imperceptible hints and touches of selective and associative detail which express shadings of moods and build up a vague illusion of the strange reality of the unreal—instead of into bald catalogues of incredible happenings which can have no substance or meaning apart from a sustaining cloud of colour and mood-symbolism. A serious adult story must be *true to something in life*. Since marvel tales cannot be true to the *events* of life, they must shift their emphasis toward something to which they *can* be true;

namely, certain wistful or restless *moods* of the human spirit, wherein it seeks to weave gossamer ladders of escape from the galling tyranny of time, space, and natural law."

The writer who comes closest toward creating these (as I view them) reasonable specifications is Algernon Blackwood *in his best moments.* He actually analyses & reproduces faithfully the details of the persistent human illusion of—& out-reaching toward—a misty world of vari-coloured wonders, transcended natural laws, limitless possibilities, delighted discoveries, & ceaseless adventurous expectancy. But he labours under three severe handicaps—an undistinguished journalistic style, a recurrent tendency to lapse into mushy sentimentality & infantile namby-pambyism of the most painful sort, & a credulousness regarding "occultism" which causes him to employ now & then a professional mediumistic jargon of woefully weakening effect. Of all Blackwood's voluminous output, only a golden minimum represents him at his best—but that is such a marvellous best that we can well forgive him all his slush & prattle. It is my firm opinion that his longish short story "The Willows" is the greatest weird tale ever written (with Machen's "The White People" as a good second.) Little is said—everything is suggested! Of his books, "Incredible Adventures", "John Silence", & "The Centaur" form the cream—though "Julius LeVallon" & the juvenile "Jimbo" are not to be despised. But heaven deliver us from crap like "The Extra Day", "The Wave", & (ugh!) "The Garden of Survival"! Next to Blackwood, Poe stands first in basic seriousness & convincingness—though his themes tend to centre in limited manifestations of the terrestrially gruesome, & in sinister twists of morbid human psychology. In *total effect* he probably *transcends* Blackwood, & indeed all rivals; that is, what he *does* tell is told with a potent art & daemonic force which no one else can even approach. One of my favourites is M. P. Shiel, whose "House of Sounds" is a marvellous tour de force comparable to its obvious Poesque prototype "The Fall of the House of Usher". The first half of Shiel's novel "The Purple Cloud" is also a veritably stupendous piece of work.

As for style & realism—I'm glad you think well of my stuff in that respect. I've always held two cardinal principles regarding weird fiction: that the structure & rhythm of the language should reflect & promote the tension, menace, gloom, dreamlike quality, cumulative mood-flow & climactic suspense of the theme; & that an air of absolute realism should be preserved (as if one were preparing an actual hoax instead of a story) *except* in the one limited field where the writer has chosen to depart (in a way consistent with actual human psychology & illusion as reflected in experience & folklore) from the order of objective reality. I haven't always succeeded in embodying these principles to the extent I'd like, but at least I've tried to do so. Commercial "pulp" fiction repudiates them altogether—glibly piling on extravagant marvels without the least relation to mankind's natural myth-making tendencies, & phrasing everything in a brisk, happy, casual, cheerful style which would be enough to kill even a good idea or plot! It is too bad that no magazine market for seriously intended weird fiction exists. One must either make the book good (which I can't) or be satisfied to have things in the pulp rags—whose editors accept a really serious story more in spite of its real merits than because of them. I see red every time I think of the number of finely-endowed fantaisistes who have been lured away from sincere writing by the rewards of the commercial magazine market. Most of them soon become so steeped in the cheap methods, puerile psychology, shoddy values, & stock characters & events of popular thrillerdom that they could never "come back" as serious literary artists even if they wished. The salient example of this kind of thing is of course *A. Merritt*—of "Moon Pool" fame. Azathoth, what a genius gone wrong! Today dishing out the usual sort of formula-tripe—yet now & then revealing flashes of descriptive or evocative power which tell the sort of titan he might have been had he elected to follow the path of Machen or de la Mare instead of that of the *Argosy* hacks!

.....I'm glad the geographical colour in some of my tales seems to ring true—as it ought to, since I was born less than a mile from this spot & have lived hereabouts all my life save for a trivial two-year period in New York City. The realistic side of me has always tended to soak up local atmosphere, & I think it's well to keep true to the characteristics of a region even when the place-names are fictitious. I like a solid, definite, visualisable, and even identifiable background behind certain types of weird fiction. In the "Haunter of the Dark" I accurately described my own abode (the old Georgian house on the hill), the westward view from my desk window (I'm looking at that darkly-looming church right now—though I regret to say it lost its spire through a lightning-stroke last summer), the general layout of Federal Hill, & various minor Providentiana. However—Arkham, Miskatonic University, Kingsport, Innsmouth, Dunwich, & certain other oft-mentioned localities (as well as poor old Abdul & his hideous *Al Azif* which the Byzantine monk Theodorus Philetas translated into Greek circa 900 A.D. as Τo Νεκρο-voμικov) are of the bubble or boil-like nature of those lands you have dreamed about—these places having slight & harmless intrusions on Massachusetts geography. Roughly speaking, "Innsmouth" (an exaggeration of quaint decaying *Newburyport*) is supposed to be on the marshy coast a bit south of the real Newburyport. "Arkham" (an idealisation of *Salem* plus a wholly gratuitous college) is a good deal south of that—a few miles inland up the imaginary river "Miskatonic", but not as far inland as Ipswich & Essex. "Kingsport" (a "stepped-up" reflection of ancient & fascinating *Marblehead*) is at the mouth of this imaginary river—bearing about the same relation to "Arkham" as that borne by the real Marblehead to the real Salem. "Dunwich" is far inland—near the headwaters of the mythical "Miskatonic". It is a sort of synthesis of the picturesquely retrograding Wilbraham country (near Springfield) with certain characteristics of southern Vermont. I have always been fond of maps & geographical details (I've drawn a map of "Arkham' to keep my local references straight), & my lifelong antiquarianism has caused me to lay zestful stress on historic backgrounds & traditional architectural minutiae. My one real avocation & hobby is the imaginative pursuit of the past—especially of the 18th century, to which I have a curious sense of inextricably belonging—& my chief avenue of century-spanning is the architectural. My supreme joy is to visit old cities where rich deposits of early architecture remain. I have never been to Europe (for ill-health in youth & bad finances in later life have severely circumscribed my travels), but I *have* managed to see—& absorb from the point of view of comparative architecture & antiquities—most of this continent's venerable cities from Quebec on the north to St. Augustine & Key West on the south & New Orleans & Natchez on the west. *Charleston* is probably my favourite of all cities.

I note your reference to the late Charles Fort—some of whose books I have read with extreme interest. I don't think his scraps of bizarre reporting made out much of a case against accepted science, but I do tremendously admire the zeal & consistency of his delvings. He makes magnificent weird source-material! As for *melancholy*—it is indeed, as old Burton realised, a fruitful field for exploration. My own temperament, I should say, is one of *scientific indifferentism* (the solar system is a meaningless drop in an unknown & purposeless cosmos, but what the hell of it?) rather than melancholy—though I suppose my constant interest in fantasy expresses a subconscious dissatisfaction with objective reality which is not far from certain phases of the genuine article. I've always been fascinated, by the way, by that engraving of Dürer's.

Well—I must apologise for this possibly boresome burst of verbosity! But genuine devotees of the weird are rare. I regret the geographical circumstances which postpone oral conversation.

. . . .

[Sincerely yours,
H. P. Lovecraft]

[3]   To Jonquil Leiber

Nov. 13, 1936

Dear Mrs. Leiber:—

. . . . . Pray convey my appreciative regards to "the governor" & tell him I shall be on the lookout for those two films. I can imagine how well he must interpret the austere Thomas Jonathan Jackson. As a native of the Mother Land, you would surely be in a position to appreciate his magnificent delivery of that "King John" finale! Those lines—& Mr. Leiber Sr.'s rendering of them— reach me with a certain extra closeness because I am nearer to Old England on the paternal side than is the average Yankee. Whilst my maternal lines are of ancient Rhode-Island stock dwelling hereabouts for the past 2½ to 3 centuries, my own paternal grandfather was born in Devonshire in 1815; reaching these shores only in 1827 when brought by his father after a sort of financial annihilation. And the wife he later married was only one generation from

"This royal throne of kings, this sceptred isle,
This earth of majesty, this seat of Wars,
This other Eden, demi-paradise,
This fortress built by Nature for herself
Against infection & the bond of war,
This happy breed of men, this little world,
This precious stone set in the silver sea,
Which serves it in the office of a wall
Or as a moat defensive to a house,
Against the envy of less happier lands,
This blessed plot, this earth, this realm, this ENGLAND."

Add to this the circumstance the fact that I am a natural-born antiquarian, prone to revel in dreams & pictures of the past & to cherish ancestral things, & one may readily see why it would take much more than a political cleavage a century & a half ago to make me anything but a British colonial at heart! And yet I have never seen Old England, & I do not know whether it will ever be financially possible for me to do so. I envy you the experience of that mouldy castle in Wales—Arthur Machen's enchanted west country "with the ancient woods hanging all about . . . & the wild domed hills, & the ragged land." I long to see the great-boled oaks I dream about, & the grassy ridges that were once Roman roads stretching through the twilight of deep forests.

As for the matter of my years & aspect—I fear the snapshot your husband saw was either very archaic or very flattering. Even "the governor" (who must have realised that an admirer of his old-time Faulconbridge & Edgar could scarcely be a youth today!) underguessed my burthen of greying winters, since as a matter of ruthless fact I shall turn 47 on the 20th of next August. Nearly a semi-centenarian, but with all my teeth, & memory still fairly dependable. The enclosed pair of snaps* (all I can find & rather crude, but betwixt them not wholly unrepresentative) give an idea of the sort of scarecrow I am. I was very glad to hear details of Mr. Leiber's appearance, & hope to gain a pictorial glimpse in the course of time. His combination of physique, features, & genius should carry him far—& I can well imagine the joint pride which you & "the governor" must take in him!

With my best regards to you, & to the Messrs. Leiber junior & senior,
. . . . . .

[Sincerely yours,
H. P. Lovecraft]

---

*One of them includes my young friend Frank Belknap Long, Jun., whose work in W T you & Mr. L. must know. This reminds me to ask whether your household would care for the loan of a collection of snaps shewing what several of the W T authors look like. I'd be very glad to lend any such an array.

[4]   To Fritz Leiber, Jr.

Nov. 15, 1936

My dear Mr. Leiber:—

. . . . . Yes—damn it all!—you are only too correct in deducing that I have not seen your father in his more recent tours as an independent star. I have at times read of his later appearances, but they have never taken place in any city simultaneously with my presence therein. My great grudge against the cinema lies is the havock it has wrought with the stage in all but the largest metropolitan centres. Twenty years ago no company like your father's could possibly have neglected the old Providence Opera House—but today, alas! Indeed, the Opera House was torn down in 1931, & its manager (with a tragic timeliness worthy of the Muse whose temple he had tended) died the following year. Would that some future dispensation might bring a Leiber Lear or Macbeth to one of our still-surviving (if less historic) theatres! My tantalisation at hearing about your father's productions would have been greater had I known that better versions than Mantell's were used. I recall that many used to criticise Mr. Mantell's choice of texts—especially his use of the Cibber "Richard III". (Personally, as a devotee of the 18th century, I forgave that—for what metaphorical periwig-wearer cou'd deem Richard truly himself without such savorous sallies as:

> Th' aspiring Youth that fir'd th' Ephesian Dome
>   (in Greek architecture!)
> Outlives in Fame the pious Fool that rais'd it.

or

> Hence, babbling Dreams; you threaten here in vain;
> Conscience, avaunt, Richard's himself again!
> Hark! the shrill Trumpet sounds, to Horse, away
> My Soul's in Arms, & eager for the Fray!

Certainly, a full or well-edited Lear comes close to forcing the high-water mark of modern (using the adjective in the sense of *non-ancient*) dramas, with its glimpses of the black, sardonic Outside pressing in upon the helpless figures driven before storms both literal & non-literal. Here is the spirit of Aeschylus & Sophocles with something added—& I pity the poor 'debunking' clod who can see in it no more than a petulant dotard backed up by John Dennis's thunder. Not only do the characters & their onrushing fates suggest the background of infinity, but every visual picture contributes to the massed, subtle impression. Man against the Abyss—blind Gloster led up to the edge of the Dover cliffs in a scene which for me conveys the most dizzying picture in all literature . . . . a scene in which your father (& now, I learn, you after him!) spoke those peculiarly potent lines about the crews & choughs & samphire-gatherers. That whole episode of Gloster, blind & deluded (for his own good) as to what is really taking place around him ("Look up a-height—the shrill-song'd lark so far cannot be seen or heard . . . . his eyes were two full means; he had a thousand noses; horns whelk'd, & wav'd like the enridged sea.") is ironically symbolic of man's whole place in the cosmic gulfs. What a picture—a blind old man racked by misery on the edge of a void & helpless to gain even the oblivion he chooses! I was indeed interested to know that you have played Edgar to your father's Lear. Certainly a noble apprenticeship! Speaking of *cutting* Lear—a friend of mine (Samuel Loveman, who now conducts the Bodley Book Shop at 104 Fifth Avenue., N.Y.C.) once went to the opposite extreme & wrote a scene (in diabolically clever Elizabethan language) to be interpolated in the tragedy! Taking the view of Sir Joshua Reynolds & Swinburne that Lear actually refers to the Fool & not to Cordelia (a view which seems doubtful, but which is at least interesting) when he says "And my poor fool is hang'd", Loveman invents a scene which in the play would break up the concluding scene somewhere betwixt the departure of Lear & Cordelia under guard & the subsequent entry of Lear bearing his dead daughter—a scene laid in the forest near the British camp, in which the Fool is brought in as a captive & killed in the presence of Lear & Cordelia, & in which Cordelia is killed before her father's eyes. Lear then departs with Cordelia's body, ready to reappear in the text proper with his memorable lines of anguish. A carping critic might pick flaws in this interpolation—but I would feel proud indeed if I could re-create the Elizabethan atmosphere as well. Loveman also did an interpolated scene for Macbeth—which I had the honour of publishing 15 or 16 years ago when I edited the official organ of the United Amateur Press Association. It pleases me very much to know that Faulconbridge was one of your father's favourite parts—indeed, I might have imagined it from the glow & spirit with which he delivered those memorable final lines. Your own very juvenile handling of the role—or parts of it—must at least have been picturesque—like the performance of the three-year-old hopeful of an English-teacher friend of mine, whose fond papa once discovered him (at a time when "Macbeth" was much under discussion in the household) with an ornate paper-knife (for he had a literal mind!) declaiming very gravely:

> "Ith dith a dagger w'ich I thee before me,
> De han'le toward muh hand? Tum, let me tlut de!"

It has always seemed to me that Faulconbridge is the *principal* character in "King John"—at least, I must say that it is the one which makes the most impression on me. The bluff, wholesome impudence ("And hang a calf's shin on those recreant limbs!") of the youth stands out notably amidst the welter of subtleties & villainies, & he leaves more of a concrete picture with the spectators than does the subtle, moody monarch—pathos, death, & all. At least, with a goodly number of the spectators, whatever be the judgment of the profound & sensitive critic. The least that can be said of Faulconbridge is that it is a nearly *equal* part—like Iago to Othello, or Antony to Brutus.

But I wander far from the weird! Let me return by saying how thoroughly I agree with you regarding Spengler's distinction betwixt the "Faustian" or modern western sense of infinity (which begins with a clearer idea of, & interest in, one's orientation in time & space) & the classical localism & lack of a time-sense. Spengler, I may add, produced a profound impression upon me when I first encountered him a decade ago—and this despite my inability to endorse completely his view of a culture as a quasi-biological organism. His pointing out of the modern time-&-space consciousness as opposed to the Hellenic indifference to long cycles and sequences (when did the Greeks ever think of their world as a momentary dot in an endless line or curve? What mind was it which created conflicts of data in its leading myths, & established as fixed chronological relationships betwixt such cycles of events as the Seven against Thebes, Trojan War, &c. &c.?) gave me almost a *shock,* because it revealed so great a streak of the non-classical in myself, who have always felt so closely akin to the Graeco-Roman as opposed to the mediaeval. Of course I had always recognised my taste for Gothic mystery & shadow as something Northern & definitely *outside* my classic intellectual orientation; but I had not previously felt that this taste was so antithetically *opposed* to the foundations of classicism, & that my fascinated preoccupation with the element of *time* was *so much more than accidentally* differentiated from Hellenic timelessness. Yet I could not help being convinced & impressed—even at the cost of admitting that a dominant part of my personality was non-classical & even anti-classical. Incidentally, this admission involves a sharp cleavage rather than a contradiction, since the purely philosophic side of me—plus a large amount of the aesthetic side—certainly *is* classical. I am a complete materialist in belief—of the line of the Ionians, Leucippus, Democritus, Epicurus, & Lucretius, & such moderns (Hobbes, Condillac, Comte, Dewey, Bertrand Russell, Santayana) as derive from this source. I abhor the mediaeval spirit of faith, dogma, & intellectual mysticism (how weary the exalters of the "great" 13th century—Cram, Chesterton, Belloc, et al.—make me!), & value as man's choicest possession the Greek spirit of free, sceptical enquiry. Moreover, in architecture (the art to which, apart from literature, I am most sensitive), decoration, sculpture & pictorial representation, my tastes run overwhelmingly to the Graeco-Roman (with, however, a parallel fondness for really *fine* Gothic design) & its Renaissance derivations. ("Functional" modernism nauseates me & makes me see red!) All this is joined to a curious *sense of identification* with classic *Rome* . . . . a psychological twist which a superstitious person would attribute to metempsychosis or something of the sort. This feeling—which runs parallel to my still stronger sense of identification with the 18th century, is independent of any intellectual appraisal of Rome on my part. I know damn well that Roman culture was infinitely inferior to its Hellenic source, & can even understand Spengler's passionate indictment of the Respublica . . . . yet not for a second can I emotionally grasp any human event anterior to 500 A.D. except through Roman eyes. Greece is "our" province of Achaia. The Orient is the scene of "our" Mithridatic wars. Egypt is the province which fell to "us" after Actium, & so on. When I run up against a person with a strong anti-Roman bias—like the late Robert E. Howard, who championed the northern barbarians—I feel an almost personal affront. I have not a drop of non-British blood, yet as I cast my fancy backward through time there comes a point when my blood-allegiance breaks, and my sense of identification & quasi-patriotism shifts from the Thames to the Tiber. In a conflict like that of the Saltus Teutober-giensis in A.D. 9 my instinct is not to exult with my blood-kinsman Arminius but to weep like Augustus for the lost legions of Quinctilius Varus. Naturally all this gives me a tremendous & particular interest in *Roman Britain,* where my two personalities, ancient & modern, meet. To think of a forum in Lon-don, of a Roman amphitheatre in Caerleon, & of the Respublica's roads & villas & camps & temples all over my ancestral soil, is intensely & peculiarly gratifying to me. The summit of my delight was reached when I read in the works of the late Arthur Weigall & other recent authorities that evidence now seems to point to the survival of vast amounts of Britanno-Roman & Roman legionary blood (largely Nordic, though, since the army was recruited most numerously in Gallia & Germania) in modern English veins. Thus it be-came a virtually literal certainty that blood forbears of mine have spoken Latin, worn togas, & borne names like C. Ulpius Silvanus, L. Valerius Celsus, P. Vicius Marcianus, A. Aufidius Olussa, L. Martius Senecianus (I quote from actual Britanno-Roman stelae) & so on. What a drama is that of Roman Brit-ain—Britannia Prima et Secunda—& its slow crumbling before the Teutonic onrush! The forts of the "Saxon shore" (some still standing!)—the naval bat-tles & massacres—the withdrawal of support from Rome—the gradual attri-tion & the heroic stands—Artorius, the Comes Britanniae ("King Arthur")—the final fight of Aurelius Candidanus at Durham in 582 A.D.—Ædepol! I don't wonder that Machen reverts again & again to the Britanno-Roman back-ground motif! But I digress. In spite of all this sense of classic identification, I must admit the parallel presence of the opposite element—the feeling of nearness to the great Abyss which my hypothetical ancestors Ulpius Silvanus & Valerius Celsus never had—or having, derived from their Teutono-Celtic tribal stream & not from their acquired Roman culture. You repeat almost verbatim something I have many times pointed out when you speak of the function of religion in assuaging Nordic mankind's impatience of temporal & spatial bounds during ages of belief—& of the need of some substitute when supernatural belief declines. The fact is, I have again & again driven home this point in repelling the charge of inconsistency levelled at me for being a complete agnostic & materialist on the intellectual side, & a confirmed fan-taisiste & myth-weaver on the aesthetic side. I have told my critics that in all probability the reason I *want* to write about circumventions of time, space, & natural law is that I *don't* believe in such! If I *believed* in the supernatural, I would not need to create the aesthetic illusion of belief. Indeed, the super-natural would not seem strange & fascinating to me. I am preoccupied with the invention of a desired thing which I can get *only* through invention. And as for the desire itself—the need to imagine a mastery of the cosmos & a satisfied curiosity anent the black outer voids—I am willing to acknowledge its alienage to the classic stream, & its characteristic position in modern western civilisation as a legacy of the northern blood side—the same Teutonic side which bequeathed us our major political principles & our tacit adoption of the *honour* (= pride in the open dealing of a strong, free man) concept in opposition to the ostensibly accepted (& really Hebraic) divine-will-&-justice concept as a primary motive in ethics.

Your remarks on my favourite writers interest me vastly, & as you now see, form an enlightening commentary on the parallel remarks in my own previous letter. Machen is a master of hints, & certainly holds the true cosmic concept in the back of his consciousness (I'll never forget that pillar raised by Flavius Senilis to Nodens, *Lord of the Great Abyss*), but he was unfortunately strongly affected by the 1890-ism & Stevenson romantic tradition of his youth. He loves stylistic effects & melodramatic climaxes; & now & then his use of coincidence, & of jaunty Victorian mannerisms, vitiates what might otherwise be well-nigh perfect. Then too, as you remark, he is often a bit hasty in having things thrown terrifically into the flames after the merest glance! "The White People" needs no excuses. Even before one read Miss Murray's "Witch Cult in Western Europe" it is disquieting; after such reading, it is diabolical. Or perhaps different temperaments would receive it differently in relation to a knowledge of the anthropological background—some finding its cosmic & sinister implications more profound in the *absence* of specific data about sabbats, estbats, & the like. Anyhow, it's a magnificent evocation of shadows from the abyss. Nowhere else, I think, have I ever seen a *landscape* so endowed with sentient evil as that series of fields through which the child advances toward the ancient wood. That picture—or phantasmagoria—haunts my memory even now. One can envisage meadows like that as meeting-places of the known & the black unknown ... like the remote Scottish island in John Buchan's "Skule Skerry"—"Insula Avium quae est ultima insula *et proxima Abysso*." If I could ever create a landscape like Machen's—or an island like the new Lord Tweedsmuir's—I'd consider that I hadn't written in vain! I think I said that I regard "The White People" as the second-greatest weird story ever written—with Blackwood's "Willows" alone ahead of it.

Your analysis of Blackwood really coincides with my own—though perhaps I am a little more sympathetic toward his serious treatment of the anatomy of our emotional out-reaching toward unreality. I agree that this treatment tends to lose effectiveness when it becomes *visibly scientific* or mixed up with the jargon of occultism—the old Lodge & Doyle & Flammarion & Chevreuil & Richet stuff. But when this acute analysis is concealed—or manifested only in the description of sensations & events (as in "The Willows" & certain of the "Incredible Adventures" ... yea, in "The Centaur" as well, though the *length* of this latter verges on tediousness)—the result is difficult to surpass. Blackwood's discouraging unevenness is his curse. It is fatally easy to misjudge him if one first approaches him through his pseudo-occult chronicles or his infantile sentimental slop. But taking "The Willows", "Incredible Adventures", "The Centaur", the tales (except the first & last) in "John Silence", & such occasional shorts as "The Wendigo", we find a body of weird writing whose authentic power proclaims its creator a master no matter what else he has perpetrated!

Dunsany has a peculiar appeal for me. Casual and tenuous though any one of his fantastic flights may seem, the massed effect of his whole cycle of theogony, myth, legend, fable, hero-epic & dream-chronicle on my consciousness is that of a most potent & particular sort of cosmic liberation. When I first encountered him (through "A Dreamer's Tales") in 1919 he seemed like a sort of gate to enchanted worlds of childhood dream, & his temporary influence on my own literary attempts (vide "Celephaïs", "The Doom That Came to Sarnath", "The Quest of Iranon", "The White Ship", &c) was enormous. Indeed, my own mode of expression almost lost itself for a time amidst a wave of imitated Dunsanianism. There seemed to me to be in Dunsany certain poetic adumbrations of the cosmic lacking elsewhere. I may have read some of them in myself, but am sure that a goodly number must have been there to start with. Dunsany knows a certain type of dream & longing and vague out-reaching natural to the Nordic mind & shaped in childhood by the early folklore and literary impressions afforded by our culture—the Germanic fairy-tale, the Celtic legend, the Biblical myth, the Arabian-Nightish Orientale, the Graeco-Roman epic, and so on. This vision or longing or out-reaching he is able to crystallise in terms of certain elements drawn from all these simple & familiar sources, & the result has an odd universal magic which few can deny. The philosophy behind his work is essentially that of the finer minds of our age—a cosmic disillusion plus a desperate effort to retain those fragments of wonder & myth of significance, direction, & purpose which intellectual progress & absorption in material things alike tend to strip away. Of course Dunsany is uneven, & his later work (despite the different sort of charm in "The Curse of the Wise Woman") cannot be compared with his early productions. As he gained in age & sophistication, he lost in freshness & simplicity. He was ashamed to be uncritically naive, & began to step aside from his tales & visibly smile at them even as they unfolded. Instead of remaining what the true fantaisiste must be—a child in a child's world of dream—he became anxious to show that he was really an adult good-naturedly pretending to be a child in a child's world. This hardening-up began to show, I think, in "The Book of Wonder"—say around 1910. It was very perceptible in "The Last Book of Wonder"—though it did not creep into the plays so soon. A decade later it relaxed slightly in the novels "Chronicles of Rodriguez" and "The King of Elfland's Daughter", but it shews at its worst in the "Jorkens" tripe. Alas that no writer can ever keep up to the level of his best! When I think of Dunsany, it is in terms of "The Gods of the Mountain", "Bethmoora", "Poltarnees, Beholder of Ocean",

"The City of Never", "The Fall of Babbulkund", "In the Land of Time", and "Idle Days on the Yann".

"The Worm Ouroboros" is indeed a familiar friend & cherished possession of mine. What a chronicle of dream! When it was first circulated around 1927 half our gang were swearing great oaths by Koshtra Piurarcha! Some may think the interest flags in spots, but it does not flag for me. It leaves the same massed impression of a gateway to dream (though I do think the supposed setting on Mercury is a bit clumsy) that the best works of Dunsany leaves. Eddie has written other things—a Norse saga called "Styrbion the Strong", & a very recent social allegory of some sort which I haven't seen. But never again has he struck the heights of Ouroboros. Koshtra Piurarcha, alas, can be scaled only once!

You are right in remarking how few can enter into the mood of the cosmically weird. I notice the element of preoccupation with local human concernments which pervades most of the attacks on my attempts. Material with a cosmic angle—in which *phenomena,* not the local inhabitants of a single negligible sphere, are the protagonists—never reaches the average man in the street. He wants something "folksy", as his more homespun representatives frequently express it. I can't seem to cater to that demand. Trends, impacts & adventures of whole culture-streams, millennial cycles of development or decay, clashes of man as a whole with the principle of time or with the terror of the outer dark—these things have always interested me more than individual biography & character-analysis. And who can write effectively or meaningfully if he has to fake an interest? So far as weird fiction is concerned, I always insist that the emphasis be kept on *the wonder of the central abnormality itself.* As I wrote once in an article, any violation of what we know as natural law is *in itself* a far more tremendous thing than any other event or feeling which could possibly affect a human being. But Holy Yuggoth, how the old man runs on! . . . .

   [Sincerely yours,
       H. P. Lovecraft]

[5]   To Fritz Leiber, Jr.

                                                    November 18, 1936
My dear Mr. Leiber:—

    . . . . . I was much interested in your allusion to the meteor-deposited strangers, the burrowing lizard-men, & the Creatures of the Peaks. I wonder how much of this is authentic (i.e., relatively diffused & spontaneous) folklore, & how much the imaginative product of your friend? Speaking of Coronado & Cibola—I once used the idea of a subterrene region beneath the southwest, peopled by the descendants of Atlanteans *& others,* into which strayed one of Coronado's men—one Panfilo de Zamacona y something-or-other. It was not in a tale of my own, but in one I ghost-wrote for a revision-client. By the way, though strange as it may seem, I did *not* invent the Mi-go or Abominable Snow Men. This is genuine Nepalese folklore surrounding the Himalayas, & I picked it up in most unscholarly fashion from the newspaper & magazine articles exploiting one or another of the attempts on Mt. Everest. Probably you are familiar with at least two stories in which this concept is very advantageously employed—E. F. Benson's "The Horror-Horn" in "Visible & Invisible", & H. R. Wakefield's "The Cairn" in "Others Who Returned". Kadath in the Cold Waste is, however, my invention. In one of my repudiated efforts—a novelette written in the winter of 1926–7 I made it my central theme, but the result was not successful.

Yes—as I said in last Sunday's instalment—I do not think our estimates of Blackwood, Machen, & Dunsany are in any sense antipodal. No one regrets more than I do the limitations besetting Blackwood, & I have often sighed at Nature's inability to effect a sort of synthesis of him & Machen—giving the composite genius Blackwood's vision & understanding of man's out-reaching emotions & illusions, plus Machen's definitely literary perspective & self-critical faculty. Machen, with all his faults, knows literature & style. He is often trivial & insipid, but never awkward nor mawkish nor silly. You make an excellent point regarding Poe. His infinity was indeed *within*— the wall of horror & darkness which is the true though unrecognised human spirit. "There are moments", he says, "when even to the sober eye of Reason the world of our sad Humanity may assume the semblance of a Hell—but the imagination of a man is as Carathis, to explore with impunity its every cavern. Alas! the grim legion of sepulchral terrors cannot be regarded as altogether fanciful—but, like the Demons in whose company Afrasiab made his voyage down the Oxus, they must sleep, or they will devour us—they must be suffered to slumber, or we perish." Today our sense of mystery & infinity shifts to a less personal realm for many reasons— a prominent one being the gradual dissociation of most of our subjective feelings into simpler & less impressive components by the processes of modern psychology. Then again, as you point out, the cheerful prosaicism of recent scientific social thinkers really invites a reaction in favour of the external, the indefinite, & the uncontrollable. Modern science may or may not leave out important elements in its view of the universe—but in either case the *emotional* revolt against prosaic certainty & limitation cannot be downed.

In my view of the universe I probably side more—objectively & intellectually—with the material man of science than with the mystic; but my repudiation of unverified trimmings causes me to reject unjustified extrapolations & dogmata on one side as well as on the other. Certainly, I have nothing but rueful & sardonic laughter of the political economist who insists that future history *must* necessarily follow this or that course (no two agree, but each one is sure of himself!), or for the biologist who (like J. B. S. Haldane) maps out a certain line of marvellous upward development for the race. I don't believe in any "cosmic consciousness" or purpose or direction, nor in any "spiritual" order of entity coexisting with the universe of electrons. But I do see existence filled with an infinity of *unrecognised* (not supernatural) & *incalculable* factors—factors involving the relationship of everything we know to the totality of space-time—whereby all supposed certainties & long-term calculations must be called into question so far as any absolute sense is concerned. We don't know what we are in time & space, or what will happen to us before our kind of matter & energy will cease to exist. Organic life is only a momentary incident—whether a local & unique accident or a widespread cosmic principle often repeated, we can never know. We can never know how far our kind of natural law holds good in the gulfs of space & time, or when some manifestation of it will change. Nor can we interpret it well enough to calculate the future of life & of the universe even if it does not change. So far as future history is concerned, I'm damned if I know what lies ahead. Probably certain philosophic historians & sociologists have a *limited* rightness in pointing out rough general trends— such as that from capitalism to *some* form of collectivism under the impact of widespread mechanisation—but the moment they try to prophesy in detail as the Marxists do they are merely weaving myths. Any one of a dozen possible courses may await mankind. Nobody knows what factors will pop up to prove the decisive ones. What will the next war bring—& leave? How much of existing knowledge & technology will survive—or leave recoverable keys—through the next dark age? How fatal will be the decadence or collapse toward which both western & eastern cultures seem to be moving? Will the modified behaviour-patterns created by the lapse of certain traditional beliefs produfce unforeseen results? To what extent will a new dark age restore or duplicate the early attitudes & superstitions of mankind? In connexion with this sort of speculation no one ought to miss reading W. Olaf Stapledon's "Last & First Men", published some six years ago. Probably you *have* read it. If not, make a bee line for library or bookstall! To give a personal guess—I look for a sharply-divided world with intervals of terrific warfare taking the general level of civilisation lower & lower each time. I doubt the probability of a general worldwide explosion—for most great decays have been gradual. Indeed, I fancy the saner nations will have many intervals of relative placidity & decency. The northern & western countries seem to have a knack of readjusting their government, economics, & society to meet changing needs without explosive disaster, & if they can be left free to evolve without encroachment, they probably have quite a future. I don't look for any social upheavals of prime magnitude in America or Great Britain (or any part of the Empire) or Scandinavia, & believe that their dangers lie in external wars. How well can they resist the encroachments of more violent neighbours? How wisely will they combine their interests & defences, & arrange their economic contacts? I don't know. Nor will I try to rival the aforementioned Mr. Stapledon in conjecturing what will come out of the next general dark age. In that matter I haven't even a guess to offer. But that a kind of dark age will come in 1000 years I feel reasonably certain. Nor will it be without its compensations, as hinted by Dunsany in his "Prayer of the Flowers" in "Fifty-One Tales".

Regarding Charles Fort—I'm not against the principle that no observed phenomenon should be ignored merely because it fails to harmonise with existing knowledge & existing ideas of natural law. Indeed, I don't think any truly scientific thinker is. It is only from the observation of numberless varied phenomenon that we have formulated "natural laws", & when we strike a new phenomena at once clearly established & definitely irreconcilable with our "laws", we know that we must seek new explanations & draw up a new code of conjectural principles. Thus perished Laplace's nebular hypothesis, the Ptolemaic system, the theory of "phlogiston", & son on. In every case the old doctrine was shelved as soon as the contrary evidence became conclusive. The thing which makes men of science hold out in certain cases is a grave doubt of the authority & conclusiveness of the contrary evidence. They know how deceptive appearances are, how spontaneously yet realistically myths arise & spread, and how minutely & painstakingly they & their predecessors had to verify, purge of illusions, & sift out from among endless examples of false appearances the body of evidential phenomena on which existing ideas are based. Knowing this, they have a right to ask that each bit of evidence challenging such ideas be examined & analysed just as thoroughly as were the evidences whence the ideas were formulated. When an overwhelming weight of tested evidence points in one direction, any lone phenomenon seeming to point in the contrary direction must surely be taken very much on probation—not brushed aside, but analysed very carefully, & not regarded too seriously until analysis & verification have established it as a certainty necessitating a general re-casting of existing ideas. My opinion of Fort as an interesting rather than intellectually revolutionary figure arises from the casual & unverified nature of his reports. He assembles odd statements of so loose & un-authoritative an origin (I speak from memory, not having read him ("The Book of the Damned", "New Lands") in a decade.) that one does not see why they form a serious challenge to existing ideas. We are all too familiar with the anthropological & sociological processes which customarily give birth to irresponsible statements of this general nature. Of course, no one would claim that all such statements ought to be dismissed without an investigation. Indeed, investigation of all strange phenomena not obviously fictitious should be encouraged. But until these reports—or some of them—have been shewn to be different from the run of wild canards common to folklore & the press, a good many solid thinkers will decline to attach too much importance to them. That, however, doesn't mean a closed frontier. See what repetitions of the Michelson-Morley experiment have done to our most cherished conceptions of time & space—& what further repetitions (as now conducted by Prof. Dayton C. Miller) may do the equally cherished relativity ideas of the moment! See how respectfully (note the article in the current *Harpers*) the general scientific public is beginning to listen to the experiments of Prof. Rhine at Duke University touching on telepathic & clairvoyant (but not, of course, really "supernatural") principles! I don't think science is quite as ruthless & arbitrary as Fort maintained. One *must* guard the frontiers of accepted learning against casual delusion & charlatanry—suppose academic authorities were to endorse phrenology, animal magnetism, psychic vibrations, ectoplasm, & all the rest of the pseudo-science peddled down the ages by fanatics & pretenders! But I get your point—& realise that there are indeed many narrow men of science whose closed minds justify all the Fortian invective. It is well, I doubt not, that healthy irritants like Fort appear from time to time to rouse the guardians of human learning from a stultifying complacency & cocksureness. By the way—I envy you the intellectual vigour & activity implied in the list of some of your studies and pursuits. I lag far behind—so that I really don't enjoy mental activity per se, but employ it only as a means to the end of gratifying curiosity shout the cosmos & the phenomena. Thus I never maintained any enthusiasm for chess—though for that matter I don't care for *any* games . . . intellectual, physical, or fortuitous. I lack most completely the competitive or sporting instinct.

I appreciated extremely the criticisms of my various tales, & believe I agree completely with all of them. *Characterisation* is undeniably a woefully weak point with me, & I am usually so intent on depicting or suggesting *phenomena* that I lack the patience to develop and motivate the human figures (of no interest to me except as indices of the phenomena) as I should in order to make the total picture convincing. The weakness is also aggravated by the *dream-attitude* which habitually underlies my attempts to crystallise moods & cosmic adumbrations. The way I think of strange phenomena & outside intrusions is as a dreamer helplessly & passively watching a panorama flit past him, or floating disconnectedly through a series of incredible pictures. Everything connected with motive & action is absent—a mad universe obeys strange new laws, & the spectator has no wish but to watch, & no acts save to stare. If the panorama or pictures happen to contain people, what they do or why they do it remains shrouded in mystery—this mystery contributing to the dream-concept part of its essential force. Of course I realise that I can't get this over to any reader, hence have to invent characters & motives. But these puppets & excuses are so objective & artificial, & so little related to what I'm really trying to do, that I tend to become weary & slight them. I felt the weakness particularly in "Whisperer", & believe I tried (albeit clumsily) to have him explain his apparently anomalous helplessness in one of his letters. In the "Haunter" I think I also tried to suggest some reason for the victim's passiveness—implying that the experience almost paralysed his will & that the Entity was exchanging personalities with him, but I know I did it badly & listlessly. I surely must pay more attention to this point. Regarding the other point—springing marvels before I've sufficiently prepared the reader—I recognise that, too. This is without question a result of my constant writing for a pulp rag like W T. The insidious influence of the cheap shocker gets at me despite my conscious efforts to exclude it. Recently I've felt this defect very keenly, & have made efforts to break away from it—though there are no results so far. I'm glad indeed to have these points emphasised, & shall double my alertness to avoid the usual kind of error. Glad you've seen "Cthulhu"—a product of 1926 which I regard as only so-so. I'll have some things to lend as soon as I get that checked list—quite a batch of previously lent material returned yesterday.......

> [Sincerely yours,
> H. P. Lovecraft]

[6]   To Jonquil Leiber

November 29, 1936

Dear Mrs. Leiber:—

..... Descending from the sublime to the ridiculous, I am interested in the impression conveyed to you & Mr. Leiber by the snap of my own grotesque & senescent mug. I lately suggested to the *Weird Tales* illustrator Finlay, to whom I had sent the same snap in response to his request, that he use it as a model for one of those nameless cosmic horrors from outside—such as he drew in his memorable design for Bloch's "Faceless God" in the issue for last May. The reading of Puritanic & witch-hanging (no witch-suspect was ever *burned* in New England) characteristics into my grim & forbidding features suggests a number of curious lines of research—ethnological, biological, psychological & what-not—in view of the fact that with one exception not a single line of my ancestry tarried for more than a few years in that part of New England where the dour Puritan theocracy held sway—Rhode Island being a colony founded by & maintained for the opponents of—& refugees from—that arrogant theocracy. Why, then, the undeniable resemblance to the popular picture of the conical-hatted whiner of tunes from the Bay Psalm-Book—a resemblance infinitely greater than that of most of the actual psalm-singers & witchcraft-judges of 17th century Massachusetts (Cotton Mather was a plump, cheerful-looking soul beneath his full-bottom'd periwig)? Excluding the fact that precisely one-half of my ancestry never touched New England till a couple of years before my birth (an exclusion justified by the fact that my features seem wholly of maternal derivation), why should a Rhode-Islander look like the folklore concept of a Bay Colony Puritan? Was it (a) origin from a similar element in Great Britain (& variations, local & social, in British ethnology are a study in themselves—as Sir Arthur Keith could attest), (b) climatic & dietary similarities in New England, promoting similar glandular functioning, (c) *rough* similarities in psychological life despite the differences between the beliefs of those within & outside the Mass.-Conn. theocracy, (d) an *individual* dourness of the Mass. type, or (e) combinations of any two or three or all four of the foregoing influences? Well—I don't know. As to the first count, I think there did tend to be a vague similarity of source in the Massachusetts & Rhode Island colonists (East Anglian lines predominating, though exceptions were bewilderingly many)—a tendency accentuated by the fact that many Rhode Islanders were either refugees from Massachusetts or of known kinship to Massachusetts families. In my own ancestry a good many lines—Perkins, Rathbone, Dyer, Place, Whipple, Field, & others I could think of if I stopped to get out my charts—did cross the sea as Massachusetts colonists (coming therefore from the usual Mass. sources), though they paused only transiently (save Perkins, which didn't reach R. I. till the 18th century) in the Bay. These names represent regions as far apart as Warwickshire & the West Riding of Yorkshire, but two are from Norfolk, & some of my non-Massachusetts lines are also East Anglian. There is, then, an undeniable East Anglian bias, like Massachusetts', in my maternal & feature-determining lineage. This argues perhaps a basis for facial differentiation—about which a first-hand student of the Eastern counties could tell better than I. Probably East Anglians, coming from the old "Litus Saxonicum" which the Teutonic invaders first occupied, have more of the tribal Teuton direct from the north of Europe, & less of the Celt & Britanno-Roman, than other English stocks—although the more southerly natives of Kent & Sussex should by the same token have at least as much. The second point—climatic & dietary similarities between Mass. & R. I.— may also be significant. The two regions are close together, & colonial eating habits were very similar. Physically, all southern N. E. colonists met a similar milieu. As the psychological element—here I think the parallelism grows weaker. Whilst Rhode-Islanders undoubtedly shared the general New-England preoccupation with ethical & theological matters, they had nothing of the savage Massachusetts approach. They fought not for the narrow enforcement of one creed but for the tolerance of all. We welcomed Jews in Newport as early as the 1670's & their synagogue of 1763 still remains in use. Not a single case of witchcraft prosecution ever occurred on our soil, & Quakers—the bane of the Bay—flourished in our midst. The Church of England became predominant in our southern counties about the time of William & Mary, & so remains to this day. These southern counties likewise diverged from the rest of New England in social & economic organisation & way of life—developing large plantations with negro slaves in the manner of the southern colonies, & fostering a patriarchal agricultural life surprisingly like that of old England, or rather (considering the colour & status of the labour) like that of Virginia or the South Carolina low country. These more or less squirearchical plantation families represented something very far from the Puritanism of the Bay—& about half of my maternal lines stem from them more or less directly. The plantation system largely collapsed with the revolution; some representatives of the planter houses being able to remain on their own lands, whilst others (many of my own forbears among them) took smaller holdings in the undeveloped region to the northward & mingled with the westward-pushing element from Providence. All of which argues a life & psychology widely different from the more narrowly centred

Massachusetts type. If *only* psychological influences moulded the "Puritan face", one would not expect to find it in the people of Rhode Island. So far as the *individual* element goes—I'm not much of a Bay-Colony theocrat. Whilst I *do* share the basic New-England respect for an orderly life & social organisation (as did also Plato, John Locke, & many other non-Yankees), I have no belief in any religion, nor any use for any state policy imposing the least curb upon intellectual & aesthetic (or religious, if anybody wishes to retain the legends of yesteryear) freedom. I likewise oppose the Puritan concept of ethics in art & literature—believing ethics itself to be an independent art & not logically miscible with any other. Any vestigial philosophic resemblance I may have to the bygone Puritan is perhaps contained in my general belief (a mere personal opinion, whose application by force I would violently oppose) that a contemplative & imaginative life is of somewhat more evolved quality, & likely to confer richer ultimate rewards upon persons of highly organised sensibilities, than is a more elemental life with its concentration on the primitive, the more simply emotional, & the orgiastic. In a word, I seem to favour the Apollonian over the Dionysian ideal as a general policy—though for purely aesthetic & scientific reasons, & without the least wish to incorporate it Nazi-fashion into a civic doctrine. Whether this perfectly tolerant attitude tends toward the creation of a Puritan bigot's physiognomy, I can't say. Possibly I am what George Santayana would call a Puritan in decay—although I lack the sense of abstract *duty* (as distinguished from the aesthetic satisfaction in symmetrical & adequate completion) which he & others find still dominant in the Puritans' agnostic descendants. As for the mere gleam of a sulky temperament or bad digestion—which so often produces the illusion of piety, asceticism, & moral fervour—I must record as a prosaic fact that I scarcely have even this. Though in very poor health prior to the age of 30, I have never been able to cultivate a picturesque melancholy. Indeed, it has never even occurred to me to try. Instead, though scarcely of a boisterous or ebullient disposition, I am a distinctly good-natured old cuss, with a kind of mild paternal benevolence toward the external world, & with no constitutional inability to twist the grim line of my mouth at least slightly in the direction of a fairly amiable & non-sardonic smile. I have also laughed aloud on at least four occasions within a memory extending back to 1892. I would not, in all probability, qualify as a Falstaff—yet scarcely fancy my temperament alone could have determined the sourness of my phiz. No—referring back to the classification near the bottom of p. I, 1—I fancy the Judge Hathorne visage must be attributed to point (e) in the end . . . . a combination of causes, & these more physical (selective ancestry & climatic-dietary milieu influencing the feature-deciding half of my lineage) than psychological. But even so, the habit of occasional (though scarcely savage or morose) analysis & reflection may have played its subtle part. It does not do to be dogmatic. However, I will say that a map like mine is more likely to *give* its possessor melancholy (unless, as I do, he avoids mirrors as much as possible) than to be a *result* of melancholy!

Proceeding to answer the questions in your letter (& trusting perhaps overconfidently that the foregoing garrulous & egocentric comment has left you with enough patience & consciousness to hear the not-quite-so-garrulous (I hope)* replies thereto)—I may say that (a) I haven't any especial claims to the title of "student", being not even a university graduate (health broken down during years which should have been collegiate), & being more or less superficial & fragmentary about everything. Whether a sort of curiosity about things in general—impelling informal dabblings in bits of history, a few of the sciences, & so on—would win me an unofficial or non-commissioned status as semi-student or pseudo-student, I really don't know. But my ignorance always impresses me more than any ill-coördinated acquirements which I may have picked up in an aimless way. As to (b) my matrimonial status—you are right to the extent that I am not married *now*, although I was from March 3, 1924 to March 25, 1929. I am very much in favour of an harmonious wedded state, but mistook superficial for basic congeniality. Small similarities did not, as expected, grow greater; nor did small differences, as expected, grow less. Instead, the reverse process occurred in both cases—aided no doubt by that financial insecurity which is ever the foe of domestic adjustment. Aspirations & environmental preferences diverged increasingly, until at length—albeit without real blame or even bitterness on either side—the Superior Court of Providence County was permitted to exercise its corrective & divisive function, & the old gentleman was ceremoniously reënthroned in a dour celibate dignity. My household is now presided over by my sole surviving aunt—my only close relative. Whether (c) I am very reserved or not depends upon one's interpretation of 'reserve'. Certainly I am not gratuitously gregarious, or prone to seek conversation whether or not I have anything to say; & consequently, I might by some be regarded as a crusty hermit. On the other hand, as various victims of my epistles can attest, I am positively loquacious whenever any topic of interest to me is to be discussed. I was not a hermit at all during the period when I lived within reach of a group whose interests were akin to mine (that was in N. Y.—but I loathed the place as a whole so vehemently that I couldn't stand it even for the sake of pleasant individual associations), & am more or less so now merely because I don't discover many thoroughly kindred spirits hereabouts. (d) The picture of me as alternately pottering over a desk ("The Haunter of the Dark" accurately describes this house & the position of my desk at a west window commanding a view) & taking long walks ((in warm weather—my optimum temperature is 80° to 90°; I can't write legibly under 75° (some cynical souls declare I can't at *any* temperature) & am very badly affected by real cold—under about +20°)) through ancient streets & slightly agrestic & sylvan scenes is a perfectly correct one—although on hot days I take my work along in a black bag & perform it

---

*Later—how vain are the hopes of mankind!

in various selected scenic spots along my chosen line of march. (e) As to what the neighbours (at present, very largely the youthful denizens of the contiguous fraternity-houses, plus the elderly respectables inhabiting the boarding-house across the back garden in a parallel street) think of me—I have never taken the trouble to ascertain, & scarcely imagine I should feel greatly complimented if I did. Your estimate is probably correct! As to (f) how the wolf is kept from the door—I can only reply (without the least pique at the query) that I presume sheer luck is the deciding factor so far, & that in the future I can't guarantee that the fanged & furry menacer *will* be kept away! No one more annoyingly lacks the least rudiments of remunerative enterprise or commercial aptitude than I. I simply don't know how to gather cash except incidentally & accidentally. I made the mistake in youth of not realising that literary endeavour does not always mean an income. I ought to have trained myself for some routine clerical work (like Charles Lamb's or Hawthorne's) affording a dependable stipend yet leaving my mind free enough for a certain amount of creative activity—but in the absence of immediate need I was too damned a fool to look ahead. I seemed to think that sufficient money for ordinary needs was something which everyone had as a matter of course—& if I ran short, I "could always sell a story or poem or something". Well—my calculations were inaccurate! The kind of poems & stories & somethings I write (& I have no more skill in the saleable commercial sort of stuff than has a coal-heaver) are *not* the kind one can translate into rent & nourishment with any degree of dependability—yet here I find myself in middle life with no trained commercial aptitude, & with the original resources of my youth disrupted & nearly exhausted. Such tales as I do sell—& more than that, such revisory & ghost-writing work as I perform—help to postpone the fatal day of reckoning; but when it comes, & I find no further trace of patrimonial reserve to draw upon, it will (in the prevailing sermo plebeius) be just too bad. So far,[†] I haven't been able to make scattered returns even roughly equal the $10.00 or $15.00 per week which would meet my drastically (tho' gradually) minimised needs—but some trace of the blind & fatuous optimism of my youth remains, conferring the hope that at some time before the final crash I can somehow stumble stupidly upon some sort of a job paying about 10 or 15 berries hebdomadally. Being of an abstract cast of mind with no interest in—or prejudices concerning—sources of subsistence, I don't care what in thunder it is so long as it is honest, adequately performable by me, and capable of yielding the modest

---

[*]You're wrong in assuming that there isn't money in the pulps for those ingenious & case-hardened enough to sink personal repugnance & cater to the artificial, puerile needs of the cheap editors. Price & Long & Wandrei & Hamilton & others thrive on pulp writing. They are able to forget literary criteria & meet the market. It is my finaicial misfortune that I can't do likewise.

[†]Except last year, when the two *Astounding* items caused me to break even.

amount necessary to provide a roof for myself, my books, and the accustomed articles of furniture, statuary, paintings, etc. which survive from my old house & without whose familiar presence I could not possibly exist. Fortunately my aunt seems independently provided for—& my own needs have been whittled down with such scientific precision that even an annual $500 ought to float me if I am not too fastidious as to neighbourhood when the next move comes. I have reduced nourishment to $2 and $3 per week, and continue to wear the raiment of yesteryear (suits: 1925, 1925, 1925, 1928. Overcoats: 1915, 1932. Hats: 1931, 1935). Nor do I resent the process—which to one of my years and unworldly temperament has something of the amusing aspect of a game. Hence I merely keep enquiring as to the various sorts of jobs—editing, elevator-running, proofreading, night-watchmanning, revising or ghost-writing on a salaried basis, door-tending, acting as publisher's reader or critic, sandwich-manning, &c.—which might be swung by an untrained & naively uncalculative but conscientious old goof whose years & physique render pickaxe-wielding or stevedoring slightly impracticable. So far my investigations have revealed little of definite value, since I have not the remotest idea how—or whom—or where—or when—one asks for a job. But like most shiftless dreamers (dislike of Victorian literature forbids me to introduce the inevitable comparison to Mr. Wilkins Micawber*—or even to the real-life figure of my happy-go-lucky fellow-Yankee, Amos Bronson Alcott, father of the celebrated author of "Little Women") I keep fancying that I shall stumble upon something—that something, as it were, will 'turn up' before I hit the relief rolls, or that I shall at length discover how 'jobs' are discerned & secured—hence refrain from the darksome wailing of lugubrious apprehension. And at that, certain 'breaks' *might* come. Conceivable changes in public taste & editorial policy might enable me to capture *every* year something like the $630 which my two novels in *Astounding* drew last year. Were that so, I would have no worries. Not that it is likely to be so, but that it might be. Or some really good revision opportunities might appear—or your letter to Mr. Rosenbach might start a Lovecraft boom at once & make me (after the deduction of your commission as agent) a plutocrat overnight—or anything might happen. Incidentally—I'm sure *I* don't mind your enquiry to Mr. Rosenbach if *he* doesn't. It won't be *I* who will be sent off on a wild-goose-chase after the nugatory & ephemeral yarns of an undesired unknown, which in the end can scarcely net more than the dime or quarter each asked by such juvenile junk dealers as Mr. Forrest J. Ackerman! That ponderous treatise (whose austere dignity as a "first" is doubtless enhanced rather than impaired by its current reprinting in the "fan" press) catalogued by Janvier in '28 *might* bring today the $3.00 as it was supposed to bring then—but wouldn't the first enquirer be tacitly expected to buy the

---

*or even to the real-life figure of my happy-go-lucky fellow-Yankee, Amos Bronson Alcott, father of the celebrated author of "Little Women".

darned thing in the event that a stray copy actually *did* turn up? Therefore
pray be cautious about seeming to investigate the ancient item. Not that *I*
mind the sending of the catalogue-leaf to the Maison Rosenbach—but that if
you did send it you might find yourself saddled with a tattered copy of the
bygone *Recluse* plus a bill even greater (in view of the 'priceless item's'
greater antiquity & presumable rarity) than the $3.00 quoted some eight
years ago! Could even the nickname-laden regards of the eminent deter from
the eternal profit-quest one who is, after all, a professional dealer?

Having inadvertently maundered on for some five pages in a more or
less autobiographical strain, I will mercifully desist. I am sorry to learn that
"Adept's Gambit" did not land with W T—I would suggest (out of a knowledge of Wright's capricious temperament) that it be resubmitted after a few
months, perhaps with nominal emendations. Wright has a curious way of
accepting things he has once rejected—especially if the rejection was reluctant or half-undecided, as is apparent in this case. Meanwhile I trust Mr. Leiber will let me see the MS., since I am eager to sample the creative efforts of
one who comprehends so fully & profoundly the nature of true cosmic horror & alienage. Indeed, he promised me a glimpse in the event of its return.

I am greatly interested in your reference to your grandfather (who might
conceivably have seen mine if he was of remembering age before 1827, though
Devon & Cornwall represent quite a few square miles betwixt them!) & his
menacing cone-topped Devil-Tower—& the strange whistles blown by no human lips & doubtless designed as signals to the Dark Ones of Outer Space. The
astronomical phase appeals to me especially, since I have been interested in
the heavens since the age of 12, have a 3" refracting telescope, & used to write
regular astronomical articles for the press. As a boy I used to haunt the Ladd
Observatory of Brown University—looking through the 12" refractor now &
then, reading the books in the library, & probably making an unmitigated nui-
sance of myself through my incessant questioning of everybody present. Curiously enough, the assistant there was one of your grandfather's humbler
compatriots—a Cornishman named John Edwards, whose capacity for mis-
placing h's was limitless. Scarcely less limitless was his mechanical skill, & in
his infinite kindness he fixed me up all sorts of devices (a long-focus celestial
camera, a set of photographic lantern slides, a diagonal eyepiece for my telescope, &c. &c) at no more than cost price. I still have the slides somewhere—
as well as lunar & other photographs I took with the camera. He is dead
now—as is Prof. Upton, the director in those days, our acquaintance with
whom gave me my passport to that dark-domed enchanted castle. My third
victim there—Associate Prof. Slocum—is now head of the observatory at
Wesleyan U. in Middletown, Conn. I would have carried astronomy further but
for the *mathematics*—but I hadn't quite the right stuff in me. Oddly enough, I
have a real astronomer in my heredity—but I have to go back to Queen
Elizabeth's reign to claim him. He was John Felde—sometimes called "The
Proto-Copernican of England" because of his "Ephemeris" of 1557 was the first
English book to contain an account of the solar system's true motions. Two of
his grandsons—John & William Field—settled in Providence in 1637, & I am

John & William Field—settled in Providence in 1637, & I am descended from three of Grandson John's grandchildren.

But since I am back on autobiography I had better call a halt. I'd surely enjoy hearing of "Old Master Stebbins'" daemon-chasing & other-world-communing in the Dark Tower!

Again, my sincerest thanks for the pictures!

Best wishes to you & Mr. Leiber—your obt. servant,

H. P. Lovecraft

[7]   To Fritz Leiber, Jr.

The Castle Called Mist
(#66 *is* on the crest of a precipitous
hill—cf. "The Haunter of the Dark")
——Dec. 19, 1936.

My dear Mr. Leiber:—

I read yours of the 3d with the keenest pleasure, but have postponed my reply till after an unhurried & appreciative perusal of the simultaneously-arriving literary products. Let me say at once that the latter brought no disappointment. On the other hand, I am delighted & enthralled by the ever-present intimations of brooding & intrusive Outsideness, & by the vivid imagery, narrative skill, & apt, musical language with which each theme is developed.

Let me consider first the slighter & more impressionistic "Demons of the Upper Air." The whole sequence seems to me to possess the power which I noticed in the previously-quoted extract, & the graphic & unhackneyed choice of symbols throughout excites fresh admiration. Especially potent are the occasional changes of mood & cadence—& the concomitant changes in linguistic method. With the second section the free verse settles down into suggestions of iambic tetrameter, & with the third there appears rhyme, & the more traditional type of utterance with goes with it. Then in Section IV the chant becomes freer again—with long, resonant lines, & a splendid contrast of the real signs with the mere stage-properties of the Outer Darkness. In the fifth section something of the spirit of folklore appears, & the reader is prepared for the regular rhyme & meter when they come. At this point, though, I must pedantically remark that in one of the lines (p. 5—5th l. from bottom) the word *al-lies'* occurs in such a place as to make the accent seem to fall on the first syllable. This, I think, deserves straightening out—& I fancy you can do it without much trouble. I won't venture to recommend a definite alternative—though something like the following might do:

Ho! Wild, / misrul'd / allies / upon / the earth

Section VI extracts genuine power from a traditional medium—the ever-repeated *beyondness* furnishing a splendid effect. Here again, though,

Grandpa's innate pedantry must crop out—for on p. 6 (ll. 11, 12) there is a *false rhyme* [*town—roun(d)*] which needs rectification. You know better than I, in all probability, how to eliminate it without loss of dramatic force. I might suggest:

> Beyond, a factory city's *found*
> With costly suburbs snuggled round.

Section VII presents a very effective "stepping-up"—& has something of the old Edda quality about it. The eighth & final division, with its interesting metrical shifts, forms an appropriate conclusion. Surveying the production as a whole, one cannot but adjudge it truly powerful, well-developed, & articulate with its chosen message. That old Satrap Pharnabazus of North Michigan Ave. turned it down—if he did—forms no reflection on its quality; for of course no poem of this length & mood could conceivably find a place in what is, despite its superiority to the worst grade of pulp rags, essentially a sensational oaf-tickler. I hope most strongly that you can get this sequence published in some not too inappropriate medium. Have you ever tried the so-called "little magazines"—non-paying, non-profit ventures which combine high standards with an absence of professional prejudices & taboos? The number of these is legion—though one might mention *Driftwind* (Walter J. Coates, N. Montpelier Vermont) and *L'Alouette* (Charles A. A. Parker, 114 Riverside Ave., Medford, Mass.) among the all-verse specimens, & *Manuscript* (17 N. Washington St., Athens, O.), *Fantasy* (450 Huberton Ave., Pittsburgh, Pa.), *The Tanager* (Grinnell, Iowa), *American Prefaces* (Iowa City, Iowa), & *Literary America* (175 Fifth Ave., New York, N.Y.) among those which are less specialised. In any case, so fine a set of intimations of the Great Abyss ought not to languish indefinitely in manuscript!

But now I approach the piece de resistance—"Adept's Gambit"—& will proceed to give vent to remarks which ... whether or not as peculiar as those of the palpitant Brother Farnsworth .... are likely to be at least sincere & appreciative. First, though, let me say, as of the poems, that pulp rejection can have no qualitative implications regarding a work like this. The cheap magazines have their set formulae, & this delectable fantasy simply doesn't happen to coincide with any of them. Magazines from the WT level down (& that there *is* a "down" no one who has seen the editorial products of one Rogers Terrill, or the happily defunct Macfadden *Ghost Stories,* can dispute) have no use for anything not simple, literal, & explicitly diagrammed enough to bore its difficult way through the densest cortical integuments of the gaping yokelry.

My appreciation & enjoyment of "Adept's Gambit" as a capturer of dark currents from the void form an especially good proof of the story's essential power, since the style & manner of approach are almost antipodal to my own. With me, the transition to the unreal is accomplished through humourless pseudo-realism, dark suggestion, & a style full of sombre menace &

tension. You, on the other hand, adopt the light, witty, & sophisticated manner of Cabell, Stephens, the later Dunsany, & others of their type—with not a few suggestions of "Vathek" & "Ouroboros". Lightness & humour impose a heavy handicap on the fantaisiste, & all too often end in triviality—yet in this case you have turned liabilities to assets & achieved a fine synthesis in which the breezy whimsicality ultimately builds up rather than dilutes or neutralises the tension & sense of impinging shadow.

The farther I read into "Adept's Gambit" the more I enjoyed it. You succeed abundantly in the difficult art of emotional modulation—heightening the tension & making each fresh turn more impressive—never less—than the preceding one. The picaresque chronicle is always in an ascending key. As the Viking & Mouser leave the low seacoast for the highlands of Turkestan & the mountains beyond the Lost City the feeling of latent evil & immanent alienage mounts, & a fascination creeps increasingly on the reader. Then—on p. 55, where the Elobeth section begins—you let the tempo change a bit & subordinate the cheerfully whimsical to the poignantly pathetic. The shift comes at the right time, & conveys the effect of the opening of some inner door. It is well synchronised with the complete following of the *current,* the vanishment of Ningauble's urchin-emissary, the steeper ascent, the wilder & more precipitous landscape, & the coming of a flaming sunset & purple twilight. Nor is there any letdown. Despite recurrences of the whimsical mood, the tension is always on the increase. The scenes within the castle are magnificently replete with cosmic fear & the sense of encroaching order upon order of alien outsideness. Nor is the ending anticlimactic—for the escape of the adept's soul in the traditional form of a mouse blends perfectly with the massed nature of what has gone before. Indeed, all the developments are gratifyingly plausible & inevitable according to the laws of that fantasy-touched world which you have chosen to depict. I could name dozens of especially tense & powerful high spots—such as the terrified glances in the Adept's sarcophagus in the lost city, the discovery of what was suspended in the box in the castle, &c. &c. &c. If anything in the plot would be the better for changing, I think it is perhaps the matter of the Adept's (or power-beyond-the-Adept's) motive in imposing an ignominious spell on Fafhrd & the Mouser. This is of course suggested on p. 29—but in view of the later doubtfulness of the source of Isaiah ben Elzhaz's volition I think the suggestion might well be a trifle more definite. Why was Isaiah— or That or Those behind him—interested in Fafhrd & his companion? Was it indeed because the Mouser's superficial magical dabblings had attracted attention? Of course the Grey One's own explanation—about having insulted the Adept in Ephesus—is ruled out, since Elobeth's story-within-the-story reveals that Isaiah cannot have walked abroad in his own body as a magician. As for possible re-proportioning—if any sections would bear condensation, it is probably those referring respectively to the action of the spell in Tyre (the story's first 8 pages) & to the conversation & combat with the Adept's corpse in the Lost City. This latter section, however, should (as just stated) contain a very specific hint of the reason for the spell cast on the adventurers. However—all these observations are very minor matters. The novelette is really very much all right just as it is!

Certainly, you have produced a remarkably fine & distinctive bit of cosmic fantasy in a vein which is, for all the Cabellian or Beckfordian comparisons, essentially your own. The basic element of allegory, the earthiness & closeness to human nature, & the curious blending of worldly lightness with the strange & the macabre, all harmonise adequately & seem to express a definite mood & personality. The result is an authentic work of art—& I certainly hope it can eventually get published somewhere even though its genre makes it the hardest conceivable sort of thing to place. Picaresque fantasy of this type generally appears only in book form—which is of course a significant commentary on the vapid formula-following of even the best periodicals. I'll be very much interested to hear your own remarks—as well as Wright's—on this not-merely-promising bit of accomplishment.

And now for a few pedantic observations on certain points in the text which I jotted down as I came to them. Some of these observations may seem trivial—others will perhaps prove helpful in correcting minor slips.

Page 1—would *Hittites*[1] have a separate identity in the great Syrian amalgam as late as Hellenistic times? Look the matter up.

General orthographical notes—note spelling of *sistrum*. One stores water in a *cistern,* but it's a *sistrum* that one rattles! The sistrum was *Egyptian* & connected with the cult of Isis, but the spread of Egyptian influence to the Syrian region probably justifies its mention in this tale.

pp. 3 & 53 The country in Asia Minor is *Cilicia* (Κιλικια), not *"Cilesia"*. *Silesia* is a region in Europe grabbed from Austria by Frederick the Great & with pieces now chipped off & allotted to Czechoslovakia & Poland.

p. 4 Philistines as a separate people[2] are less & less heard from as the Hellenistic age advances. The last specific mention of them is in the Book of Maccabees—2nd cent. B.C. But your reference is all right.

p. 9—I fear that the allusion to Tamerlane's later building of Samarcand must come out, since this ancient city was in existence & already venerable in the Hellenistic

Regarding any possibly anachronistic national names—you could substitute another known to belong to the Hellenistic period—such as Idumaean or Cydonian or Rhodian or Cyprian or Chalcidian or Libanian or Sabaean.

---

1. Last-minute conclusions after combing my library a bit: I think the name *Hittite* could *not* have survived to Hellenistic times. No classical text known to me records it, & the last mention of the race seems to be in Assyrian inscriptions far antedating the Greek period in the East.

2. though they left their name *geographically* in the word Παλαιστινη or Palaestina.

age of Fafhrd & the Grey Mouser. The town antedates the recorded history of its region, & appears in Persian days as *Maracanda,* capital of Sogdiana. It was a thriving place, with walls extending 90 stadia. Alexander the Great destroyed it—but it survived & did well in the days of the Graeco-Bactrian kingdom. In Arabic times it appears under its corrupted name *Samarcand*—being captured by Kataiba ibn Moslim in A.D. 712 ... the period of my fictitious *Necronomicon* author Abdul Alhazred. It became a mighty metropolis & seat of Saracenic culture under the Arabs, but was destroyed by Genghis Khan in 1219. Nearly a couple of centuries after that, Tamerlane made it his capital & (together with his successors) adorned it with fine buildings & institutions—but as you may see, it can scarcely be considered as *built* by him. So far as our historic vision can reach, we always find a great city on the site.

p. 14. Here is something a bit puzzling to an old gent not so quick on the uptake. You have the Mouser speak of a supposed work

[d]

whose title is the *Duocedahe[d]ron of Artemi"s"orus*—these names having been altered in the text from a better to a worse state—but I can't quite figure out the intention. Is the Mouser supposed to be inventing names with a clumsiness & erroneousness greater than usual? What holds me up is that the erroneousness is *too great to be convincing.* Artemidorus (gift of Artemis— Αρτεμιδορος) was too common a Greek name (especially in the Orient)—too typical in form—to be mis-rendered as "Artemisorus" by anyone who had knocked about the Hellenistic world as the Mouser presumably had. I'm not sure of your chronology—but if the period is as late as B.C. 100 (which I doubt) the great geographer Artemidorus of Ephesus ought to be on the scene. The name of the book is another tough nut. I assume that the intent is to give a corruption of *Dodecahedron* (Δωδεκαέδρον) or its possible variant *Duokaidecahedron* (Δυοκαιδεκαέδρον) [for δυο-και-δεκα or two-and-ten often subbed for δωδεκας, twelve]—"The Twelve-Sided Thing"—but here again the problem of *degree of illiteracy* comes up. Δωδεκαέδρον [I never saw the δυοκαιδεκα substitution applied to this particular word, though I suppose it could be done] was a very well-known & typical word, so how could the Mouser very well hash it up so badly? Wouldn't it be more in character for him to invent a *fictitious work,* but have the title & author in *correct Greek?* Thus I'd vote for the "*Dodecahedron* (Or *Duokaidecahedron*) *of Artemidorus*" as the supposed title. Incidentally—I haven't yet figured out the Mouser's nationality. Fafhrd calls him "scum of wit-weighted culture", so I put him down as some sort of Levantine or Hellenistic half-Greek. Anyhow, I seem to envisage him as speaking Greek very glibly & reasonably correctly. By the way—*Artemidorus* was a favourite name in Ephesus, because of the deeply-seated cult of Artemis (or rather, of an earlier Asiatic goddess whom the Greeks identified with Artemis) there. "Great is Diana of the Ephesians". There was a later Artemidorus born there (2nd cent. A.D.) who wrote a learned treatise on the interpretation of dreams. Pardon all this vacuous rambling—& use your judgment about the name of the supposed treatise & its author.

p. 15—avoid the non-existent "thusly" for *thus.*

p. 19—here's a fine point. You speak of the "Endless Caverns"—but are you sure this won't arouse jarringly prosaic associations based on the fairly well-known Endless Caverns near New Market, Va., U.S.A.? I can testify that the Caverns in Virginia are the very reverse of prosaic—Ædepol, what a subterrene world of wonder!—but there is always a suggestion of anticlimax when a name supposed to figure in an ancient & exotic scene duplicates something in the modern & nearby world.

p. 20—& elsewhere. Avoid split infinitives in spite of all the modern libertarian ballyhoo in their favour.

p. 23—*insignia* should not be used in the *singular*

p. 24—*went* should be *gone.*

p. 25—note correct spelling of metamorphosed. I never heard the form "metamorphised".

p. 42—The names Arachni and *Altaeoni* sound somehow off-key to me as Greek. *Arachne* is a name figuring in mythology (with an etymological significance), but you ought to have something less weighted with associations. How about *Aganippe* and *Authemius* for the two names?

p. 44—avoid ultra-modern coinages like *recontacted. Contact* really ought never to be used as a *verb*—the recent custom in "business English" to the contrary notwithstanding. Why not say *rediscovered?*

p. 52—use of verb *typed* doubtful. Better say "whom they instantly classified as a street gamin". This change also eliminates another error (the insertion of a redundant "that of") which needed attention.

p. 65—I hate to see the modern twisted use of *intrigue* as a verb meaning to interest or fascinate. It really ought to be discouraged. Could you substitute *fascinating* or *intriguing?* Of course, this use of "intrigue" is sadly widespread—but in the present novel the quasi-archaic, traditional tone of the style makes it seem doubly inappropriate.

pp. 70 & 72—lack of uniform usage in name of Ishtar-Astarte. You say *Astarte* in other places, so better not say *Istarte* here.

p. 75—no such word[3] as *"constrictious".* Why not say constrictive?

p. 82—"react" for respond in a general sense is a somewhat needless modernism. Why not say *respond?*

p. 83—no such word (as far as I know) as *necrous.* Try *necrose, necrosed,* or *necrotic.* Never mind the medical connotation.

pp. 92 & 95—*activated* was in old English, but long ago disappeared. The use of this resurrected word by scientific students has spread until ultra-

---

3. Whenever I say "no such word" in so apparently pontifical a manner, I mean merely that *I don't know of it,* & that I can't find it in either of the two dictionaries—a Stormonth & an 1890 Webster's International—which I possess. In some cases a recent unabridged dictionary might reveal such a word as existing—but even in that case I'd be inclined to consider it a bit too obscure or modern for a style as traditional as the novel's.

moderns are dragging it into the general field—but such an extension has nothing to recommend it. Better say *moved*.

p. 99—there is no such word as *"unbeknownst"*—this form being merely a comic coinage. Even *"unbeknown"* is wholly colloquial. The best thing to say is *unknown*. Pardon all this pedantry—but I spent most of the summer & autumn revising & partly ghost-writing a manual on "Well-Bred English" for a private school in Washington, D.C., & I can't get the damned influence out of my system!

Realising its connexion with the Fafhrd-Mouser myth-cycle, I saved the extract from Mr. Fischer's letter to read *after* my perusal of "Adept's Gambit"—a thing I am very glad I did, since it gave me a truer perspective of the background out of which the epistolary fragment grew. Needless to say, I enjoyed the episodic bit tremendously, & conceived an instant admiration for the gifted creator. A two-way correspondence full of these isolated episodes must surely be a test of creative fancy—an even better form of literary exercise than the participants consciously realise. Both of you ought to keep carbons of these beginningless & endingless passages—some day coördinating them & developing them into a series of mood-studies for publication. It is easy to see how "Adept's Gambit" grew out of this play & interchange of fancy, & I do not wonder at the graceful dedication—which must surely be greatly appreciated by its object. Let us hope that your mental collaboration will give rise to a long sequence of tales about Fafhrd & the Mouser—figures which I somehow visualise as stylised & exaggerated projections of the two unquenchable correspondents—projections, at least, so far as basic outlines & imaginative flights are concerned. Mr. Fischer's style has a marked kinship to that of your own more whimsical passages—& I suppose the nature & typical actions of Fafhrd, the Mouser, Ningauble, & perhaps other recurrent characters are equally well-known to you both through the long exchange of imaginings such as this. It interested me greatly (as when I met my old pal Cthulhu in "Adept's Gambit") to come across an Entity whose name synthesised two of my own geographical creations . . . the mountain Kadath in the Cold Waste, & the vague trans-galactic hell called Yaddith. Kaddith would seem to have been (or should I still use the present tense despite what happened to the soul-image?) an extremely formidable Entity, & I shudder to think of what would have become of the Mouser had that "scum of wit-weighted culture" been less adroit or less protected! Some later episode, I hope, will chronicle the Small Grey One's fortunes after his emergence from the Place of Black Stones—his Asking of the Questions, & his presumable rescue of Fafhrd from captivity. Indeed, an added note on the MS. leads one to think that such a hope may not be wholly vain. This picaresque kind of writing has a strong fascination, & I once attempted it myself (1926–7) in a long novelette called "The Dream-Quest of Unknown Kadath" . . . . of which the central figure was that rather shadowy & flexible dummy Randolph Carter. The tale did not, however, satisfy my critical sense when completed, so I marked it off my list & did not type it. Years later my young friend Barlow asked for the MS., & proposed to type me a copy (for preservation as a sort of quarry of imagery & incidents for possible future tales) in exchange—but although I gave him the rough draught, he has so far returned less than half of the text in typed form. Barlow suggests that my attempt might make a passable *juvenile* item—but I have my doubts as to whether's it's good for anything in its present form. Thanks immensely for Fischer's address. I am dropping him a line of appreciation anent his fragment—& the myth-cycle behind it—& shall surely be more than delighted to hear from him directly. The fragment itself I return to you herewith—for I fancy you will want it for your permanent archives. Incidentally—I hope those tales about the godlet in the Chicago Aquarium, the penultimate goblin, & the god-isolating mortal will all eventually get written. As the Mouser himself says, the possibilities of professional publication for such elusively fantastic material are sadly limited; but that does not lessen the joy of creation, or imply that ways of reasonable circulation cannot in the end be found. About Mr. Fischer's non-appreciation of music—I suppose my own case is not very remote from his. I am by no means indifferent to some forms of melody, but have no power of discrimination betwixt the classically good & the tawdry. I am like a person who could read Balzac, the *Saturday Evening Post,* & *Wild Western Stories* with almost equal relish & emotional response. My lines of preference ignore quality, but include *some* good music, *some* mediocre music, & *some* tin-pan tripe (the latter all antedating 1910 or so). Much of what I *think* is musical liking is merely *associative*—I like this or that piece because it gratifies a patriotic emotion ("Rule, Britannia", "The Star-Spangled Banner", &c.), evokes some folklore vista of yesterday ("Suwanee River", "Ben Bolt", &c.), or calls up memories of my own youth ("Sweet Adeline", tunes from "Floradora", "The Burgomaster", & so on). By chance, I may be strongly moved by some genuine classic— Wagner, MacDowell, Schubert, Beethoven—but other classics of equal reputation either leave me cold or actually repel me. I remember *tunes* with fair tenacity, but am very bad at correlating them with their *names*. Some of my friends refer familiarly to the so-and-so'th movement of what's-his-name's N[th] Symphony—& I don't know what the hell they mean, although I could probably identify the tune if they whistled it recognisably. Nor do I have the *craving* for music which some people speak of. I like an occasional ditty, but I could do without the sound of kilipat, tittibuk, & zootibar indefinitely without getting badly steamed up. On the other hand, I'd be utterly sunk—or driven to tearing the anaemic grey lint that fringes my bald spot—if I were cut off from books, opportunities to write, or the sight of certain forms of architectural, decorative, pictorial, & landscape art. Decidedly, Grandpa is an eye-man & not an ear-man! If any one thing killed my musical taste it was the violin-lessons I took betwixt the ages of 7 & 9. Back in '97 I thought I liked music, but a year or two of classico-academic drill on a 3/4 size fiddle soured me completely. They wouldn't let me scrape the tunes I wanted, but confined me to useful exercises & insipid folk-tunes out of a book. As a result, practicing became a hell, & the whole damn practicing became a hell, & the whole damn business drove me so close to nervous exhaustion that two physicians (I was little short of a neurotic semi-invalid as a kid) told my mother that a halt would have to be called. Thus ended the Kreislerian career of the Old Man Without a Beard. Today I can scarcely tell one end of a violin from another, & don't recall a cursed thing about reading music except that the spaces spell F-A-C-E, & that the lines represent the initials of the phrase Every Good Boy Does Finely. My only spontaneous melodic memories of that age are of "Sweet Rosie O'Grady", "Dolly Gray", & Paul Dresser's "Banks of the Wabash" [whose chorus the now-eminent Theodore Dreiser wrote to help out his brother Paul] & "Just Tell Then That You Saw Me", & a few assorted coon songs like "Oh, Oh, Miss Phoebe". Well—who knows? Perhaps some of my native tolklorish recollections are more significant than classic recollections would be . . . for did not those old coon-songs form the birth of *syncopation*—a principle perhaps destined (under various modified & elaborated forms) to become dominant in the future music of Western Civilisation? Let no cultural snob scorn me because of the vividness with which I recall fat Peter F. Dailey (today I suppose they've forgotten even the cigar named after him) cavorting over the boards & unctuously intoning "Cindy" or "Mah Sunflower Sue"! But I don't believe I quite share Mr. Fischer's refined *nasal* discrimination. While I *am* peculiarly repelled by unpleasant odours, I have no vast hankering after perfumes, & always urge barbers not to smell up my old bean with patent citified lotions. I like the fresh scent of springtide on the hills, & the August aura of new-mown hay, but I'd never go to the trouble of building an organ of olfactory notes—with perfume-phials for pipes—as did des Esseintes in the tenth chapter of "A Rebours"! I surely hope that your recently intensified sensitiveness to music may yield adequate returns in pleasure & aesthetic creation. It flatters me to learn that a passage in my "Witch-House" has evoked an experiment in musical composition from you—& I hope the projected piece may develop successfully. *Weird music* is a subject all in itself—& one of which the *idea* fascinates me tremendously. I've dragged allusions to such into many of my tales—the impression being derived from composite memories of Saint-Saëns' "Dans Macabre", Grieg's "Peer Gynt" suite, & other stuff by Tchaikowsky, Rimsky-Korsakov, Debussey, Sibelius, et al. Incidentally, two of my "Fungi from Yuggoth" ("Mirage" & "The Elder Pharos") were set to weird music a few years ago by someone in your neighbour-town of Los Angeles—one Harold S. Farnese (a native of Monaco, trained in Paris & specialising in fantastic airs), Dean of the local Institute of Musical Education. Unfortunately, I never had a chance to hear his compositions. He had an idea at one time of writing an opera bringing in my synthetic pantheon of Yog-Sothoth, Cthulhu, Nyarlathotep, Nug, Yeb, Azathoth, &c. (in fact, he first asked me to attempt the libretto, though I knew damn well I couldn't swing such an enterprise without experience), but I don't know whether he ever developed it or not. It must be a couple of years since I last heard from him.

I'm glad the small magazines safely arrived, & that you found my contributions therein tolerable. If you get the new *Fanciful Tales* pray let me know, & I will send you a table of errata listing the 59—count 'em—59 bad boners in the text of my "Nameless City." Glad you liked "Sarnath", although I see a good deal of the merely picturesque & imitative in it. Certainly, that kind of style is almost inevitable if one is to parallel Dunsany's themes—but alas! not everyone can tread those paths as successfully as Edward John Moreton Drax Plunkett! "The Dunwich Horror" attempts a certain composite realism in setting—engrafting certain characteristics of Southern Vermont upon the retrogressive countryside of the region near Springfield, Mass. It is, in a way, an echo of a visit to Wilbraham, Mass. in 1928, during which my hosts related much of the local traditions, & had much to say of the state of the contemporary peasantry. "The Thing on the Doorstep" is, contrary to my usual practice, more of a character study than a geographical study. I'll be interested to learn of the reason for your particular interest in it. Here, possibly, the reason why the terror-ridden character doesn't break away sooner is less obscure than in other tales of mine. But regarding those other cases—as you agree, the problem has many aspects. What really should be done is to provide a proper motivation without rubbing it into the reader. Let the vague, dreamlike impression remain, but see that troublesome questions are unobtrusively anticipated. A more careful story-teller than I ought to be able to do that.

I am delighted to know that somebody besides myself likes good old Colley Cibber's "Richard III" version! To my mind, the borrowing of material from "Henry VI" adds vastly to the unity of the thing, & I don't wonder that it has persisted as an acting text. I've tried off & on to get a copy for the past 35 years, but haven't succeeded. Evidently it is now to be commonly found only in sets of the British Dramatists. I read it in an early collection of the sort belonging to the public library. However—other Shakespearian dramas did not fare well in the classick aera, as the operatick fate of "The Tempest" at the hands of Dryden & Davenant, the *rhymed* "Macbeth" & "Julius Caesar" of Davenant alone, the "improved" "Timon of Athens" of Shadwell, the stepped-up "Troilus & Cressida" of Dryden [in the prologue to which he speaks of Avon's Bard as "Untaught, unpractis'd, in a barb'rous Age"], & the cheerful Tate "King Lear" with a new fifth act mournfully attest. In considering poor "Lear" I blush to think that my Phillips great-great-grandfather has a Tate & Brady epitaph on his tombstone: "The sweet Remembrance of the Just / Shall flourish when he sleeps in Dust." Lear was certainly pretty well mangled by the time decorous Mr. Winter prepared his version for Edwin Booth. Incidentally—if you like, I'll be glad to lend you the old amateur papers containing Loveman's interpolated "Lear" & "Macbeth" scenes. I hope you will some time attempt the possible Goneril-Regan scene before the battle!

It interests me immensely to learn that your father has varied artistic endowments outside the dramatic field, & I surely hope you will let me see photographs of his recent sculptural achievements. No one, surely, is better qualified than he for any task depending upon a sympathetic understanding of Shakespeare's characters! I hope—& am led to believe by the word *casting*—that his process is of a sort to permit of duplication, rather than one yielding only a single copy of the embodied item. Did I mention that the weird writer Clark Ashton Smith is also a sculptor of sorts, & that an exhibition of his grotesque & fantastic statuettes (one of which, I learn with becoming pride, is a monstrosity 11 inches tall entitled "Cthulhu's Child") will next month be held at the Croker Art Gallery in Sacramento? Virgil Finlay—the gifted new WT artist—also experiments in carving & modelling.

I am delighted to hear that classic Rome forms your favourite historic period, even though you have not that curious sense of personal membership in it which has always haunted me. Incidentally, very few seem to have that acute feeling of belonging to some remote age, race, & region. The closest parallel to myself in that respect whom I have known was the late Robert E. Howard, with his veritably atavistic participation in the life of ancient tribal Gaul & Britain. I appreciate very strongly the force of the dramatic contrast formed by those occasional contacts of the classical & northern worlds which history records—Goths in the Euxine & Mediterranean lands, the Massilian Greek Pytheas in Iceland in the time of Alexander the Great, &c. &c. &c. Just as you think of Vikings in the Hellenistic-Roman world, so do I think of Roman navigators in strange & distant parts—washed across the Western Ocean to unknown shores, camping on the future site of Providence & fighting the coppery predecessors of the Narragansetts & Wampanoags, or captured by the soldiers of the Mayas & forced to escape from ornately carven dungeons in Guatemalan jungles . . . . . or circumnavigating Africa & sampling the exotic marvels of India, China, & lost Polynesian lands of which there remain today only the vine-grown megaliths of Ponape & the cryptic eidola of Easter Island . . . . or trading overland with vanished peoples in the Gobi, & perchance for a moment glimpsing immemorial Shamballah behind its curtain of oblivion . . . . . . or penetrating south into Africa beyond the mark set by Maternus, skirting the Niger, threading through steaming jungles, fighting savages, pygmies, & apes, killing lions & rhinocerases, & finally coming upon that Kingdom of Elder Horror whereof there survives today only the ruined masonry of the Great Zimbabwe. . . . A knowledge of the hellish Dianic cult that festered underground in Europe adds to the fascination of the pageant—& one might add hints of straggling Neanderthal survivors in some of the great limestone cavern systems . . . . survivors whom stray legionaries encounter sane, but from whom they escape as madmen. I'm glad you've secured "The Witch-Cult in Western Europe", which certainly throws a clear light on many aspects of Machen, Blackwood, & others. The theories of Miss Murray regarding the source of the cult have been attacked from different angles by scholars as antipodal as Joseph McCabe & the Rev. Montague Summers, but I still think they are as plausible as any yet advanced. You will, I think, appreciate "The White Peo-

ple" anew upon giving it a post-Murray re-reading. What I like about it is its
subtlety & slow, cumulative convincingness—qualities in which, to my mind,
it excels "The Black Seal." The device of a child-narrator for the most hellish
parts is exceedingly clever—& those sinister landscape-descriptions can
wring a shudder from me even after numberless re-readings:

> "I looked out from them & saw the country, but it was strange. It
> was winter time, & there were black terrible woods hanging from the
> hills all round; it was like seeing a large room hung with black curtains,
> & the shape of the trees seemed quite different from any I had seen be-
> fore. I was afraid. Then beyond the woods there were other hills round
> in a great ring, but I had never seen any of them; it all looked black, &
> everything had a voor over it. It was all so still & silent, & the sky was
> heavy & grey & sad, like a wicked voorish dome in Deep Dendo. I went
> on into the dreadful rocks."

I hope you'll write that play about the Caesars—& meanwhile I am intensely interested in your present epic of Fafhrd & the Mouser in the Julio-
Claudian world. I note that you have them *reincarnated* rather than preserved
from the earliest Hellenistic period through the action of some cryptical
elixir. Which reminds me—about what *is* the approximate period of "Adept's
Gambit"? You seem to suggest a Hellenised Orient—which fixes the time as
after Alexnader—but introduce an allusion to Italy as rustic or provincial,
which places things well before the Mithridatic wars . . . . & perhaps before
the Macedonian & Syrian wars as well, since Asiatics would not be likely to
speak patronisingly of Rome after Magnesia. Perhaps, then, we may call the
period around B.C. 250—is this reasonably correct? As I have said before, I
fear that the mention of *Hittites* as a living nationality as late as Greek times
(the period is conclusively fixed as post-Socratic on p. 6) constitutes an
anachronism. Most of the ancient separate races had then so far coalesced,
& had been so overridden by the Persian & (if post-Alexandrine, as seems
indicated) Greek civilisations, that only a few of the very ancient distinctions
then held good. Jews & Phoenicians were distinct, & Philistines were only
just dissolving. But I doubt the survival of the Hittites. And yet it does not do
to be dogmatic. This matter is worth a bit of special research on your part—
or I'll transmit any conclusive information which may come my way.

All of which brings me to your question about the status of anachronisms in general, as occurring in the course of historical romances with invented characters. In reply, I would say that *small* slips do not generally seem
like grave defects, though very flagrant errors (such as the "Ephesian Dome"
which our friend Cibber engrafted on the stamping-ground of Fafhrd & the
Mouser, or some representation of a Persian Empire [other than the Parthian
region which revolted in B.C. 250 & became a new Persian Empire under the
Sassanidae in A.D. 224] after Alexander the Great) are to be frowned upon.
When we come upon too many—or too great—lapses from what we know

to be fact, we tend to find a narrative less convincing than it would otherwise be. Shakespeare gets away with such things because in him the setting
is only a vague background for character-studies—but in any ordinary tale,
anachronisms ought to be kept within bounds. However—that does not
mean that one needs to retreat to a fantastic or prehistoric dream age, or to
a Dunsanian realm beyond the edge of the world. Some types of fiction
thrive much better in genuine historic settings—& I believe this is true of
your projected novel. The thing to do is to meet the difficulty with a bit of
special reading, & with the critical advice of a few qualified scholars. It is not
hard to brush up passably on a given period—& with such a passable brush-
ing-up one may easily avoid such major errors as would affect the main plot
& action. It is well, of course, to take care that these elements depend as
little as possible on any historical or antiquarian details which might be
called into question. Refer knotty points to specialists—in this case, teachers
of ancient history—when it seems necessary, & let such authorities go over
your rough draught after its completion. With such precautions, you are
pretty sure of escaping any mistakes so bad as to imperil the success of the
story. "Adept's Gambit" is all right except for the few small points mentioned, & there is no reason why the Julio-Claudian novel should not be the
same. I certainly vote for the Roman setting—the advantages of which are
easily obvious.

Now as to the books[4] on this subject which would help to eliminate
anachronisms. First of all, perhaps, one ought to brush up by reading the
relevant sections of some popular text-book like Myers' "Ancient History".*
That gives a fresh general hang of the age, & the relative time of occurrence
of the various major events. It provides a framework of freshened connected
knowledge on which to drape the more detailed & atmospheric results of
later researches. Then it would be a good idea to absorb some general
manuals on Roman life under the Empire—of which there are fortunately a
good number. The best starter that I know of is *"Roman Life in Pliny's Time"*,
by Maurice Pellison. Never mind the later period—the essentials will hold
good for the Julio-Claudian as well as the Domitiano-Trajanic age, & you can
check up on details with larger works. This gives a fine generalised picture—
& they used to use it in the old Chautauqua reading courses. Read also the
useful little *"Roman Antiquities"** by A. S. Wilkins in the old Science Primer series. I've seen *Thomas's "Roman Life"* recommended, but haven't read it myself. Also *Davis's "A Way in Old Rome"*. Of the formal encyclopaedic &
statistical manuals you can't beat that old standby—Fiske's translation of *J. J.
Eschenburg's Manual of Classical Literature*. It is about as thorough as anything
I know, & the century-ago scholarship is not such as to mislead. It may be
hard to get hold of now, but my grandpaternal copy (1846) is at your dis-

---

4. Books marked with an asterisk are owned by me, & at your disposal as loans. I
have also the large Harper Dictionary—but I need that so often myself that I
wouldn't dare lend it, lest I be caught in a tight place.

posal. Of shorter manuals James S. S. *Baird's Classical Manual** is probably the
best, although the *"Classical Handbook"** of T. P. & W. F. Allen is not to be despised. These latter are very concise, & have some extremely useful tables. In
Baird there is a table by which any modern date can be translated into its
Roman equivalent—thus a glance shews that today, Dec. 19, is A.D. XIV. KAL.
IAN. (A.D. signifying *ante diem,* not *anno Domini!*). All these general manuals
have sections on classical geography which would save one from bad boners,
but I find it fascinating to read separate works on ancient geography—in
fact, such works are really necessary if one is to speak in much detail of this
or that region in Italia or the provinces. The best such work—by an infinitely
wide margin—is *Charles Anthon's "System of Ancient & Mediaeval Geography"**.
(1850) Good old Charlie! He certainly started classical scholarship in America,
& compares well with many a European figure! Shorter & less thorough is
*Mitchell's Ancient Geography**—with its running-mate *Mitchell's Ancient Atlas.* I
used to have the atlas, but it was lost during a household removal. (Three
removes, said old Dr. Franklin, are as bad as a fire!) For the geography of the
city of Rome—hills, topography, nature & location of streets, buildings, fora,
statues, &c.—nothing can excel *"Rome of Today & Yesterday: The Pagan City"**,
by John Dennie. However, John was pre-Mussolini, so take the "today" descriptions with reservations. Archaeology has done its stuff since then!
Meanwhile arrange to have constant access, throughout the composition of
the story, to some inclusive & convenient reference-work such as *Harper's
Dictionary of Classical Literature & Antiquities.* That's a volume without which I
could not exist. Ædepol, the questions it settles every day! I have also two
smaller reference volumes which, added together, make a very passable substitute—& these (*Smith's Smaller Classical Dictionary** & *Smith's Smaller Dictionary of Greek & Roman Antiquities**) I'd be glad to shoot along for a long-term
loan. With such a handy reservoir of facts at one's side as a guide in moments of doubt, the chances of falling into serious errors are vastly de-
creased. Oh, yes—& in order to be sure of accuracy in architectural or other
art matters, better get some good classical museum handbook or some such
brace of popular manuals as *Tarbell's "History of Greek Art"** & *Goodyear's "Roman & Mediaeval Art"*.* I could also lend you *Smith & Slater's "Classic Architecture"**, a rather more thorough work within its field, & very useful if you have
occasion to describe any building (especially a *fictitious* building, where fancy
might otherwise run riot) in detail. [I also have the companion Gothic & Renaissance work.] Well—so much for the groundwork. Now as for added atmosphere—there are a few modern novels which help pretty well to evoke
the spirit of Roman times, & which are distinctly worth reading. Avoid the
conventional "Quo Vadis" junk, with its mawkish & distorted emphasis on
early Christianity. Take only such novels as shew the Roman scene normally
through Roman eyes. *"A Friend of Caesar"**, by William Stearns Davis,* is a bit
insipid, but nevertheless worth going through. *Desider Kostolanyi's "The
Bloody Poet"*—a study of the emperor Nero—also reflects its time & theme
very well. Better still, as I am told (though I haven't yet read them), are the

two recent companion novels *"I, Claudius", & "Claudius the God", by Robert Graves*. But the finest modern fictional reflections that *I've* ever seen—the most Roman-like re-creations of the daily life & manners—are the two novels by *Edward Lucas White* (also a *weird* author. Poor old duffer—he committed suicide two or three years ago) *"The Unwilling Vestal"* & *"Andivius Hedulio"**. This latter, a picaresque novel of great length & wide scope, forms a magnificent pageant of every phase of life, urban & rural, in Imperial Italy. Read it by all means if you don't know it already. Both of these tales are laid in the age of the Antonines—rather late for your purposes—but even within them there is enough explicit differentiation betwixt the permanent & the new to make them extremely useful. Now for a little more concrete & specific historic dope—read *Suetonius' "Lives of the Caesars"** & the relevant parts of *Velleius Paterculus* (remembering, however, that the former runs to slander, & the latter to flattery). Of modern works, try *Bury's "Student's Roman Empire"*, *Cope's "The Early Empire"*, *Merivale's "History of the Romans Under the Empire"*, & *Gage's "Society in Rome Under the Caesars"*. Bits of *Montesquieu* & *Michelet* are also useful, & for heavier dope don't forget *Mommsen's "Provinces of the Roman Empire from Caesar to Diocletian"*. Well—all this takes you pretty well along. For the most minute details, & such valuable colour-touches as the names of consuls in given years, there's nothing like going back to the two *original* authorities who best cover the period—*Tacitus** & *Dio Cassius*. I have Murphy's Tacitus, & would give a good deal to get hold of a translated set of Dio Cassius, which I've read at the library. As a final word—all Roman imperial themes bring in the Hellenistic world to a great extent, so don't fail to keep brushed up on the late-Greek dope. Your best guide, I think, will be good old *Mahaffy*—the following three works by whom you ought to peruse: *"Survey of Greek Civilisation"**, *"Old Greek Life"**, & *"The Greek World Under Roman Sway"*. So much for bibliography. Of course you don't have to read *all* of these items—& indeed, if you secure good critics of the manuscript, you could whittle your preparation down to a minimum. One might suggest a *short* reading course something like this:

Another fine sidelight— Lecky's "History of European Morals*"

West's "Ancient History*
Pellison's "Roman Life in Pliny's Time"*
Wilkins' "Roman Antiquities"*
Baird's "Classical Manual*"
Anthon's "Anc. & Med. Geog.*"
Dennie's "Rome*"
Harper's Dictionary (or equivalent*)
White's "Andivius Hedulio*"
Cope's "The Early Empire"
Access to Tacitus & Dio Cassius for consultation
Mahaffy's "Old Greek Life*"

Edgar Saltus's "The Imperial Purple" is pleasant—if somewhat sketchy, flashy & over-"smart"—reading in this line. Ed was a sort of Manhattan Suetonius & Petronius in one.

Even the longer course isn't as dry & pedantic as it sounds, since the whole subject is so damned interesting & full of unparalleled drama that sheer fascination & historic curiosity keeps one's nose glued to the various enlightening authorities. Even more fascinating to me is the sturdy republican age of ruthless expansion when Spain, Carthage, & the East fell before the Roman eagles, & "Mare Nostrum" became a living reality. Also there is a melancholy magic about the final period of decay—when national ennui & administrative & economic complexities lowered the Roman morale, & the vast Imperium began to crumble, decline in art & scholarship, & finally dissolve before the Teutonic inroads—leaving only its eastern half to revert to the Hellenism (or, rather, *remain in* the Hellenism—or Byzantine successor to Hellenism) from which it had never been wrenched. I am fascinated by such questions as that of *when Latin ceased to be spoken in this or that place . . .* when Constantinopolis became *thoroughly* Greek, when the patois of increasingly Teutonised Gaul became openly known as *Lingua Romana* instead of *Lingua Latina* [have you never seen the text of the Strasburg Oath, A.D. 842?][5], & when men in Italy habitually called themselves *Tullio, Varrone, & Luigi* instead of *Tullius, Varro, & Lucius.* What pathos in the brief semi-comebacks toward the last—when the Eastern Empire under Justinianus (one of the last Imperatores who really spoke Latin as a mother-tongue) reconquered North Africa from the Vandals, & in A.D. 553 regained Italia itself . . . as the "Exarchate of Ravenna"! Even a bit of Hispania was reclaimed from the Visigoths—but how long did it all last? The Spanish conquests were merely nominal, & were lost within 70 years. North Africa—& with it Egypt & Syria—was gone to the Arabs within a century & a half. And in two centuries the last Italian fragment had been detached by Franks & Lombards, & the way paved for the ironically named "Holy Roman Empire" (neither holy nor Roman, & seldom a true empire) of Charlemagne & his successors! There is a fascination in this decay—but a sad one. And what a confusion & complexity of manners & customs, with dozens of nations intermixing, & the folkways of each one of them in a state of rapid flux! Here, truly, even the greatest student must unconsciously wallow in anachronisms if he try to depict the age in fiction or drama!

I'm glad to hear of your perusal of "The Last & First Men"—a volume which to my mind forms the greatest of all achievements in the field that Master Ackerman would denominate "scientifiction". Its scope is dizzying— & despite a somewhat disproportionate acceleration of the tempo toward the end, & a few scientific inferences which might legitimately be challenged, it remains a thing of unparalleled power. As you say, it has the truly basic quality of a myth, & some of the episodes are of matchless poignancy & dramatic intensity. This work has evoked dozens of imitations in the pulp magazines—the least absurd of which is a novelette by the brothers Binder,

---

5. in a dialect curiously midway between Latin & what we now call French.

whose title eludes my memory. It is itself perhaps an echo of the spacious speculations of Prof. J. B. S. Haldane regarding the future of mankind both on & off this planet. Have you ever seen the two little books—"Daedalus" [this ably answered by Bertrand Russell in "Icarus"] & "The Last Judgment"— in which Haldane gives free rein to his speculative imagination? Verily, they might form a source-book for dozens of romances enthralling to the "scientifan"! I have both, & would be glad to lend them if you'd like. As for Shiel— his unevenness is surely enough to reduce one to sulphureous eloquence! It would be difficult to find anything more trivial, affected, & flamboyant than his worst stuff—or more vivid, menacing, & genuinely moving than his two high spots—"The House of Sounds" [which represents a 1907 recasting of a florid 1896 attempt whose title I forget] & the first part of "The Purple Cloud." Sorry the "Cloud" seemed a bit disappointing—but possibly I laid the superlatives on too thick when describing it. It is of course riddled with crude & extravagant spots, & the occasional prosaic explanations tend to jar. Likewise, its concluding portions flop miserably into callow romance. But with all its faults it remains great stuff! That panorama of a dead world has no parallel in literature. I own "The Purple Cloud", but "The House of Sounds" has so far eluded my acquisitive attempts. It occurs in a volume called "The Pale Ape & Other Stories", published in London by T. Werner Laurie in 1908. When Knopf & the Vanguard begna reviving interest in Shiel a decade ago—reprinting several of his works—I hoped that "The Pale Ape" might be offered in a new edition—but the boom collapsed before they got around to it. I'm thankful enough that "The Purple Cloud" was reissued in time! Yes—I wish the *right* person might illustrate "Ouroboros"—what a chance for somebody like Sime! If the new WT artist Virgil Finlay (age 22) lives up to his present promise, he'll be a logical candidate for the job in a decade or so. He has his lapses—I didn't care much for that text-belying design for my "Haunter"—but at his best he can knock all rivals sou'sou'west for a triple colonnade of Ceylonese snow-shovels! His drawing for Bloch's "Faceless God" (which Wright has framed for the WT office) is his high spot, but the one for my "Doorstep" is no slouch. Some of the illustrations inflicted upon WT writers are indeed pathetic—almost as bad as the stories! The give-away heading of my "Whisperer" has me still seeing red after 5 years & more! No—I don't think weird illustrations should be detailed. They should have the vagueness & suggestions of instability & mutation characteristic of true dreams. That is why, in WT, I have always preferred Hugh Rankin to others who are better draughtsmen. Finlay, as he matures, is acquiring the right idea—which I think his "Doorstep" design embodies to a perceptible extent. Here's something, by the way, which I lately ground out about Finlay's masterpiece:

To Mr. Finlay, *upon his Design for*
Mr. Bloch's *Tale,* The Faceless God:

In dim Abysses pulse the Shapes of Night,
    Hungry and hideous, with strange Mitres crown'd;
Black Pinions beating in phantastick Flight
    From Orb to Orb thro' sunless Voids profound.
None dares to name the Cosmos whence they course,
    Or guess the Look on each amorphous Face,
Or speak the Words that with resistless Force
    Would draw them from the Hells of outer Space.

Yet here upon a Page our frighten'd Glance
    Finds monstrous Forms no human Eye shou'd see;
Hints of those Blasphemies whose Countenance
    Spreads Death and Madness thro' Infinity.
What Limner he who braves black Gulphs alone,
    And lives to make their alien Horrors known?

N.B. Do you know the work of William Hope Hodgson? It is very obscure, yet almost makes the Machen & Blackwood grade. You ought to read "The Boats of the Glen Carrig", "The House on the Borderland", & "The Night Land". If you wish, I'll have the owner of these books put your name on the list of borrowers among whom they are circulating.

I learn with great interest of Messrs. Nemo & Murphet Leiber, & wish my own household were able to harbour their counterparts. As it is, my aunt & I have reluctantly agreed that our very light scale of housekeeping—involving irregular hours & occasional long absences (as when I paid 2 & 3 month visits in Florida in '34 & '35) on my part—render the tenure of any non-inorganic companions impracticable. Consequently, I am forced to content myself with playing occasional host to varied felidae of the neighbourhood—especially the inhabitants of the boarding-house in a parallel street whose rear abuts on our back garden. For this purpose I always have a supply of catnip on hand, & many an afternoon as I sit writing I have some black or tiger or grey or black-&-white caller racing around the floor after spools or chewing the papers on my desk or alternately purring & dozing in a neighbouring easy-chair, according to his age & temperament. The little garden beside & behind this house is so completely cut off from the world that it forms a favourite congregating-place for local Mousers, grey or otherwise—who tend to choose as their social centre the roof of a small shed directly in line with my west windows. This group of shed-sprawlers has so many of the earmarks of a definite organisation that I have come to regard it (on the analogy of the numerous Greek-letter fraternities which form our neighbours on the ancient hill) as the Providence Chapter of the earthwide Kappa Alpha Tau society—an institution whose initials may be interpreted as the words *Κομπσον Αιλυρον Ταξις* (band of elegant or well-dress'd cats), though low punsters persist in reading a shorter & more phonetic meaning into our corporate initials K.A.T. Of this band, notwithstanding the inapplicability of the adjective top me, I consider myself an honorary member by virtue of my lifelong regard for the feline species. I am sure that Nemo & Murphet are high officials of the Southern California Chapter—just as Mother Simaetha, the incredibly aged coal-black witch-cat of Clark Ashton Smith, heads the Ladies' Auxiliary of the Central California Chapter. Enclosed you will find a small tribute which the Providence K.A.T. is sending, with its compliments, to Nemo & Murphet. I believe you have not seen this tale—or at least, that you do not have it permanently—hence I trust that its new furry owners will permit you to glance through it at least once or twice. It is rather a favourite of mine, as my own junk goes, & last Christmas my young friend Barlow astonished me with this special edition of 40 copies, which he sent to most of our circle in lieu of a greeting card. He gave me several, but unfortunately my duplicates have narrowed down to the present rather seedy copy which borrowers have harshly handled, & for whose condition I must very sincerely apologise. I ought not to have allowed this gift-edition to piece out my battery of WT lending copies . . . . . but I am sure that Nemo & Murphet have a generous share of civilised tolerance. By the way—I hope to read at some time of Yanquisaga & his War-Cats, who respond to the summons of a silver whistle. They remind me of some of the characters in my repudiated fantasy "The Dream-Quest of Unknown Kadath". The peculiar charm of the felidae is a composite thing difficult to analyse. It seems to arise on the one hand from the utter grace & harmony of the cat—a perfect eurythmy pervading outlines & motions alike—plus those marks of cool, superior independence & self-sufficiency which remove Sir Thomas from the realm of human satellitism & make him the aristocratic exponent of another order of being—proud, alien in motives, values, & objectives, & linked with the mysteries of those black outer gulfs whence surely the first terrestrial felines lithely sprang long ago when Mu & Hyperborea were young. The ardent ailurophile is in good company, for does he not number eminent men as varied as Mohammed, Richelieu, Dr. Johnson, Poe, Baudelaire, & Vilfredo Pareto among his fellows?

As for the attitude of rational men of science toward the marvellous—the whole thing goes back into the remotest beginnings of epistemology. What do we know? How do we know we know it? Where the hell do all our ideas & impressions & perspectives come from, anyhow? Obviously, our traditional heritage of beliefs is of no use as a guide to truth, since it is predominantly an indiscriminate mass of primitive personifications, childish animistic pseudo-explanations, & ignorant inferences made from a background of subjective emotions & typical mental illusions—the whole developed & crystallised at a prehistoric date when the race knew nothing of the facts behind its environment, of cause & effect as related to terrestrial & celestial phenomena, or of the workings of its own consciousness & feelings. In an honest attempt to learn what the cosmos is, how it works, what its trends & directions are, & what relation to it is borne by organic life (including ourselves), religion & folklore are absolutely out [save as illustrations of human psychological processes]. Our only possible method is to observe the phenomena of the external world at first-hand—excluding all hereditary or preconceived ideas—& to form from an accurate study of these phenomena a set of inferences based on those same dependable & verifiable principles of cognition whereby we recognise intrinsic similarities & differences in immediate things such as temperature, degree of light, colour, odour, texture, sound, taste, & so on. It is of course understood that such an inferential process necessarily involves not only a minute biological study of those human channels through which our impressions come, but likewise a close survey (so far as our position & limitations allow) of those cognitive functions whereby we unconsciously select & emphasise & classify impressions, & draw conclusions from them. In these latter studies we must be prepared to realise that our images of things are arbitrarily limited by the accidents of our physical equipment (we, a spider, a snake, & a bird see & hear & feel & smell & taste altogether different things when experiencing the same objective environment), & that the concepts we deduce from these images are themselves altogether dependent upon a physiological state of things conditioned by racial history & swayed by numberless obscure factors. Ability to perceive & infer, a quality at first developed solely in the interest of primitive needs & gratifications, is constantly at the mercy of the crude instincts & emotions which called it forth, & can only with the most supreme difficulty be dissociated from the irrational hereditary delusions, material interests, & childish desires & perspectives with which it has for hundreds of thousands of years—or countless millions, if we go behind the human & primate & mammal stages—been inextricably intertwined. The stimulation of a nerve-centre, the hypertrophy or atrophy ofan endocrine gland, the prior presence of a given concept or impression—any of these things may, wholly apart from truth or from any legitimate evidence, totally alter the conclusions which a given mind will draw from a given set of external impressions. Our subjective life is an utter, unreliable chaos from which no truth may be extracted, & which we must examine with the utmost closeness—studying its principles & characteristic tendencies—in order to allow for its effect on the objective concepts that we try to form. It is, then, no wonder that rational observers are cautious in advancing claims of the marvellous which on the one hand bear a suspicious resemblance to traditional notions of known erroneousness, & which on the other hand are sustained only feebly or not at all by any genuine or verifiable evidence in the external world. Of course, there are iconoclastic zealots who *overdo* the matter of caution—tending to minimise the evidence in behalf of things which seem at first sight unusual or opposed to the recognised scheme of Nature, & to magnify the defects & unreliability of our cognitive apparatus—but it is not the conclusions of these pedantic enthusiasts which triumph in the long run. Normal scientific progress generally makes steadily for increased truth—hence the tragedy of those new philosophies, so popular in totalitarian dictatorships, which exalt unreason & demand that scholarship be used only to serve preconceived propagandist ends. Nor will science ever be able to kill the feeling of wonder in the human spirit. The mystery of the black outer gulfs, & of the deepest cognitive processes within us, must always remain unplumbed—& against these limitations the ego-driven restlessness of the human consciousness & imagination must always frantically pound. It is phlegmatic complacency or a callous absorption in material things, which—rather than scientific truth—forms wonder's greatest foe. ¶ And now let me apologise for this extreme & tedious verboseness. Pray convey my compliments to Mrs. Leiber, whose interesting letter of the 8th I am about to answer. ¶ Yr obt Servt—The Old Man Without a Beard

P.S. As per instructions, I am holding the two MSS. for further discussion. I hope they may—if not destined for early publication—be circulated (as has other similar material) among a choice circle of the elect—such as Barlow, Clark Ashton Smith, Miss Moore, H. C. Koenig, & so on. Koenig (450 E. 80th St., N.Y. City) is the owner of those W. H. Hodgson books which I'm suggesting that you borrow from him if you can't get them locally.

[8]   To Jonquil Leiber

December 20, 1936

Dear Mrs. Leiber:—
      . . . . . Concerning the matter of prosaic toil—I can scarcely rejoice that I have not discovered & engaged in some more regular & remunerative form of it than free-lance revision, since the tangible results would be distinctly more helpful than the psychological atmosphere would be harmful! Instead, if ever I *do* stumble upon an opening, the picturesque conception of me as a non-time-clock-puncher will swiftly & ruthlessly vanish. However, I shall probably be available a decade hence—if still living at so advanced an age—for that good-weird-magazine editorship which Mr. Leiber has in mind! Such a magazine would surely be welcomed by a limited & devoted circle—though in harsh fact I gravely doubt its practicability as a commercial or even self-sustaining venture. The old W.T. group has many a time discussed something of the sort—pointing out that virtually all of the world's first-rate authors (for example—Henry James, Rudyard Kipling, Edith Wharton, F. Marion Crawford, Theodore Dreiser, Guy de Maupassant, &c. &c. &c) have at one time or another written weird material, & arguing that they would probably produce a great deal more if a definite & dependable market existed. With this potential source of contents (to which would of course be added the presumably increased output of such acknowledged fantaisistes as Blackwood, Machen, Dunsany, de la Mare, &c.), argued the optimists, the right sort of publisher might float a weird magazine of the very highest grade, commanding a select & dependable public, & reaching persons who would toss aside a cheap rag like W.T. with contempt. A pleasing picture! But there were not lacking pessimists to point out that this select & faithful public would of necessity be woefully small. After all, a taste for fantasy in large doses is a rather unusual thing. Most readers like it only occasionally—relishing a Machen book now &

then, or faintly appreciating the timid & insipid bits (like "The House of the Laburnums" in the Dec. *Harpers*) sparingly scattered through the conventional magazines, but becoming distinctly bored when confronted by a solid or frequent diet of shadow & bizarrerie. Hence the reluctance of book publishers to issue collections of weird short stories . . . . & hence, by inference, the impossibility of finding enough readers among the literate to keep a cosmic-spectral periodical alive. That Farnsworth Wright & his congeners recognise this dilemma is very obvious—for their output is deliberately designed to attract the limitless hordes of the crude & illiterate. They tap a class which a civilised magazine could not reach—the coarse sensation-seeker, the superstitious séance-devotee, & so on—& yet they manage to retain a small literate following through the insertion of a few passable yarns, & because of the fact that no other magazines of the like subject-matter exist. The editors are glad to hold this handful of the civilised if they can do so without alienating their bread-&-butter-yielding yokelry—but when it comes to a choice betwixt the two, the yokelry wins every time. Caeteris paribus, the cheap, sensational story is preferred to the sincere artistic effort. And the sad thing is that the editors are probably commercially right. That's what business is! If they tried to present an all-civilised programme of fiction their circulation would probably dwindle below the self-supporting limit. But let us hope—for the sake of weird literature as well as of that editorship—that conditions may somehow miraculously change before 1947. Good luck to the future *Leiber Fabularum Pavidorum* . . . . if one may attempt a base but classic example of paronomasia.

    I can appreciate the startling contrast which would have been afforded if—in consonance with the whimsical wish of Fafhrd the Viking—I had suddenly appeared, like some skeleton at the feast, at Mr. John Barrymore's Anacreontic gathering. That your genial host would have 'gone to pieces over me' (albeit for a far different reason than that which caused his disintegration over your distinguished 'governor's' visage) I can well imagine; for even the most potent distillate of the golden maize never produced a pink elephant quite so grotesque & terrifying as the thing he would have beheld! Alas that I was unavoidably absent—for might not the shock have permanently flung the ivy-wreathed genius upon a water-wagon destined to bear him to new heights of accomplishment? By such little slips is the course of history & of the arts sometimes irrevocably changed! Yes, indeed, I have frequently encountered Mr. Barrymore's name in the press, & must congratulate him on his ability to remain in touch with romance to an extent not common among those of our greying generation! It is only in an earlier & widely different phase that this luminary & I have any point of resemblance—this being our common difficulty in establishing contact with systematic toil. I have always appreciated that oft-repeated anecdote of his youth—when, as a somewhat elegant but scarcely industrious flaneur in '06, he was engulfed in the chaos of the San Francisco disaster. Along with others he was drafted into emergency rescue & ruin-clearing service by the military authorities in charge of the stricken area—upon hearing of which his illustrious uncle, Mr. John Drew, is reported to have exclaimed, "By god, it took an earthquake & the United States Army to put John to work!" And yet the parallel is by no means perfect, since there is no period of my life in which I could not have been driven into useful pursuits by an earthquake alone—or by an army without an earthquake! No use trying to compete with the great in colour or intensity!

Speaking of industrio-economic matters—let me assure you that a 2-or-3-dollar-a-week dietary programme need not involve even a particle of malnutrition or unpalatability if one but knew what to get & where to get it. The tin can & delicatessen conceal marvellous possibilities! Porridge? Mehercule! On the contrary, my tastes call for the most blisteringly highly-seasoned materials conceivable, & for desserts as close to 100% $C_{12}H_{22}O_{11}$ as possible. Indeed, of this latter commodity I never employ less than four teaspoons in an average cup of coffee. Favourite dinners—Italian spaghetti, chile con carne, Hungarian goulash (save when I can get white meat of turkey with highly-seasoned dressing). If this be asceticism, make the most of it! As for the expense element—to begin with, I eat only twice daily from choice . . . or rather, digestive advisability. I adopted this two-meal programme long before I had to economise. The rest is merely a matter of judicious and & far from self-denying choice. Let us investigate a typical day's rations.

(a) *Breakfast* (whether I eat it before or after retiring depends on whether I retire at 2 a.m. or 9 a.m. or 3 p.m. or 9 p.m. or some other hour. My programme of sleeping & waking is very flexible.)
Doughnut from Weybosset Pure Food Market..................................0.015
York State Medium Cheese (for sake of round numbers) 0.060
Coffee + Challenge Brand Condensed Milk + $C_{12}H_{22}O_{11}$..................<u>0.025</u>
Total Breakfast.................0.100

(b) *Dinner* (occurring vaguely betwixt 6 & 9 or 10 p.m.)
1 can Rath's Chili con Carne*...0.100
2 slices Bond Bread...0.025
Coffee (with accessories as noted above)...0.025
Slice of cake or quadrant (or octant) of pie.....................................<u>0.050</u>
Total Dinner 0.200

Grand Total for Entire Day....0.30
7

Average Total per Week........2.10

---

*(or Armour's Corned Beef Hash or baked beans from delic., or Armour's Frankfort Sausage or Boiardi Meat Balls & Spaghetti or chop suey from delicatessen or Campbell's Vegetable Soup, &c. &c. &c.)

Occasionally, of course, extravagant additions occur—such as fruit with breakfast, or cheese with pie at dinner, or a chocolate bar or ice cream at an odd hour, or a meat-course costing more than a dime, or other sybaritic luxuries. But even the most Lucullan indulgence seldom tops an hebdomadal 3 bucks. And the old man still lives—in a fairly hale & hearty state, at that! Oddly enough, I was a semi-invalid in the old days when I *didn't* economise. Porridge? Not for Grandpa! . . . . . .

. . . . . I can endorse with the most profanely fervent emphasis your appraisal of American Business Push! The fact is, an ideal of toil for its own sake, & an exaltation of the grasping, aggressively acquisitive type, have always seemed to me so self-evidently barbarous & ignominious that I have never quite been able to realise their existence as important factors. Commercial ideals are a trifle better camouflaged in New England than in other parts of America; & as one more disposed to draw ideas from books than to absorb the spirit of my physical environment, I managed to grow up with a European rather than pioneer-American scale of values regarding the individual & society. Not that I have ever scorned honest industry—for should not every person contribute all he can to society, in exchange for the organised benefits it extends him?—but that I have scorned the notion of industry *as an end in itself.* I cannot comprehend the exaltation of a mere *process* as distinguished from its *objects. Working to live* I can understand—but not *living to work!* And the poisonous, cheapening vulgarity of the commercial mind— the readiness to haggle, the tendency to relate all ideas & impressions to material advantage, & the rat-like intensiveness associated with 'business enterprise'—has always nauseated me so violently that the notion of a social order founded on it has seemed to partake of fantastic nightmare rather than sober reality. Yet I suppose such a reign of commercial ideals does exist—indeed, I see many evidences of it when I view the objective phenomena of today. But I fancy its triumph will be short-lived. Mechanisation of industry & diffusion of knowledge are laying the foundations for widespread change, & squirearchy & capitalism must alike go down in time before some planned society more rational & equitable than either. Let us only hope that in this part of the world the coming transition will be evolutionary rather than revolutionary—as indeed we may expect of any fabric whose cultural roots are of Northwestern Europe. But so far as the past & present are concerned, I would certainly be more at home in England than in America. Indeed—if I were not so wrapped up in antiquarianism that I virtually *am* in England spiritually, I would probably find my milieu psychologically unendurable. I get by because I have blinders on!

It is interesting to know that you have a touch of piracy in your ancestry! I have a *counterfeiter* as a great-great-grand-uncle about whom I'll tell you some time. He was also a silversmith—with pieces surviving in the Metropolitan Museum of N. Y., the Boston Museum of Fine Arts, & elsewhere. He'd have been hanged in 1770 if his neighbours (who were probably implicated in the coining—such offences being lightly regarded in the colonies) hadn't effected a gaol-delivery. I am lineally descended from his elder brother, born in 1723. I wish I could see your ancestral crag of St. Michael's Mount—descriptions of which have always fascinated me. If pictures speak truly, the castle on its summit must be one of the loveliest & most ethereally fantastic objects outside the pages of Dunsany—to which is added the charm of its long history, & the rumour that a giant's skeleton was discovered in a secret dungeon beneath it a century or so ago. The appearance of the Mount with its pinnacled citadel under certain lighting & atmospheric conditions—as, for instance, outlined against an orange sunset—must be exquisite beyond description. And the little village on the shore doubtless shares that fascinating quality which all Cornish seaports seem to possess. (Which reminds me—I suppose you have read E. F. Benson's splendid weird tale "Negotium Perambulans", which is laid in a typical Cornish village betwixt the sea & an overshadowing crag.) Mount's Bay, I believe, still reveals at low tide the spectral black trunks which bespeak its former life as a forest above the water. One can imagine dark and curious things in connexion with a wood beneath the waves! All told, I believe that Cornwall must form the most picturesque & fascinating spot in England, with its plenteous reliques of the past, its bold topography, its ancient villages, its tenacious folkways, its suggestions of subtropical vegetation (this in the latitude of northern Newfoundland—so potent are the subtler elements of climate-formation!), & its legends of dim yesterdays & of the sunken land of Lyonesse. I have several ancestral lines which remotely extend back to Cornwall—Carew, Edgecome, Trefusis—hence feel that it is no alien soil. It is in ancient Damnonia, however, that Lovecrafts are chiefly scattered—largely in the valley of the Teign near Newton-Abbot. Historically, Cornwall & Devon are pretty much a unit. Both may have known the footstep of the Phoenician trader as far back as 100 B.C.—& in Egypt tin vases, perhaps of Cornubian origin, have been found in tombs even older than that. That is the kind of contrast which ought to appeal to Fafhrd the Viking. And not very far from your St. Michael's Mount—at St. Hilary on the mainland—there is a stone with a Roman inscription—FLAVIO. IVLIO. CONSTANTIN. PII. CAESARI. DVC. CONSTANTINI. PII. AUGUSTI. FILIO—dating from A.D. 307 & bringing the region vividly into the stream of classical history. Truly, a fitting locale for Adrian Stephens & his Devil-Tower!

I note with great interest the list of Mr. Leiber's Novanglian lives, & regret that none of them are in my own ancestry. My aunt knows *Bronsons* in this city—indeed, until recently two maiden ladies of that name conducted Providence's most select school for small children. The Bronson School was in Hope St.—next the Hope St. High School which I attended 1904-8—& in those days we used to tell fellow-students whose egos we wished to deflate that they were in the wrong building—implying that they belonged over at the Misses Bronson's with the five-year-olds! *Temple* is also represented hereabouts—indeed, if the rain lets up this afternoon my aunt & I are going to hear a lecture on old textiles at the School of Design half way down the

hill by one who combines a Temple line with our *Casey* line—the latter the
one on which the counterfeiter of 1770 occurs. Rather odd, by the way, to
find an Irish name like Casey in early Rhode Island. That's my only line of
ancestry outside England and Wales. The Caseys—seated in Tyrone & of the
Anglo-Irish Protestant persuasion—were engulfed in the massacre of 1641,
& of this branch only a 6-year-old boy named Thomas survived. He was res-
cued by his nurse & taken to his mother's family in Gloucestershire, whence
he emigrated to Newport, Rhode Island, in 1658. Sam the Counterfeiting
Silversmith (b. 1724) & my ancestor John (b. 1723) were his grandsons. Other
descendants appear elsewhere in history. Capt. Wanton Casey fought with
the rebels in the trouble of 1775–83. Gen. Silas Casey was the author of a
book of military tactics & died in the Mexican War. Another of them was the
engineer who either started or finished (I forget which) the Washington
Monument, whilst a later scion was (may gawd forgive him) the architect of
Washington's baroque & bedizened Library of Congress. Foine bhoys, ahl av
thim, aven if wan av thim did go a bit wrong toward the end of the 1760's, &
misapply his talent in constructing near-silver bas-reliefs of the reigning
Bourbons & Broganzas (the *corpora delicti* were fake Spanish milled dollars &
Portugese Moidares). The lecturer we are (perhaps) about to hear is Miss
Elizabeth Temple Casey, Asst. Curator of the School of Design Mu-
seum. . . . . . .
       Yr. Obdt &c. H P L

[9]   To Fritz Leiber, Jr.
                                    DATA. PROVIDENTIAE.
                                         VIII. A. K. FEBR.
                                             Jany. 25, 1937
FLAVIUS. SENILIS. P. CORNELIO. SCIPIONI. S. P. D.
       The reprehensibly late date of this bulletin may be charged jointly to the
plethora of tasks currently pressing on me, & to the reduced amount of energy available for their performance. For the past month I have been more or
less on the semi-invalid list—with a recurrent winter malady manifested in
swollen feet & ankles, plus a curiously persistent combination of intestinal
indigestion & general weakness perhaps allied to the prevailing grippe. Not
that I've been laid flat—indeed, I've managed to take regular walks for my
health on warm days in a pair of cut & stretched old shoes, & have attended
most of the recent college lectures . . . on subjects as diverse as Peruvian
antiquities, Italian Romanesque architecture, biological implications in philosophy, modern French painters, & Greek astronomical hypotheses. But I've
had to rest frequently, & it has taken me a hell of a while to get anything
done. Meanwhile I have heard most interestingly from the grey mouser of
Louisville (who I hope is still above water despite the floods now visiting his
section)—his latest epistle being a marvellously brilliant document accom-

panied by a generously proportioned pastel drawing of our curious friend Ningauble from the crayon of his gifted wife. In an earlier epistle the Gray One most kindly quoted for my benefit the opening paragraphs of the Fafhrd-Mouser cycle, which gave a certain feeling of orientation regarding the series as a whole. . . . . . .

. . . . . It is with the greatest interest that I learn of your plans for revising the "Gambit", & I shall surely welcome the new version when it reaches me. The plan for greater indefiniteness in allusions will surely dispose of all the anachronisms—though if you wished to avoid an excess of compound words you could call a "scientist" either a *philosopher* or a *cunning artificer,* depending on which side of his activities you wished to emphasise. Your suggestion for an era-fixing first paragraph sounds very fruitful—& that possible allusion to Hamilcar & his small son at the end provides another distinctly fascinating link with the historic stream. Regarding the basic plot & motivation changes—these all seem eminently in the right direction. It is one of my fictional axioms that, although a writer should feel perfectly free to change his plot or characters or emphasis during the course of composition, he ought to be scrupulously careful to go over the finished MS. & reconcile very part with the dominant design finally adopted. I don't believe your revision will injure the style, since you seem to have a natural & easy mastery of the chosen type of prose rhythm. Naturally, the later sections will need but little change. Would you like your original MS. returned directly? It seems as if you might use many of the pages & avoid retyping. Let me know. I am very grateful for permission to circulate the MS. among a select circle, & will take pains to confine the list to the extremely appreciative—thus avoiding both delay & wear & tear on the MS. You notes on Fafhrd's & the Mouser's possible antecedents are extremely interesting—& I wish good old Two-gun Bob Howard were alive to see this echo of his virile & adventurous heroics. Some day I surely hope a great deal of the Fafhrd cycle will get into print—leading off with "Adept's Gambit". I fancy you are wise, after all, in choosing an imaginary age for the forthcoming story—especially since you wish to include dealings with monarchs & leaders. R E H had a splendidly self-consistent world of pre-history mapped out for his King Kull & Conan tales, & he made it vital & vivid despite his very unfortunate use (how vainly Price & I have lectured him on this point!) of a nomenclature fraught with misleading historical suggestions. Have you seen the issues of the little *Phantagraph* containing Howard's own serial account of his legendary lands—"The Hyborian Age"? If not, you really ought to get hold of them. Only about a quarter has yet appeared, but the size of instalments may be increased. I'll gladly lend you the issues in question—or you can get them permanently from Donald A. Wollheim, 801 West End Ave., N. Y. City. Not that you'll want to copy anything, but that you'll take pleasure in the vigour & lifelikeness of the coördinated pseudo-historic picture, & will appreciate the Conan tales all the more for having imbibed it. Klarkash-Ton, High Priest of Tsathoggua, likewise has two very well-coördinated mythical worlds—the *Hyperboria* of the fabulous past & the *Zothique* of the infinite future—in addition to his enchanted mediaeval-French world of *Averoigne*—which latter is a sort of European "Arkham country" of 800 years ago. I have helped C A S give *Averoigne* a pseudo-history extending back to Gallic days, when the *Averones* trickled in from a sunken western land & brought with them the hellish tome known in later years as Liber Ivonis or Livre d'Eibon. This dark people set up the worship of Tsathoggua, Sodaqui, or Sadoqua in the region where they settled, so that by the Gallo-Roman period the *Regio Averonum* or *Averonia* was feared as the abode of a black and unearthly sorcery. Especially dreaded were the towns of Simaesis (Ximes) & Avionium (Yvones), where certain cults obscurely flourished. Timid references to the Averones & Avernia occur in certain unknown Gallo-Roman authors such as Flavius Alesius (whose "Annales" tell of the Dark Ones' coming) & the poet Valerius Trevirus. Trevirus, in his hideously necromantic poem "De Noctis Rebus" (circa. A.D. 390), thus alludes to the Averones:

NIGER. INFORMISQUE. VT. NUMEN. AVERONUM. SADOQUA.

—which, in Theobald's privately printed English translation (1711), runs:

> Black & unform'd, as pestilent a Clod
> As dread Sadoqua, Averonia's God.

Merovingian & Carlovingian legends hold dark allusions to the Averones, & by the 11th century the Catholic hierarchy of Averoigne was thoroughly tainted with diabolism. For accounts of mediaeval conditions in this shadowy land, C A S is a better authority than I. As you know, Gaspard du Nord's translation of the Liber Ivonis (whether from the corrupt Latin text or from the accursed Hyperborean original we cannot be sure—his accomplishments were dark & obscure) into mediaeval French in the 12th century brought about frightful consequences—the popular diffusion of certain rites & incantations causing Averoigne to receive that shadow of concentrated necromancy from which it has never quite emerged.

. . . .

> [Your obt. servant,
> H. P. Lovecraft]

STORIES AND POEMS BY
FRITZ LEIBER

ADEPT'S GAMBIT

I. Tyre

It happened that while Fafhrd and the Gray Mouser were dallying in a wine shop near the Sidonian Harbor of Tyre, where all wine shops are of doubtful repute, a long-limbed yellow-haired Galatian girl lolling in Fafhrd's lap turned suddenly into a wallopingly large sow. It was a singular occurrence, even in Tyre. The Mouser's eyebrows arched as the Galatian's breasts, exposed by the Cretan dress that was the style revival of the hour, became the uppermost pair of slack white dugs, and he watched the whole proceeding with unfeigned interest.

The next day four camel traders, who drank only water disinfected with sour wine, and two purple-armed dyers, who were cousins of the host, swore that no transformation took place and that they saw nothing, or very little out of the ordinary. But three drunken soldiers of King Antiochus and the four women with them, as well as a completely sober Armenian juggler, attested the event in all its details. An Egyptian mummy-smuggler won brief attention with the claim that the oddly garbed sow was only a semblance, or phantom, and made dark references to visions vouchsafed men by the animal gods of his native land, but since it was hardly a year since the Seluicids had beaten the Ptolomies out of Tyre, he was quickly shouted down. An impecunious travelling lecturer from Jerusalem took up an even more attenuated position, the semblance of a semblance of a sow.

Fafhrd, however, had no time for such metaphysical niceties. When, maintaining that the sow was not a sow, or even a semblance, but only with a roar of disgust not unmingled with terror, he had shoved the squealing monstrosity halfway across the room so that it fell with a great splash into the water tank, it turned back again into a long-limbed Galatian girl and a very angry one, for the stale water in which the sow had floundered drenched her garments and plastered down her yellow hair (the Mouser murmured, "Aphrodite!") and the sow's uncorsettable bulk had split the tight Cretan waist. The stars of midnight were peeping through the skylight above the tank, and the wine cups had been many times refilled, before her anger was dissipated. Then, just as Fafhrd was impressing a re-introductory kiss upon her melting lips, he felt them once again become slobbering and tusky. This time she picked herself up from between two wine casks and, ignoring the shrieks, excited comments, and befuddled stares as merely part of a rude mystification that had been carried much too far, she walked with Amazonian dignity from the room. She paused only once, on the dark and deep-worn threshold, and then but to hurl at Fafhrd a small dagger, which he absentmindedly deflected upward with his copper goblet, so that it struck full in the mouth a wooden satyr on the wall, giving that deity the appearance of introspectively picking his teeth.

Fafhrd's sea-green eyes became likewise thoughtful. He slowly scanned the wine-shop patrons, face by sly-eyed face, pausing doubtfully when he came to a tall, dark-haired girl beyond the water tank, finally returning to the Mouser. There he stopped, and a certain suspiciousness became apparent in his gaze.

The Mouser folded his arms, flared his snub nose, and returned the stare with all the sneering suavity of a Parthian ambassador. Abruptly he turned, embraced and kissed the cross-eyed Greek girl sitting beside him, grinned wordlessly at Fafhrd, dusted from his coarse-woven gray silk robe the antimony that had fallen from her eyelids, and folded his arms again.

Fafhrd began softly to beat the base of his goblet against the butt of his palm. His wide, tight-laced leather belt, wet with the sweat that stained his white linen tunic, creaked faintly.

Meanwhile murmured speculation as to the person responsible for casting a spell on Fafhrd's Galatian eddied around the tables and settled uncertainly on the tall, dark-haired girl, probably because she was sitting alone and therefore could not join in the suspicious whispering.

"She's an odd one," Chloe, the cross-eyed Greek, confided to the Mouser. "Silent Salmacis they call her, but I happen to know that her real name is Ahura."

"A Persian?" asked the Mouser.

Chloe shrugged. "She's been around for years, though no one knows exactly where she lives or what she does. She used to be a gay, gossipy little thing, though she never would go with men. Once she gave me an amulet, to protect me from someone, she said—I still wear it. But then she was away for a while," Chloe continued garrulously, "and when she came back she was just like you see her now—shy, and tight-mouthed as a clam, with a look in her eyes of someone peering through a crack in a brothel wall."

"Ah," said the Mouser. He looked at the dark-haired girl, and continued to look, appreciatively, even when Chloe tugged at his sleeve. Chloe gave herself a mental bastinado for having been so foolish as to call a man's attention to another girl.

Fafhrd was not distracted by this byplay. He continued to stare at the Mouser with the stony intentness of a whole avenue of Egyptian colossi. The cauldron of his anger came to a boil.

"Scum of wit-weighted culture," he said, "I consider it the nadir of base perfidy that you should try out on me your puking sorcery."

"Softly, man of strange loves," purred the Mouser. "This unfortunate mishap has befallen several others besides yourself, among them an ardent Assyrian warlord whose paramour was changed into a spider between the sheets, and an impetuous Ethiop who found himself hoisted several yards into the air and kissing a giraffe. Truly, to one who knows the literature, there is nothing new in the annals of magic and thaumaturgy."

"Moreover," continued Fafhrd, his low-pitched voice loud in the silence, "I regard it an additional treachery that you should practice your pig-trickery on me in an unsuspecting moment of pleasure."

"And even if I should chose sorcerously to discommode your lechery," hypothesized the Mouser, "I do not think it would be the woman that I would metamorphose."

"Furthermore," pursued Fafhrd, leaning forward and laying his hand on the large sheathed dirk beside him on the bench, "I judge it an intolerable and direct affront to myself that you should pick a Galatian girl, member of a race that is cousin to my own."

"It would not be the first time," observed the Mouser portentously, slipping his fingers inside his robe, "that I have had to fight you over a woman."

"But it would be the first time," asserted Fafhrd, with an even greater portentousness, "that you had to fight me over a pig!"

For a moment he maintained his belligerent posture, head lowered, jaw outthrust, eyes slitted. Then he began to laugh.

It was something, Fafhrd's laughter. It began with windy snickers through the nostrils, next spewed out between clenched teeth, then became a series of jolting chortles, swiftly grew into a roar against which the barbarian had to brace himself, legs spread wide, head thrown back, as if against a gale. It was a laughter of the storm-lashed forest or the sea, a laughter that conjured up wide visions, that seemed to blow from a more primeval, heartier, lusher time. It was the laughter of the Elder Gods observing their creature man and noting their omissions, miscalculations and mistakes.

The Mouser's lips began to twitch. He grimaced wryly, seeking to avoid the infection. Then he joined in.

Fafhrd paused, panted, snatched up the wine pitcher, drained it.

"Pig-trickery!" he bellowed, and began to laugh all over again.

The Tyrian riff-raff gawked at them in wonder—astounded, awestruck, their imaginations cloudily stirred.

Among them, however, was one whose response was noteworthy. The dark-haired girl was staring at Fafhrd avidly, drinking in the sound, the oddest sort of hunger and baffled curiosity—and calculation—in her eyes.

The Mouser noticed her and stopped his laughter to watch. Mentally Chloe gave herself an especially heavy swipe on the soles of her bound, naked feet.

Fafhrd's laughter trailed off. He blew out the last of it soundlessly, sucked in a normal breath, hooked his thumbs in his belt.

"The dawn stars are peeping," he commented to the Mouser, ducking his head for a look through the skylight, "It's time we were about the business."

And without more ado he and the Mouser left the shop, pushing out of their way a newly arrived and very drunken merchant of Pergamum, who looked after them bewilderedly, as if he were trying to decide whether they were a tall god and his dwarfish servitor, or a small sorceror and the great-thewed automaton who did his bidding.

Had it ended there, two weeks would have seen Fafhrd claiming that the incident of the wine shop was merely a drunken dream that had been dreamed by more than one—a kind of coincidence with which he was by no means unfamiliar. But it did not. After "the business" (which turned out to be much more complicated than had been anticipated, evolving from a fairly simple affair of Sidonian smugglers into a glittering intrigue studded with Cilician pirates, a kidnapped Cappadocian princess, a forged letter of credit on a Syracusian financier, a bargain with a female Cyprian slave-dealer, a rendezvous that turned into an ambush, some priceless tomb-filched Egyptian jewels that no one ever saw, and a band of Idumean brigands who came galloping out of the desert to upset everyone's calculations) and after Fafhrd and the Gray Mouser had returned to the soft embraces and sweet polyglot of the seaport ladies, pig-trickery befell Fafhrd once more, this time ending in a dagger brawl with some men who thought they were rescuing a pretty Bithynian girl from death by salty and odorous drowning at the hands of a murderous red-haired giant—Fafhrd had insisted on dipping the girl, while still metamorphosed, into a hogshead of brine remaining from pickled pork. This incident suggested to the Mouser a scheme he never told Fafhrd: namely, to engage an amiable girl, have Fafhrd turn her into a pig, immediately sell her to a butcher, next sell her to an amorous merchant when she had escaped the bewildered butcher as a furious girl, have Fafhrd sneak after the merchant and turn her back into a pig (by this time he ought to be able to do it merely by making eyes at her), then sell her to another butcher and begin all over again. Low prices, quick profits.

For a while Fafhrd stubbornly continued to suspect the Mouser, who was forever dabbling in black magic and carried a gray leather case of bizarre instruments picked from the pockets of wizards and recondite books looted from Chaldean libraries—even though long experience had taught Fafhrd that the Mouser seldom read systematically beyond the prefaces in the majority of his books (though he often unrolled the later portions to the accompaniment of penetrating glances and trenchant criticisms) and that he was never able to evoke the same results two times running with his enchantments. That he could manage to transform two of Fafhrd's lights of love was barely possible; that he should get a sow each time was unthinkable. Besides the thing happened more than twice; in fact, there never was a time when it did not happen. Moreover, Fafhrd did not really believe in magic, least of all the Mouser's. And if there was any doubt left in his mind, it was dispelled when a dark and satiny-skinned Egyptian beauty in the Mouser's close embrace was transformed into a giant snail. The Gray One's disgust at the slimy tracks on his silken garments was not to be mistaken, and was not lessened when two witnesses, traveling horse doctors, claimed that they had seen no snail, giant or ordinary, and agreed that the Mouser was suffering from an obscure kind of wet rot that induced hallucinations of animals in its victim, and for which they were prepared to offer a rare Median remedy at the bargain price of nineteen drachmas a jar.

Fafhrd's glee at his friend's discomfiture was short-lived, for after a night of desperate and far-flung experimentation, which, some said, blazed from the Sidonian harbor to the Temple of Melkarth a trail of snail tracks that next morning baffled all the madams and half the husbands in Tyre, the Mouser discovered something he had suspected all the time, but had hoped was not the whole truth: namely, that Chloe alone was immune to the strange plague his kisses carried.

Needless to say, this pleased Chloe immensely. An arrogant self-esteem gleamed like two clashing swords from her crossed eyes and she applied nothing but costly scented oil to her poor, mentally bruised feet—and not only mental oil, for she quickly made capital of her position by extorting enough gold from the Mouser to buy a slave whose duty it was to do very little else. She no longer sought to avoid calling the Mouser's attention to other women, in fact she rather enjoyed doing so, and the next time they encountered the dark-haired girl variously called Ahura and Silent Salmacis, as they were entering a tavern known as the Murex Shell, she volunteered more information.

"Ahura's not so innocent, you know, in spite of the way she sticks to herself. Once she went off with some old man—that was before she gave me the charm—and once I heard a primped-up Persian lady scream at her, 'What have you done with your brother?' Ahura didn't answer, just looked at the woman coldly as a snake, and after a while the woman ran out. Brr! You should have seen her eyes!"

But the Mouser pretended not to be interested.

Fafhrd could undoubtedly have had Chloe for the polite asking, and Chloe was more than eager to extend and cement in this fashion her control over the twain. But Fafhrd's pride would not allow him to accept such a favor from his friend, and he had frequently in past days, moreover, railed against Chloe as a decadent and unappetizing contemplater of her own nose.

So he perforce led a monastic life and endured contemptuous feminine glares across the drinking table and fended off painted boys who misinterpreted his misogyny and was much irritated by a growing rumor to the effect that he had become a secret eunuch priest of Cybele. Gossip and speculation had already fantastically distorted the truer accounts of what had happened, and it did not help when the girls who had been transformed denied it for fear of hurting their business. Some people got the idea that Fafhrd had committed the nasty sin of bestiality and they urged his prosecution in the public courts. Others accounted him a fortunate man who had been visited by an amorous goddess in the guise of a swine, and who thereafter scorned all earthly girls. While still others whispered that he was a brother of Circe and that he customarily dwelt on a floating island in the Tyrrhenian Sea, where he kept cruelly transformed into pigs a whole herd of beautiful ship-wrecked maidens. His laughter was heard no more and dark circles appeared in the white skin around his eyes and he began to make guarded inquiries among magicians in hopes of finding some remedial charm.

"I think I've hit on a cure for your embarrassing ailment," said the Mouser carelessly one night, laying aside a raggedy brown papyrus. "Came across it in this obscure treatise, 'The Demonology of Isaiah ben Elshaz.' It seems that whatever change takes place in the form of the woman you love, you should continue to make love to her, trusting to the power of your passion to transform her back to her original shape."

Fafhrd left off honing his great sword and asked, "Then why don't you try kissing snails?"

"It would be disagreeable and, for one free of barbarian prejudices, there is always Chloe."

"Pah! You're just going with her to keep your self-respect. I know you. For seven days now you'd had thoughts for no one but that Ahura wench."

"A pretty chit, but not to my liking," said the Mouser icily. "It must be your eye she's the apple of. However, you really should try my remedy; I'm sure you'd prove so good at it that the shes of all the swine in the world would come squealing after you."

Whereupon Fafhrd smote at the Mouser and a scuffle ensued which did not end until the Gray One was half strangled and one of Fafhrd's arms dislocated by a method generally known only to men from beyond the Indus.

However, Fafhrd did go so far as to hold firmly at arm's length the next sow his pent passion created, and feed it slops in the hope of accomplishing something by kindness. But in the end he had once again to admit defeat and assuage with owl-stamped Athenian silver didrachmas an hysterically angry Scythian girl who was sick at the stomach. It was then that an ill-advised curious young Greek philosopher suggested to the Northman that the soul or inward form of the thing loved is alone of importance, the outward form having no ultimate significance.

"You belong to the Socratic school?" Fafhrd questioned gently.

The Greek nodded.

"Socrates was the philosopher who was able to drink unlimited quantities of wine without blinking?"

Again the quick nod.

"That was because his rational soul dominated his animal soul?"

"You are learned," replied the Greek, with a more respectful but equally quick nod.

"I am not through. Do you consider yourself in all ways a true follower of your master?"

This time the Greek's quickness undid him. He nodded, and two days later he was carried out of the wine shop by friends, who found him cradled in a broken wine barrel, as if new born in no common manner. For days he remained drunk, time enough for a small sect to spring up who believed him a reincarnation of Dionysos and as such worshipped him. The sect was dissolved when he became half sober and delivered his first oracular address, which had as its subject the evils of drunkenness.

The morning after the deification of the rash philosopher, Fafhrd awoke when the first hot sunbeams struck the flat roof on which he and the Mouser had chosen to pass the night. Without sound or movement, suppressing the urge to groan out for someone to buy him a bag of snow from the white-capped Lebanons (over which the sun was even now peeping) to cool his aching head, he opened an eye on the sight that he in his wisdom had expected: the Mouser sitting on his heels and looking at the sea.

"Son of a wizard and a witch," he said, "it seems that once again we must fall back upon our last resource."

The Mouser did not turn his head, but he nodded it once, deliberately.

"The first time we did not come away with our lives," Fafhrd went on.

"The second time we lost our souls to the Other Creatures," the Mouser chimed in, as if they were singing a dawn chant to Isis.

"And the last time we fell through the Hole in the World."

"He may trick us into drinking the drink, and we not awake for another five hundred years."

"He may send us to our deaths and we not to be reincarnated for another two thousand," Fafhrd continued.

"He may show us Pan, or offer us to the Elder Gods, or send us back to Lankhmar," the Mouser concluded.

There was a pause of several moments.

Then the Gray Mouser whispered, "Nevertheless, we must visit Ningauble of the Seven Eyes."

And he spoke truly, for as Fafhrd had guessed, his soul was hovering over the sea dreaming of dark-haired Ahura.

2. Ningauble

So they crossed the snowy Lebanons and stole three camels, virtuously choosing to rob a rich landlord who made his tenants milk rocks and sow the shores of the Dead Sea, for it was unwise to approach the Gossiper of the Gods with an overly dirty conscience. After seven days of pitching and tossing across the desert, furnace days that made Fafhrd curse Muspelheim's fire gods, in whom he did not believe, they reached the Sand Combers and the Great Sand Whirlpools, and warily slipping past them while they were only lazily twirling, climbed the Rocky Islet. The city-loving Mouser ranted at Ningauble's preference for "a godforsaken hole in the desert," although he suspected that the Newsmonger and his agents came and went by a more hospitable road than the one provided for visitors, and although he knew as well as Fafhrd that the Snarer of Rumors (especially the false, which are the more valuable) must live as close to India and the infinite garden lands of the

Yellow Men as to barbaric Britain and marching Rome, as close to the heaven-steaming trans-Ethiopian jungle as to the mystery of lonely table-lands and star-scraping mountains beyond the Caspian Sea.

With high expectations they tethered their camels, took torches, and fearlessly entered the Bottomless Caves, for it was not so much in the visiting of Ningauble that danger lay as in the tantalizing charm of his advice, which was so great that one had to follow wherever it led.

Nevertheless Fafhrd said, "An earthquake swallowed Ningauble's house and it stuck in his throat. May he not hiccup."

As they were passing over the Trembling Bridge spanning the Pit of Ultimate Truth, which could have devoured the light of ten thousand torches without becoming any less black, they met and edged wordlessly past a helmeted, impassive fellow whom they recognized as a far-journeying Mongol. Safely across, they speculated as to whether he too were a visitor of the Gossiper, or a spy—Fafhrd had no faith in the clairvoyant powers of the seven eyes, averring that they were merely a sham to awe fools and that Ningauble's information was gathered by a corps of pedlars, panders, slaves, urchins, eunuchs, and midwives, which outnumbered the grand armies of a dozen kings.

Presently they saw a faint light flickering on the stalactited roof, reflected from a level above them. Soon they were struggling toward it up the Staircase of Error, an agglomeration of great rough rocks. Fafhrd stretched his long legs; the Mouser leapt catlike. The little creatures that scurried about their feet, brushed their shoulders in slow flight, or merely showed their yellow, insatiably curious eyes from crevice and rocky perch, multiplied in number; for they were nearing the Archeavesdropper.

A little later, having wasted no time in reconnoitering, they stood before the Great Gate, whose iron-studded upper reaches disdained the illumination of the tiny fire. It was not the gate, however, that interested them, but its keeper, a monstrously paunched creature sitting on the floor beside a vast heap of potsherds, and whose only movement was a rubbing of what seemed to be his hands. He kept them under the shabby but voluminous cloak which also completely hooded his head. A third of the way down the cloak, two large bats clung.

Fafhrd cleared his throat.

The movement ceased under the cloak.

Then out of the top of it sinuously writhed something that seemed to be a serpent, only in place of a head it bore an opalescent jewel with a dark central speck. Nevertheless, one might finally have judged it a serpent, were it not that it also resembled a thick-stalked exotic bloom idly waved by an exquisite. It restlessly turned this way and that until it pointed at the two strangers. Then it went rigid and the bulbous extremity seemed to glow more brightly. There came a low purring and five similar stalks twisted rapidly from under the hood and aligned themselves with their companion. Then the six black pupils dilated.

"Fat-bellied rumor monger!" hailed the Mouser nervously. "Must you forever play at peep show?"

For one could never quite get over the faint initial uneasiness that came with meeting Ningauble of the Seven Eyes.

"Is it not time," a voice from under the hood thinly quavered, "that you ceased to impose on me, because you once got me an unborn ghoul that I might question it of its parentage? The service to me was slight, accepted only to humor you; and I, by the name of the Spoorless God, have repaid it twenty times over."

"Nonsense, Midwife of Secrets," retorted the Mouser, stepping forward familiarly, his gay impudence almost restored. "You know as well as I that deep in your great paunch you are trembling with delight at having a chance to mouth your knowledge to two such appreciative listeners as we."

"That is as far from the truth as I am from the Secret of the Sphinx," commented Ningauble, four of his eyes following the Mouser's advance, one keeping watch on Fafhrd, while the sixth looped back around the hood to reappear on the other side and gaze suspiciously behind them.

"But, Ancient Talebearer, I am sure you have been closer to the Sphinx than any of her stony lovers. Very likely she first received her paltry riddle from your great store."

Ningauble quivered like jelly at this tickling flattery.

"Nevertheless," he piped, "today I am in a merry humor and will give ear to your question. But remember that it will almost certainly be too difficult for me."

"We know your great ingenuity in the face of insurmountable obstacles," rejoined the Mouser in the properly soothing tones.

"Why doesn't your friend come forward?" asked Ningauble, suddenly querulous again.

Fafhrd had been waiting for that question. It always went against his grain to have to behave congenially toward one who called himself the Mightiest Magician as well as the Gossiper of the Gods. But that Ningauble should let hang from his shoulders two bats whom he called Hugin and Munin in open burlesque of Odin's ravens, was too much for him. It was more a patriotic than religious matter with Fafhrd. He believed in Odin only during moments of sentimental weakness.

"Slay the bats or send them slithering and I'll come, but not before," he dogmatized.

"Now I'll tell you nothing," said Ningauble pettishly, "for, as all know, my health will not permit bickering."

"But, Schoolmaster of Falsehood," purred the Mouser, darting a murderous glance at Fafhrd, "that is indeed to be regretted, especially since I was looking forward to regaling you with the intricate scandal that the Friday concubine of the satrap Philip withheld even from her body slave."

"Ah well," conceded the Many-Eyed One, "it is time for Hugin and Munin to feed."

The bats reluctantly unfurled their wings and flew lazily into the darkness.

Fafhrd stirred himself and moved forward, sustaining the scrutiny of the majority of the eyes, all six of which the Northman considered artfully manipulated puppet-orbs. The seventh no man had seen, or boasted of having seen, save the Mouser, who claimed it was Odin's other eye, stolen from sagacious Mimer—this not because he believed it, but to irk his northern comrade.

"Greetings, Snake Eyes," Fafhrd boomed.

"Oh, is it you, Hulk?" said Ningauble carelessly. "Sit down, both, and share my humble fire."

"Are we not to be invited beyond the Great Gate and share your fabulous comforts too?"

"Do not mock me, Gray One. As all know, I am poor, penurious Ningauble."

So with a sigh the Mouser settled himself on his heels, for he well knew that the Gossiper prized above all else a reputation for poverty, chastity, humility, and thrift, therefore playing his own doorkeeper, except, on certain days when the Great Gate muted the tinkle of impious sistrum and the lascivious wail of flute and the giggles of those who postured in the shadow shows.

But now Ningauble coughed piteously and seemed to shiver and warmed his cloaked members at the fire. And the shadows flickered weakly against iron and stone, and the little creatures crept rustling in, making their eyes wide to see and their ears cupped to hear; and upon their rhythmically swinging, weaving stalks pulsated the six eyes. At intervals, too, Ningauble would pick up, seemingly at random, a potsherd from the great pile and rapidly scan the memorandum scribbled on it, without breaking the rhythm of the eye-stalks or, apparently, the thread of his attention.

As Fafhrd started to speak, Ningauble questioned rapidly, "And now, my children, you had something to tell me concerning the Friday concubine—"

"Ah, yes, Artist of Untruth," the Mouser cut in hastily, "concerning not so much the concubine as three eunuch priests of Cybele and a slave-girl from Samos—a tasty affair of wondrous complexity, which you must give me leave to let simmer in my mind so that I may serve it up to you skimmed of the slightest fat of exaggeration and with all the spice of true detail."

"And while we wait for the Mouser's mind-pot to boil," said Fafhrd casually, at last catching the spirit of the thing, "you may the more merrily pass the time by advising us as to a trifling difficulty." And he gave a succinct account of their tantalizing bedevilment by sow- and snail-changed maidens.

"And you say that Chloe alone proved immune to the spell?" queried Ningauble thoughtfully, tossing a potsherd to the far side of the pile. "Now that brings to my mind—"

"The exceedingly peculiar remark at the end of Diotima's fourth epistle to Socrates," interrupted the Mouser brightly. "Am I not right, Father?"

"You are not," replied Ningauble coldly. "As I was about to observe, when this tick of the intellect sought to burrow the skin of my mind, there must be something that throws a protective influence around Chloe. Do you know of any god or demon in whose special favor she stands, or any incantation or rune she habitually mumbles, or any notable talisman, charm, or amulet she customarily wears or inscribes on her body?"

"She did mention one thing," the Mouser admitted diffidently after a moment. "An amulet given her years ago by some Persian, or Greco-Persian girl. Doubtless a trifle of no consequence."

"Doubtless. Now, when the first sow-change occurred, did Fafhrd laugh the laugh? He did? That was unwise, as I have many times warned you. Advertise often enough your connection with the Elder Gods and you may be sure that some greedy searcher from the pit . . ."

"But what *is* our connection with the Elder Gods?" asked the Mouser, eagerly, though not hopefully. Fafhrd grunted derisively.

"Those are matters best not spoken of," Ningauble ordained. "Was there anyone who showed a particular interest in Fafhrd's laughter?"

The Mouser hesitated. Fafhrd coughed. Thus prodded, the Mouser confessed, "Oh, there was a girl who was perhaps a trifle more attentive than the others to his bellowing. A Persian girl. In fact, as I recall, the same one who gave Chloe the amulet."

"Her name is Ahura," said Fafhrd. "The Mouser's in love with her."

"A fable!" the Mouser denied laughingly, double-daggering Fafhrd with a surreptitious glare. "I can assure you, Father, that she is a very shy, stupid girl, who cannot possibly be concerned in any way with our troubles."

"Of course, since you say so," Ningauble observed, his voice icily rebuking. "However, I can tell you this much: the one who has placed the ignominious spell upon you is, insofar as he partakes of humanity, a man . . ."

(The Mouser was relieved. It was unpleasant to think of dark-haired, lithe Ahura being subjected to certain methods of questioning which Ningauble was reputed to employ. He was irked at his own clumsiness in trying to lead Ningauble's attention away from Ahura. Where she was concerned, his wit failed him.)

". . . and an adept," Ningauble concluded.

The Mouser started. Fafhrd groaned, "Again?"

"Again," Ningauble affirmed. "Though why, save for your connection with the Elder Gods, you should interest those most recondite of creatures, I cannot guess. They are not men who wittingly will stand in the glaringly illuminated foreground of history. They seek——"

"But who is it?" Fafhrd interjected.

"Be quiet, Mutilator of Rhetoric. They seek the shadows, and surely for good reason. They are the glorious amateurs of high magic, disdaining practical ends, caring only for the satisfaction of their insatiable curiosities, and therefore doubly dangerous. They are . . ."

"But what's his name?"

"Silence, Trampler of Beautiful Phrases. They are in their fashion fearless, irreligiously considering themselves the coequals of destiny and having only contempt for the Demigoddess of Chance, the Imp of Luck, and the

Demon of Improbability. In short, they are adversaries before whom you should certainly tremble and to whose will you should unquestionably bow."

"But his name, Father, his name!" Fafhrd burst out, and the Mouser, his impudence again in the ascendant, remarked, "It is he of the Sabihoon, is it not, Father?"

"It is not. The Sabihoon are an ignorant fisher folk who inhabit the hither shore of the far lake and worship the beast god Wheen, denying all others," a reply that tickled the Mouser, for to the best of his knowledge he had just invented the Sabihoon.

"No, his name is . . ." Ningauble paused and began to chuckle. "I was forgetting that I must under no circumstances tell you his name."

Fafhrd jumped up angrily. "What?"

"Yes, Children," said Ningauble, suddenly making his eye-stalks staringly rigid, stern, and uncompromising. "And I must furthermore tell you that I can in no way help you in this matter . . ." (Fafhrd clenched his fists) ". . . and I am very glad of it too. . ." (Fafhrd swore) ". . . for it seems to me that no more fitting punishment could have been devised for your abominable lecheries, which I have so often bemoaned . . ." (Fafhrd's hand went to his sword hilt) ". . . in fact, if it had been up to me to chastise you for your manifold vices, I would have chosen the very same enchantment . . ." (But now he had gone too far; Fafhrd growled, "Oh, so it is you who are behind it!" ripped out his sword and began to advance slowly on the hooded figure) ". . .Yes, my children, you must accept your lot without rebellion or bitterness . . ." (Fafhrd continued to advance) ". . . Far better that you should retire from the world as I have and give yourselves to meditation and repentance. . . ." (The sword, flickering with firelight, was only a yard away) ". . . Far better that you should live out the rest of this incarnation in solitude, each surrounded by his faithful band of sows or snails . . ." (The sword touched the ragged robe) ". . . devoting your remaining years to the promotion of a better understanding between mankind and the lower animals. However—" (Ningauble sighed and the sword hesitated) ". . . if it is still your firm and foolhardy intention to challenge this adept, I suppose I must aid you with what little advice I can give, though warning you that it will plunge you into maelstroms of trouble and lay upon you geases you will grow grey in fulfilling, and incidentally be the means of your deaths."

Fafhrd lowered his sword. The silence in the black cave grew heavy and ominous. Then, in a voice that was distant yet resonant, like the sound that came from the statue of Memnon at Thebes when the first rays of the morning sun fell upon it, Ningauble began to speak.

"It comes to me, confusedly, like a scene in a rusted mirror; nevertheless, it comes, and thus: You must first possess yourselves of certain trifles. The shroud of Ahriman, from the secret shrine near Persepolis—"

"But what about the accursed swordsmen of Ahriman, Father?" put in the Mouser. "There are twelve of them. Twelve, Father, and all very accursed and hard to persuade."

"Do you think I am setting toss-and-fetch problems for puppy dogs?" wheezed Ningauble angrily. "To proceed: You must secondly obtain powdered mummy from the Demon Pharaoh, who reigned for three horrid and unhistoried midnights after the death of Ikhnaton—"

"But, Father," Fafhrd protested, blushing a little, "you know who owns that powdered mummy, and what she demands of any two men who visit her."

"Shh! I'm your elder, Fafhrd, by eons. Thirdly, you must get the cup from which Socrates drank the hemlock, fourthly a sprig from the original Tree of Life, and lastly . . ." He hesitated as if his memory had failed him, dipped up a potsherd from the pile, and read from it: "And lastly, you must procure the woman who will come when she is ready."

"What woman?"

"The woman who will come when she is ready." Ningauble tossed back the fragment, starting a small landslide of shards.

"Corrode Loki's bones!" cursed Fafhrd, and the Mouser said, "But Father, no woman comes when she's ready. She always waits."

Ningauble sighed merrily and said, "Do not be downcast, Children. Is it ever the custom of your good friend the Gossiper to give simple advice?"

"It is not," said Fafhrd.

"Well, having all these things, you must go to the Lost City of Ahriman that lies east of Armenia—whisper not its name—"

"Is it Khatti?" whispered the Mouser.

"No, Blowfly. And furthermore, why are you interrupting me when you are supposed to be hard at work recalling all the details of the scandal of the Friday concubine, the three eunuch priests, and the slave girl from Samos?"

"Oh truly, Spy of the Unmentionable, I labor at that until my mind becomes a weariness and a wandering, and all for love of you." The Mouser was glad of Ningauble's question, for he had forgotten the three eunuch priests, which would have been most unwise, as no one in his senses sought to cheat the Gossiper of even a pinch of misinformation promised.

Ningauble continued, "Arriving at the Lost City, you must seek out the ruined black shrine, and place the woman before the great tomb, and wrap the shroud of Ahriman around her, and let her drink the powdered mummy from the hemlock cup, diluting it with a wine you will find where you find the mummy, and place in her hand the sprig from the Tree of Life, and wait for the dawn."

"And then?" rumbled Fafhrd.

"And then the mirror becomes all red with rust. I can see no farther, except that someone will return from a place which it is unlawful to leave, and that you must be wary of the woman."

"But Father, all this scavenging of magical trumpery is a great bother," Fafhrd objected. "Why shouldn't we go at once to the Lost City?"

"Without the map on the shroud of Ahriman?" murmured Ningauble.

"And you still can't tell us the name of the adept we seek?" the Mouser ventured. "Or even the name of the woman? Puppy dog problems indeed!

We give you a bitch, Father, and by the time you return her, she's dropped a litter."

Ningauble shook his head ever so slightly, the six eyes retreated under the hood to become an ominous multiple gleam, and the Mouser felt a shiver crawl on his spine.

"Why is it, Riddle-Vendor, that you always give us half knowledge?" Fafhrd pressed angrily. "Is it that at the last moment our blades may strike with half force?"

Ningauble chuckled.

"It is because I know you too well, Children. If I said one word more, Hulk, you could be cleaving with your great sword—at the wrong person. And your cat-comrade would be brewing his child's magic—the wrong child's magic. It is no simple creature you foolhardily seek, but a mystery, no single identity but a mirage, a stony thing that has stolen the blood and substance of life, a nightmare crept out of dream."

For a moment it was as if, in the far reaches of that nighted cavern, something that waited stirred. Then it was gone.

Ningauble purred complacently, "And now I have an idle moment, which, to please you, I will pass in giving ear to the story that the Mouser has been impatiently waiting to tell me."

So, there being no escape, the Mouser began, first explaining that only the surface of the story had to do with the concubine, the three priests, and the slave girl; the deeper portion touching mostly, though not entirely, on four infamous handmaidens of Ishtar and a dwarf who was richly compensated for his deformity. The fire grew low and a little, lemurlike creature came edging in to replenish it, and the hours stretched on, for the Mouser always warmed to his own tales. There came a place where Fafhrd's eyes bugged with astonishment, and another where Ningauble's paunch shook like a small mountain in earthquake, but eventually the tale came to an end, suddenly and seemingly in the middle, like a piece of foreign music.

Then farewells were said and final questions refused answer, and the two seekers started back the way they had come. And Ningauble began to sort in his mind the details of the Mouser's story, treasuring it the more because he knew it was an improvisation, his favorite proverb being, "He who lies artistically, treads closer to the truth than ever he knows."

Fafhrd and the Mouser had almost reached the bottom of the boulder stair when they heard a faint tapping and turned to see Ningauble peering down from the verge, supporting himself with what looked like a cane and rapping with another.

"Children," he called, and his voice was tiny as the note of the lone flute in the Temple of Baal, "it comes to me that something in the distant spaces lusts for something in you. You must guard closely what commonly needs no guarding."

"Yes, Godfather of Mystification."

"You will take care?" came the elfin note. "Your beings depend on it."

"Yes, Father."

And Ningauble waved once and hobbled out of sight. The little creatures of his great darkness followed him, but whether to report and receive orders or only to pleasure him with their gentle antics, no man could be sure. Some said that Ningauble had been created by the Elder Gods for men to guess about and so sharpen their imaginations for even tougher riddles. None knew whether he had the gift of foresight, or whether he merely set the stage for future events with such a bewildering cunning that only an efreet or an adept could evade acting the part given him.

3. The Woman Who Came

After Fafhrd and the Gray Mouser emerged from the Bottomless Caves into the blinding upper sunlight, their trail for a space becomes dim. Material relating to them has, on the whole, been scanted by annalists, since they were heroes too disreputable for classic myth, too cryptically independent ever to let themselves be tied to a folk, too shifty and improbable in their adventurings to please the historian, too often involved with a riff-raff of dubious demons, unfrocked sorcerors, and discredited deities—a veritable underworld of the supernatural. And it becomes doubly difficult to piece together their actions during a period when they were engaged in thefts requiring stealth, secrecy, and bold misdirection. Occasionally, however, one comes across the marks they left upon the year.

For instance, a century later the priests of Ahriman were chanting, although they were too intelligent to believe it themselves, the miracle of Ahriman's snatching of his own hallowed shroud. One night the twelve accursed swordsmen saw the blackly scribbled shroud rise like a pillar of cobwebs from the altar, rise higher than mortal man, although the form within seemed anthropoid. Then Ahriman spoke from the shroud, and they worshipped him, and he replied with obscure parables and finally strode giantlike from the secret shrine.

The shrewdest of the century-later priests remarked, "I'd say a man on stilts, or else—" (happy surmise!) "—one man on the shoulders of another."

Then there were the things that Nikri, body slave to the infamous False Laodice, told the cook while she anointed the bruises of her latest beating. Things concerning two strangers who visited her mistress, and the carousal her mistress proposed to them, and how they escaped the black eunuch scimitarmen she had set to slay them when the carousal was done.

"They were magicians, both of them," Nikri averred, "for at the peak of the doings they transformed my lady into a hideous, wiggly-horned sow, a horrid chimera of snail and swine. But that wasn't the worst, for they stole her chest of aphrodisiac wines. When she discovered that the demon mummia was gone with which she'd hoped to stir the lusts of Ptolemy, she screamed in rage and took her backscratcher to me. Ow, but that hurts!"

The cook chuckled.

But as to who visited Hieronymus, the greedy tax farmer and connoisseur of Antioch, or in what guise, we cannot be sure. One morning he was found in his treasure room with his limbs stiff and chill, as if from hemlock, and there was a look of terror on his fat face, and the famous cup from which he had often caroused was missing, although there were circular stains on the table before him. He recovered, but would never tell what had happened.

The priests who tended the Tree of Life in Babylon were a little more communicative. One evening just after sunset they saw the topmost branches shake in the gloaming and heard the snick of a pruning knife. All around them, without other sound or movement, stretched the desolate city, from which the inhabitants had been herded to nearby Seleucia three-quarters of a century before and to which the priests crept back only in great fear to fulfill their sacred duties. They instantly prepared, some of them to climb the Tree armed with tempered golden sickles, others to shoot down with gold-tipped arrows whatever blasphemer was driven forth, when suddenly a large gray batlike shape swooped from the Tree and vanished behind a jagged wall. Of course, it might conceivably have been a gray-cloaked man swinging on a thin, tough rope, but there were too many things whispered about the creatures that flapped by night through the ruins of Babylon for the priests to dare pursuit.

Finally Fafhrd and the Gray Mouser reappeared in Tyre, and a week later they were ready to depart on the ultimate stage of their quest. Indeed, they were already outside the gates, lingering at the landward end of Alexander's mole, spine of an ever-growing isthmus. Gazing at it, Fafhrd remembered how once an unintroduced stranger had told him a tale about two fabulous adventurers who had aided mightily in the foredoomed defense of Tyre against Alexander the Great more than a hundred years ago. The larger had heaved heavy stone blocks on the attacking ships, the smaller had dove to file through the chains with which they were anchored. Their names, the stranger had said, were Fafhrd and the Gray Mouser. Fafhrd had made no comment.

It was near evening, a good time to pause in adventurings, to recall past escapades, to hazard misty, wild, rosy speculations concerning what lay ahead.

"I think any woman would do," insisted the Mouser bickering. "Ningauble was just trying to be obscure. Let's take Chloe."

"If only she'll come when she's ready," said Fafhrd, half smiling.

The sun was dipping ruddy-golden into the rippling sea. The merchants who had pitched shop on the landward side in order to get first crack at the farmers and inland traders on market day were packing up wares and taking down canopies.

"Any woman will eventually come when she's ready, even Chloe," retorted the Mouser. "We'd only have to take along a silk tent for her and a few pretty conveniences. No trouble at all."

"Yes," said Fafhrd, "we could probably manage it without more than one elephant."

Most of Tyre was darkly silhouetted against the sunset, although there were gleams from the roofs here and there, and the gilded peak of the Temple of Melkarth sent a little water-borne glitter track angling in toward the greater one of the sun. The fading Phoenician port seemed entranced, dreaming of past glories, only half listening to today's news of Rome's implacable eastward advance, and Philip of Macedon's loss of the first round at the Battle of the Dog's Heads, and now Antiochus preparing for the second, with Hannibal come to help him from Tyre's great fallen sister Carthage across the sea.

"I'm sure Chloe will come if we wait until tomorrow," the Mouser continued. "We'll have to wait in any case, because Ningauble said the woman wouldn't come until she was ready."

A cool little wind came out of the wasteland that was Old Tyre. The merchants hurried; a few of them were already going home along the mole, their slaves looking like hunchbacks and otherwise misshapen monsters because of the packs on their shoulders and heads.

"No," said Fafhrd, "we'll start. And if the woman doesn't come when she's ready, then she isn't the woman who will come when she's ready, or if she is, she'll have to hump herself to catch up."

The three horses of the adventurers moved restlessly and the Mouser's whinnied. Only the great camel, on which were slung the wine-sacks, various small chests, and snugly-wrapped weapons, stood sullenly still. Fafhrd and the Mouser casually watched the one figure on the mole that moved against the homing stream; they were not exactly suspicious, but after the year's doings they could not overlook the possibility of death-dealing pursuers, taking the form either of accursed swordsmen, black eunuch scimitarmen, gold-weaponed Babylonian priests, or such agents as Hieronymus of Antioch might favor.

"Chloe would have come on time, if only you'd helped me persuade her," argued the Mouser. "She likes you, and I'm sure she must have been the one Ningauble meant, because she has that amulet which works against the adept."

The sun was a blinding sliver on the sea's rim, then went under. All the little glares and glitters on the roofs of Tyre winked out. The Temple of Melkarth loomed black against the fading sky. The last canopy was being taken down and most of the merchants were more than halfway across the mole. There was still only one figure moving shoreward.

"Weren't seven nights with Chloe enough for you?" asked Fafhrd. "Besides, it isn't she you'll be wanting when we kill the adept and get this spell off us."

"That's as it may be," retorted the Mouser. "But remember we have to catch our adept first. And it's not only I whom Chloe's company could benefit."

A faint shout drew their attention across the darkling water to where a lateen-rigged trader was edging into the Egyptian Harbor. For a moment they thought the landward end of the mole had been emptied. Then the figure moving away from the city came out sharp and black against the sea, a slight figure, not burdened like the slaves.

"Another fool leaves sweet Tyre at the wrong time," observed the Mouser. "Just think what a woman will mean in those cold mountains we're going to, Fafhrd, a woman to prepare dainties and stroke your forehead."

Fafhrd said, "It isn't your forehead, little man, you're thinking of."

The cool wind came again and the packed sand moaned at its passing. Tyre seemed to crouch like a beast against the threats of darkness. A last merchant searched the ground hurriedly for some lost article.

Fafhrd put his hand on his horse's shoulder and said, "Come on."

The Mouser made a last point. "I don't think Chloe would insist on taking the slave girl to oil her feet, that is, if we handled it properly."

Then they saw that the other fool leaving sweet Tyre was coming toward them, and that it was a woman, tall and slender, dressed in stuffs that seemed to melt into the waning light, so that Fafhrd found himself wondering whether she truly came from Tyre or from some aerial realm whose inhabitants may venture to earth only at sunset. Then, as she continued to approach at an easy, swinging stride, they saw that her face was fair and that her hair was raven; and the Mouser's heart gave a great leap and he felt that this was the perfect consummation of their waiting, that he was witnessing the birth of an Aphrodite, not from the foam but the dusk; for it was indeed his dark-haired Ahura of the wine shops, no longer staring with cold, shy curiosity, but eagerly smiling.

Fafhrd, not altogether untouched by similar feelings, said slowly, "So you are the woman who came when she was ready?"

"Yes," added the Mouser gayly. "And did you know that in a minute more you'd have been too late?"

4. The Lost City

During the next week, one of steady northward journeying along the fringe of the desert, they learned little more of the motives or history of their mysterious companion than the dubious scraps of information Chloe had provided. When asked why she had come, Ahura replied that Ningauble had sent her, that Ningauble had nothing to do with it and that it was all an accident, that certain dead Elder Gods had dreamed her a vision, that she sought a brother lost in a search for the Lost City of Ahriman; and often her only answer was silence, a silence that seemed sometimes sly and sometimes mystical. However, she stood up well to hardship, proved a tireless rider, and did not complain at sleeping on the ground with only a large cloak snuggled around her. Like some especially sensitive migratory bird, she seemed possessed of an even greater urge than their own to get on with the journey.

Whenever opportunity offered, the Mouser paid assiduous court to her, limited only by the fear of working a snail-change. But after a few days of this tantalizing pleasure, he noticed that Fafhrd was vying for it. Very swiftly the two comrades became rivals, contesting as to who should be the first to offer Ahura assistance on those rare occasions when she needed it, striving to top each other's brazenly boastful accounts of incredible adventures, constantly on the alert lest the other steal a moment alone. Such a spate of gallantry had never before been known on their adventurings. They remained good friends—and they were aware of that—but very surly friends—and they were aware of that too. And Ahura's shy, or sly, silence encouraged them both.

They forded the Euphrates south of the ruins of Carchemish, and struck out for the headwaters of the Tigris, intersecting but swinging east away from the route of Xenophon and the Ten Thousand. It was then that their surliness came to a head. Ahura had roamed off a little, letting her horse crop the dry herbage, while the two sat on a boulder, and expostulated in whispers, Fafhrd proposing that they both agree to cease paying court to the girl until their quest was over, the Mouser doggedly advancing his prior claim. Their whispers became so heated that they did not notice a white pigeon swooping toward them until it landed with a downward beat of wings on an arm Fafhrd had flung wide to emphasize his willingness to re- nounce the girl temporarily—if only the Mouser would.

Fafhrd blinked, then detached a scrap of parchment from the pigeon's leg, and read, "There is danger in the girl. You must both forgo her."

The tiny seal was an impression of seven tangled eyes.

"Just *seven* eyes!" remarked the Mouser. "Pah, He is modest!" And for a moment he was silent, trying to picture the gigantic web of unknown strands by which the Gossiper gathered his information and conducted his business.

But this unexpected seconding of Fafhrd's argument finally won from him a sulky consent, and they solemnly pledged not to lay hand on the girl, or each in any way to further his cause, until they had found and dealt with the adept.

They were now in a townless land that caravans avoided, a land like Xenophon's, full of chill misty mornings, dazzling noons, and treacherous twilights with hints of shy, murderous, mountain-dwelling tribes recalling the omnipresent legends of "little people" as unlike men as cats are unlike dogs. Ahura seemed unaware of the sudden cessation of the attentions paid her, remaining as provocatively shy and indefinite as ever.

The Mouser's attitude toward Ahura, however, began to undergo a gradual but profound change. Whether it was the souring of his inhibited passion, or the shrewder insight of a mind no longer abubble with the fash- ioning of compliments and witticisms, he began to feel more and more that the Ahura he loved was only a faint spark almost lost in the darkness of a stranger who daily became more riddlesome, dubious, and even, in the end, repellent. He remembered the other name Chloe had given Ahura, and found himself brooding oddly over the legend of Hermaphroditus bathing in the Carian fountain and becoming joined in one body with the nymph Salmacis. Now when he looked at Ahura he could see only the avid eyes that peered secretly at the world through a crevice. He began to think of her chuckling soundlessly at night at the mortifying spell that had been laid upon himself and Fafhrd. He became obsessed with Ahura in a very different way, and took to spying on her and studying her expression when she was not looking, as if hoping in that way to penetrate her mystery.

Fafhrd noticed it and instantly suspected that the Mouser was contemplating going back on his pledge. He restrained his indignation with difficulty and took to watching the Mouser as closely as the Mouser watched Ahura. No longer when it became necessary to procure provisions was either willing to hunt alone. The easy amicability of their friendship deteriorated. Then, late one afternoon while they were traversing a shadowy ravine east of Armenia, a hawk dove suddenly and sank its talons in Fafhrd's shoulder. The Northerner killed the creature in a flurry of reddish feathers before he noticed that it too carried a message.

"Watch out for the Mouser," was all it said, but coupled with the smart of the talon-pricks, that was quite enough for Fafhrd. Drawing up beside the Mouser while Ahura's horse pranced skittishly away from the disturbance, he told the Mouser his full suspicions and warned him that any violation of their agreement would at once end their friendship and bring them into deadly collision.

The Mouser listened like a man in a dream, still moodily watching Ahura. He would have liked to have told Fafhrd his real motives, but was doubtful whether he could make them intelligible. Moreover, he was piqued at being misjudged. So when Fafhrd's direful outburst was finished, he made no comment. Fafhrd interpreted this as an admission of guilt and cantered on in a rage.

They were now nearing that rugged vantage-land from which the Medes and the Persians had swooped down on Assyria and Chaldea, and where, if they could believe Ningauble's geography, they would find the forgotten lair of the Lord of Eternal Evil. At first the archaic map on the shroud of Ahriman proved more maddening than helpful, but after a while, clarified in part by a curiously erudite suggestion of Ahura, it began to make disturbing sense, showing them a deep gorge where the foregoing terrain led one to expect a saddle-backed crest, and a valley where ought to have been a mountain. If the map held true, they would reach the Lost City in a very few days.

All the while, the Mouser's obsession deepened, and at last took definite and startling form. He believed that Ahura was a man.

It was very strange that the intimacy of camp life and the Mouser's own zealous spying should not long ago have turned up concrete proof or disproof of this clearcut supposition. Nevertheless, as the Mouser wonderingly realized on reviewing events, they had not. Granted, Ahura's form and movements, all her least little actions were those of a woman, but he recalled painted and padded minions, sweet not simpering, who had aped femininity almost as well. Preposterous—but there it was. From that moment his obsessive curiosity became a compulsive sweat and he redoubled his moody peering, much to the anger of Fafhrd, who took to slapping his sword hilt at unexpected intervals, though without ever startling the Mouser into looking away. Each in his way stayed as surly-sullen as the camel that displayed a more and more dour balkiness at this preposterous excursion from the healthy desert.

Those were nightmare days for the Gray One, as they advanced ever closer through gloomy gorges and over craggy crests toward Ahriman's primeval shrine. Fafhrd seemed an ominous, white-faced giant reminding him of someone he had known in waking life, and their whole quest a blind treading of the more subterranean routes of dream. He still wanted to tell the giant his suspicions, but could not bring himself to it, because of their monstrousness and because the giant loved Ahura. And all the while Ahura eluded him, a phantom fluttering just beyond reach; though, when he forced his mind to make the comparison, he realized that her behavior had in no way altered, except for an intensification of the urge to press onward, like a vessel nearing its home port.

Finally there came a night when he could bear his torturing curiosity no longer. He writhed from under a mountain of oppressive unremembered dreams and, propped on an elbow, looked around him, quiet as the creature for which he was named.

It would have been cold if it had not been so still. The fire had burned to embers. It was rather the moonlight that showed him Fafhrd's touseled head and elbow outthrust from shaggy bearskin cloak. And it was the moonlight that struck full on Ahura stretched beyond the embers, her lidded, tranquil face fixed on the zenith, seeming hardly to breathe.

He waited a long time. Then, without making a sound, he laid back his gray cloak, picked up his sword, went around the fire, and kneeled beside her. Then, for another space, he dispassionately scrutinized her face. But it remained the hermaphroditic mask that had tormented his waking hours—if he were still sure of the distinction between waking and dream. Suddenly his hands grasped at her—and as abruptly checked. Again he stayed motionless for a long time. Then, with movements as deliberate and rehearsed-seeming as a sleep-walker's, but more silent, he drew back her woolen cloak, took a small knife from his pouch, lifted her gown at the neck, careful not to touch her skin, slit it to her knee, treating her chiton the same.

The breasts, white as ivory, that he had known would not be there, were there. And yet, instead of his nightmare lifting, it deepened.

It was something too profound for surprise, this wholly unexpected further insight. For as he knelt there, somberly studying, he knew for a certainty that this ivory flesh too was a mask, as cunningly fashioned as the face and for as frighteningly incomprehensible a purpose.

The ivory eyelids did not flicker, but the edges of the teeth showed in what he fancied was a deliberate, flickery smile.

He was never more certain than at this moment that Ahura was a man.

The embers crunched behind him.

Turning, the Mouser saw only the streak of gleaming steel poised above Fafhrd's head, motionless for a moment, as if with superhuman forbearance a god should give his creature a chance before loosing the thunderbolt.

The Mouser ripped out his own slim sword in time to ward the titan blow. From hilt to point, the two blades screamed.

And in answer to that scream, melting into, continuing, and augmenting it, there came from the absolute calm of the west a gargantuan gust of wind that sent the Mouser staggering forward and Fafhrd reeling back, and rolled Ahura across the place where the embers had been.

Almost as suddenly the gale died. As it died, something whipped batlike toward the Mouser's face and he grabbed at it. But it was not a bat, or even a large leaf. It felt like papyrus.

The embers, blown into a clump of dry grass, had perversely started a blaze. To its flaring light he held the thin scrap that had fluttered out of the infinite west.

He motioned frantically to Fafhrd, who was clawing his way out of a scrub pine.

There was squid-black writing on the scrap, in large characters, above the tangled seal.

"By whatever gods you revere, give up this quarrel. Press onward at once. Follow the woman."

They became aware that Ahura was peering over their abutting shoulders. The moon came gleamingly from behind the small black tatter of cloud that had briefly obscured it. She looked at them, pulled together chiton and gown, belted them with her cloak. They collected their horses, extricated the fallen camel from the cluster of thorn bushes in which it was satisfiedly tormenting itself, and set out.

After that the Lost City was found almost too quickly; it seemed like a trap or the work of an illusionist. One moment Ahura was pointing out to them a boulder-studded crag; the next, they were looking down on a narrow valley choked with crazily-leaning, moonsilvered monoliths and their accomplice shadows.

From the first it was obvious that "city" was a misnomer. Surely men had never dwelt in those massive stone tents and huts, though they may have worshipped there. It was a habitation for Egyptian colossi, for stone automata. But Fafhrd and the Mouser had little time to survey its entirety, for without warning Ahura sent her horse clattering and sliding down the slope.

Thereafter it was a harebrained, drunken gallop, their horses plunging shadows, the camel a lurching ghost, through forests of crude-hewn pillars, past teetering single slabs big enough for palace walls, under lintels made for elephants, always following the elusive hoofbeat, never catching it, until they suddenly emerged into clear moonlight and drew up in an open space between a great sarcophagus-like block or box with steps leading up to it, and a huge, crudely man-shaped monolith.

But they had hardly begun to puzzle out the things around them before they became aware that Ahura was gesturing impatiently. They recalled Ningauble's instructions, and realized that it was almost dawn. So they unloaded various bundles and boxes from the shivering, snapping camel, and Fafhrd unfolded the dark, cobwebby shroud of Ahriman and wrapped it around Ahura as she stood wordlessly facing the tomb, her face a marble portrait of eagerness, as if she sprang from the stone around her.

While Fafhrd busied himself with other things, the Mouser opened the ebony chest they had stolen from the False Laodice. A fey mood came upon him, and dancing cumbrously in imitation of a eunuch serving man, he tastefully arrayed a flat stone with all the little jugs and jars and tiny amphorae that the chest contained. And in an appropriate falsetto he sang:

> "I laid a board for the Great Seleuce,
> I decked it pretty and abstruse;
> And he must have been pleased,
> For when stuffed, he wheezed,
> 'As punishment castrate the man.'"

Then Fafhrd handed him Socrates' cup and, still prancing and piping, the Mouser measured into it the mummy powder and added the wine and stirred them together and, dancing fantastically toward Ahura, offered it to her. When she made no movement, he held it to her lips and she greedily gulped it without taking her eyes from the tomb.

Then Fafhrd came with the sprig from the Babylonian Tree of Life, which still felt marvellously fresh and firm-leafed to his touch, as if the Mouser had only snipped it a moment ago. And he gently pried open her clenched fingers and placed the sprig inside them and folded them again.

Thus ready, they waited. The sky reddened at the edge and seemed for a moment to grow darker, the stars fading and the moon turning dull. The outspread aphrodisiacs chilled, refusing the night breeze their savor. And the woman continued to watch the tomb, and behind her, seeming to watch the tomb too, as if it were her fantastic shadow, loomed the man-shaped monolith, which the Mouser now and then scrutinized uneasily over his shoulder, being unable to tell whether it were of primevally crude workmanship or something that men had laboriously defaced because of its evil.

The sky paled until the Mouser could begin to make out some monstrous carvings on the side of the sarcophagus—of men like stone pillars and animals like mountains—and until Fafhrd could see the green of the leaves in Ahura's hand.

Then he saw something astounding. In an instant the leaves withered and the sprig became a curled and blackened stick. In the same instant Ahura trembled and grew paler still, snow pale, and to the Mouser it seemed

that there was a tenuous black cloud forming around her head, that the riddlesome stranger he hated was pouring upward like a smoky jinni from her
body, the bottle.

The thick stone cover of the sarcophagus groaned and began to rise.

Ahura began to move toward the sarcophagus. To the Mouser it seemed
that the cloud was drawing her along like a black sail.

The cover was moving more swiftly, as if it were the upper jaw of a
stone crocodile. The black cloud seemed to the Mouser to strain trium-
phantly toward the widening slit, dragging the white wisp behind it. The
cover opened wide. Ahura reached the top and then either peered down
inside or, as the Mouser saw it, was almost sucked in along with the black
cloud. She shook violently. Then her body collapsed like an empty dress.

Fafhrd gritted his teeth, a joint cracked in the Mouser's wrist. The hilts
of their swords, unconsciously drawn, bruised their palms.

Then, like an idler from a day of bowered rest, an Indian prince from the
tedium of the court, a philosopher from quizzical discourse, a slim figure
rose from the tomb. His limbs were clad in black, his body in silvery metal,
his hair and beard raven and silky. But what first claimed the sight, like an
ensign on a masked man's shield, was a chatoyant quality of his youthful
olive skin, a silvery gleaming that turned one's thoughts to fishes' bellies and
leprosy—that, and a certain familiarity.

For the face of this black and silver stranger bore an unmistakable resemblance to Ahura.

5. Anra Devadoris

Resting his long hands on the edge of the tomb, the newcomer surveyed
them pleasantly and nodded as if they were intimates. Then he vaulted
lightly over and came striding down the steps, treading on the shroud of
Ahriman without so much as a glance at Ahura.

He eyed their swords. "You anticipate danger?" he asked, politely
stroking the beard which, it seemed to the Mouser, could never have grown
so bushily silky except in a tomb.

"You are an adept?" Fafhrd retorted, stumbling over the words a little.

The stranger disregarded the question and stopped to study amusedly
the zany array of aphrodisiacs.

"Dear Ningauble," he murmured, "is surely the father of all seven-eyed
Lechers. I suppose you know him well enough to guess that he had you fetch
these toys because he wants them for himself. Even in his duel with me, he
cannot resist the temptation of a profit on the side. But perhaps this time
the old pander had curtsied to destiny unwittingly. At least, let us hope so."

And with that he unbuckled his sword belt and carelessly laid it by,
along with the wondrously slim, silver-hilted sword. The Mouser shrugged
and sheathed his own weapon, but Fafhrd only grunted.

"I do not like you," he said. "Are you the one who put the swine-curse on us?"

The stranger regarded him quizzically.

"You are looking for a cause," he said. "You wish to know the name of an agent you feel has injured you. You plan to unleash your rage as soon as you know. But behind every cause is another cause, and behind the last agent is yet another agent. An immortal could not slay a fraction of them. Believe me, who have followed that trail farther than most and who have had some experience of the special obstacles that are placed in the way of one who seeks to live beyond the confines of his skull and the meager present—the traps that are set for him, the titanic enmities he awakens. I beseech you to wait a while before warring, as I shall wait before answering your second question. That I am an adept I freely admit."

At this last statement the Mouser felt another light-headed impulse to behave fantastically, this time in mimicry of a magician. Here was the rare creature on whom he could test the rune against adepts in his pouch! He wanted to hum a death spell between his teeth, to flap his arms in an incantational gesture, to spit at the adept and spin widdershins on his left heel thrice. But he too chose to wait.

"There is always a simple way of saying things," said Fafhrd ominously.

"But there is where I differ with you," returned the adept, almost animatedly. "There are no ways of saying certain things, and others are so difficult that a man pines and dies before the right words are found. One must borrow phrases from the sky, words from beyond the stars. Else were all an ignorant, imprisoning mockery."

The Mouser stared at the adept, suddenly conscious of a monstrous incongruity about him—as if one should glimpse a hint of double-dealing in the curl of Solon's lips, or cowardice in the eyes of Alexander, or imbecility in the face of Aristotle. For although the adept was obviously erudite, confident, and powerful, the Mouser could not help thinking of a child morbidly avid for experience, a timid, painfully curious small boy. And the Mouser had the further bewildering feeling that this was the secret for which he had spied so long on Ahura.

Fafhrd's sword-arm bulged and he seemed about to make an even pithier rejoinder. But instead he sheathed his sword, walked over to the woman, held his fingers to her wrists for a moment, then tucked his bearskin cloak around her.

"Her ghost has gone only a little way," he said. "It will soon return. What did you do to her, you black and silver popinjay?"

"What matters what I've done to her or you, or me?" retorted the adept, almost peevishly. "You are here, and I have business with you." He paused. "This, in brief, is my proposal: that I make you adepts like myself, sharing with you all knowledge of which your minds are capable, on condition only that you continue to submit to such spells as I have put upon you and may put upon you in future, to further our knowledge. What do you say to that?"

"Wait, Fafhrd!" implored the Mouser, grabbing his comrade's arm. "Don't strike yet. Let's first look at the statue from all sides. Why, magnanimous magician, have you chosen to make this offer to us, and why have you brought us out here to make it, instead of getting your yes or no in Tyre?"

"An adept," roared Fafhrd, dragging the Mouser along. "Offers to make me an adept! And for that I should go on kissing swine! Go spit down Fenris' throat!"

"As to why I have brought you here," said the adept coolly, "there are certain limitations on my powers of movement, or at least on my powers of satisfactory communication. There is, moreover, a special reason, which I will reveal to you as soon as we have concluded our agreement—though I may tell you that, unknown to yourselves, you have already aided me."

"But why pick on *us*? Why?" persisted the Mouser, bracing himself against Fafhrd's tugging.

"Some whys, if you follow them far enough, lead over the rim of reality," replied the black and silver one. "I have sought knowledge beyond the dreams of ordinary men, I have ventured far into the darkness that encircles minds and stars. But now, midmost of the pitchy windings of that fearsome labyrinth, I find myself suddenly at my skein's end. The tyrant powers who ignorantly guard the secret of the universe without knowing what it is, have scented me. Those vile wardens of whom Ningauble is the merest agent and even Ormadz a cloudy symbol, have laid their traps and built their barricades. And my best torches have snuffed out, or proved too flickery-feeble. I need new avenues of knowledge."

He turned upon them eyes that seemed to be changing to twin holes in a curtain. "There is something in the inmost core of you, something that you, or others before you, have close-guarded down the ages. Something that lets you laugh in a way that only the Elder Gods ever laughed. Something that makes you see a kind of jest in horror and disillusionment and death. There is much wisdom to be gained by the unravelling of that something."

"Do you think us pretty woven scarves for your slick fingers to fray," snarled Fafhrd. "So you can piece out that rope you're at the end of, and climb all the way down to Niflheim?"

"Each adept must fray himself, before he may fray others," the stranger intoned unsmilingly. "You do not know the treasure you keep virgin and useless within you, or spill in senseless laughter. There is much richness in it, many complexities, destiny-threads that lead beyond the sky to realms undreamt." His voice became swift and invoking. "Have you no itch to understand, no urge for greater adventuring than schoolboy rambles? I'll give you gods for foes, stars for your treasure-trove, if only you will do as I command. All men will be your animals; the best, your hunting pack. Kiss snails and swine? That's but an overture. Greater than Pan, you'll frighten nations, rape the world. The universe will tremble at your lust, but you will master it and force it down. That ancient laughter will give you the might—"

"Filth-spewing pimp! Scabby-lipped pander! Cease!" bellowed Fafhrd.

"Only submit to me and to my will," the adept continued rapturously, his lips working so that his black beard twitched rhythmically. "All things we'll twist and torture, know their cause. The lechery of gods will pave the way we'll tramp through windy darkness 'til we find the one who lurks in senseless Odin's skull twitching the strings that move your lives and mine. All knowledge will be ours, all for us three. Only give up your wills, submit to me!"

For a moment the Mouser was hypnotized by the glint of ghastly wonders. Then he felt Fafhrd's biceps, which had slackened under his grasp—as if the Northerner were yielding too—suddenly tighten, and from his own lips he heard words projected coldly into the echoing silence.

"Do you think a rhyme is enough to win us over to your nauseous titillations? Do you think we care a jot for your high-flown muck-peering? Fafhrd, this slobberer offends me, past ills that he has done us aside. It only remains to determine which one of us disposes of him. I long to unravel him, beginning with the ribs."

"Do you not understand what I have offered you, the magnitude of the boon? Have we no common ground?"

"Only to fight on. Call up your demons, sorcerer, or else look to your weapon."

An unearthly lust receded, rippling from the adept's eyes, leaving behind only a deadliness. Fafhrd snatched up the cup of Socrates and dropped it for a lot, swore as it rolled toward the Mouser, whose cat-quick hand went softly to the hilt of the slim sword called Scalpel. Stooping, the adept groped blindly behind him and regained his belt and scabbard, drawing from it a blade that looked as delicate and responsive as a needle. He stood, a lank and icy indolence, in the red of the risen sun, the black anthropomorphic monolith looming behind him for his second.

The Mouser drew Scalpel silently from its sheath, ran a finger caressingly down the side of the blade, and in so doing noticed an inscription in black crayon which read, "I do not approve of this step you are taking. Ningauble." With a hiss of annoyance the Mouser wiped it off on his thigh and concentrated his gaze on the adept—so preoccupiedly that he did not observe the eyes of the fallen Ahura quiver open.

"And now, Dead Sorcerer," said the Gray One lightly, "my name is the Gray Mouser."

"And mine is Anra Devadoris."

Instantly the Mouser put into action his carefully weighed plan: to take two rapid skips forward and launch his blade-tipped body at the adept's sword, which was to be deflected, and at the adept's throat, which was to be sliced. He was already seeing the blood spurt when, in the middle of the second skip, he saw, whirring like an arrow toward his eyes, the adept's blade. With a belly-contorted effort he twisted to one side and parried blindly. The adept's blade whipped in greedily around Scalpel, but only far enough to snag and tear the skin at the side of the Mouser's neck. The Mouser recovered balance crouching, his guard wide open, and only a backward leap saved him from Anra Devadoris' second serpentlike strike. As he gathered himself to meet the next attack, he gaped amazedly, for never before in his life had he been faced by superior speed. Fafhrd's face was white. Ahura, however, her head raised a little from the furry cloak, smiled with a weak and incredulous, but evil joy—a frankly vicious joy wholly unlike her former sly, intangible intimations of cruelty.

But Anra Devadoris smiled wider and nodded with a patronizing gratefulness at the Mouser, before gliding in. And now it was the blade Needle that darted in unhurried lightning attack, and Scalpel that whirred in frenzied defense. The Mouser retreated in jerky, circling stages, his face sweaty, his throat hot, but his heart exulting, for never before had he fought this well—not even on that stifling morning when, his head in a sack, he had disposed of a whimsically cruel Egyptian kidnaper.

Inexplicably, he had the feeling that his days spent in spying on Ahura were now paying off.

Needle came slipping in and for the moment the Mouser could not tell upon which side of Scalpel it skirred and so sprang backward, but not swiftly enough to escape a prick in the side. He cut viciously at the adept's withdrawing arm—and barely managed to jerk his own arm out of the way of a stop thrust.

In a nasty voice so low that Fafhrd hardly heard her, and the Mouser heard her not at all, Ahura called, "The spiders tickled your flesh ever so lightly as they ran, Anra."

Perhaps the adept hesitated almost imperceptibly, or perhaps it was only that his eyes grew a shade emptier. At all events, the Mouser was not given that opportunity, for which he was desperately searching, to initiate a counterattack and escape the deadly whirligig of his circling retreat. No matter how intently he peered, he could spy no gap in the sword-woven steel net his adversary was tirelessly casting toward him, nor could he discern in the face behind the net any betraying grimace, any flicker of eye hinting at the next point of attack, any flaring of nostrils or distension of lips telling of gasping fatigue similar to his own. It was inhuman, unalive, the mask of a machine built by some Daedalus, or of a leprously silver automaton stepped out of myth. And like a machine, Devadoris seemed to be gaining strength and speed from the very rhythm that was sapping his own.

The Mouser realized that he must interrupt that rhythm by a counterattack, any counterattack, or fall victim to a swiftness become blinding.

And then he further realized that the proper opportunity for that counterattack would never come, that he would wait in vain for any faltering in his adversary's attack, that he must risk everything on a guess.

His throat burned, his heart pounded on his ribs for air, a stinging, numbing poison seeped through his limbs.

Devadoris started a feint, or a deadly thrust, at his face.

Simultaneously, the Mouser heard Ahura jeer, "They hung their webs on your beard and the worms knew your secret parts, Anra."

He guessed—and cut at the adept's knee.

Either he guessed right, or else something halted the adept's deadly thrust.

The adept easily parried the Mouser's cut, but the rhythm was broken and his speed slackened.

Again he developed speed, again at the last possible moment the Mouser guessed. Again Ahura eerily jeered, "The maggots made you a necklace, and each marching beetle paused to peer into your eye, Anra."

Over and over it happened, speed, guess, macabre jeer, but each time the Mouser gained only momentary respite, never the opportunity to start an extended counterattack. His circling retreat continued so uninterruptedly that he felt as if he had been caught in a whirlpool. With each revolution, certain fixed landmarks swept into view: Fafhrd's blanched agonized face; the hulking tomb; Ahura's hate-contorted, mocking visage; the red stab of the risen sun; the gouged, black, somber monolith, with its attendant stony soldiers and their gigantic stone tents; Fafhrd again. . . .

And now the Mouser knew his strength was failing for good and all. Each guessed counterattack brought him less respite, was less of a check to the adept's speed. The landmarks whirled dizzily, darkened. It was as if he had been sucked to the maelstrom's center, as if the black cloud which he had fancied pouring from Ahura were enveloping him vampirously, choking off his breath.

He knew that he would be able to make only one more counter-cut, and must therefore stake all on a thrust at the heart.

He readied himself.

But he had waited too long. He could not gather the necessary strength, summon the speed.

He saw the adept preparing the lightning death-stroke.

His own thrust was like the gesture of a paralyzed man seeking to rise from his bed.

Then Ahura began to laugh.

It was a horrible, hysterical laugh; a giggling, snickering laugh; a laugh that made him dully wonder why she should find such joy in his death; and yet, for all the difference, a laugh that sounded like a shrill, distorted echo of Fafhrd's or his own.

Puzzledly, he noted that Needle had not yet transfixed him, that Devadoris' lightning thrust was slowing, slowing, as if the hateful laughter were failing in cumbering swathes around the adept, as if each horrid peal dropped a chain around his limbs.

The Mouser leaned on his own sword and collapsed, rather than lunged, forward.

He heard Fafhrd's shuddering sigh.

Then he realized that he was trying to pull Scalpel from the adept's chest and that it was an almost insuperably difficult task, although the blade had gone in as easily as if Anra Devadoris had been a hollow man. Again he tugged, and Scalpel came clear, fell from his nerveless fingers. His knees shook, his head sagged, and darkness flooded everything.

Fafhrd, sweat-drenched, watched the adept. Anra Devadoris' rigid body teetered like a stone pillar, slim cousin to the monolith behind him. His lips were fixed in a frozen, foreknowing smile. The teetering increased, yet for a while, as if he were an incarnation of death's ghastly pendulum, he did not fall. Then he swayed too far forward and fell like a pillar, without collapse. There was a horrid, hollow crash as his head struck the black pavement.

Ahura's hysterical laughter burst out afresh.

Fafhrd ran forward calling to the Mouser, anxiously shook the slumped form. Snores answered him. Like some spent Theban phalanxman drowsing over his pike in the twilight of the battle, the Mouser was sleeping the sleep of complete exhaustion. Fafhrd found the Mouser's gray cloak, wrapped it around him, and gently laid him down.

Ahura was shaking convulsively.

Fafhrd looked at the fallen adept, lying there so formally outstretched, like a tomb-statue rolled over. Dead, Devadoris' lankness was skeletal. He had bled hardly at all from the wound given him by Scalpel, but his forehead was crushed like an eggshell. Fafhrd touched him. The skin was cold, the muscles hard as stone.

Fafhrd had seen men go rigid immediately upon death—Macedonians who had fought too desperately and too long. But they had become weak and staggering toward the end. Anra Devadoris had maintained the appearance of ease and perfect control up to the last moment, despite the poisons that must have been coursing through his veins almost to the exclusion of blood. All through the duel, his chest had hardly heaved.

"By Odin crucified!" Fafhrd muttered. "He was something of a man, even though he was an adept."

A hand was laid on his arm. He jerked around. It was Ahura come behind him. The whites showed around her eyes. She smiled at him crookedly, then lifted a knowing eyebrow, put her finger to her lips, and dropped suddenly to her knees beside the adept's corpse. Gingerly she touched the satin smooth surface of the tiny blood-clot on the adept's breast. Fafhrd, noting afresh the resemblance between the dead and the crazy face, sucked in his breath. Ahura scurried off like a startled cat.

Suddenly she froze like a dancer and looked back at him, and a gloating, transcendent vindictiveness came into her face. She beckoned to Fafhrd. Then she ran lightly up the steps to the tomb and pointed into it and beckoned again. Doubtfully the Northerner approached, his eyes on her strained and unearthly face, beautiful as an efreet's. Slowly he mounted the steps.

Then he looked down.

Looked down to feel that the wholesome world was only a film on primary abominations. He realized that what Ahura was showing him had somehow been her ultimate degradation and the ultimate degradation of the thing that had named itself Anra Devadoris. He remembered the bizarre taunts that

Ahura had thrown at the adept during the duel. He remembered her laughter, and his mind eddied along the edge of suspicions of pit-spawned improprieties and obscene intimacies. He hardly noticed that Ahura had slumped over the wall of the tomb, her white arms hanging down as if pointing all ten slender fingers in limp horror. He did not know that the blackly puzzled eyes of the suddenly awakened Mouser were peering up at him.

Thinking back, he realized that Devadoris' fastidiousness and exquisitely groomed appearance had made him think of the tomb as an eccentric entrance to some luxurious underground palace.

But now he saw that there were no doors in that cramping cell into which he peered, nor cracks indicating where hidden doors might be. Whatever had come from there, had lived there, where the dry corners were thick with webs and the floor swarmed with maggots, dung beetles, and furry black spiders.

6. *The Mountain*

Perhaps some chuckling demon, or Ningauble himself, planned it that way. At all events, as Fafhrd stepped down from the tomb, he got his feet tangled in the shroud of Ahriman and bellowed wildly (the Mouser called it "bleating") before he noticed the cause, which was by that time ripped to tatters.

Next Ahura, aroused by the tumult, set them into a brief panic by screaming that the black monolith and its soldiery were marching toward them to grind them under stony feet.

Almost immediately afterwards the cup of Socrates momentarily froze their blood by rolling around in a semicircle, as if its learned owner were invisibly pawing for it, perhaps to wet his throat after a spell of dusty disputation in the underworld. Of the withered sprig from the Tree of Life there was no sign, although the Mouser jumped as far and as skittishly as one of his namesakes when he saw a large black walking-stick insect crawling away from where the sprig might have fallen.

But it was the camel that caused the biggest commotion, by suddenly beginning to prance about clumsily in a most uncharacteristically ecstatic fashion, finally cavorting up eagerly on two legs to the mare, which fled in squealing dismay. Afterwards it became apparent that the camel must have gotten into the aphrodisiacs, for one of the bottles was pashed as if by a hoof, with only a scummy licked patch showing where its leaked contents had been, and two of the small clay jars were vanished entirely. Fafhrd set out after the two beasts on one of the remaining horses, hallooing crazily.

The Mouser, left alone with Ahura, found his glibness put to the test in saving her sanity by a barrage of small talk, mostly well-spiced Tyrian gossip, but including a wholly apocryphal tale of how he and Fafhrd and five small Ethiopian boys once played Maypole with the eye-stalks of a drunken Ningauble, leaving him peering about in the oddest directions. (The Mouser was wondering why they had not heard from their seven-eyed mentor. After victories Ningauble was always particularly prompt in getting in his demands for payment; and very exacting too—he would insist on a strict accounting for the three missing aphrodisiac containers.)

The Mouser might have been expected to take advantage of this opportunity to press his suit with Ahura, and if possible assure himself that he was now wholly free of the snail-curse. But, her hysterical condition aside, he felt strangely shy with her, as if, although this was the Ahura he loved, he were now meeting her for the first time. Certainly this was a wholly different Ahura from the one with whom they had journeyed to the Lost City, and the memory of how he had treated that other Ahura put a restraint on him. So he cajoled and comforted her as he might have some lonely Tyrian waif, finally bringing two funny little hand-puppets from his pouch and letting them amuse her for him.

And Ahura sobbed and stared and shivered, and hardly seemed to hear what nonsense the Mouser was saying, yet grew quiet and sane-eyed and appeared to be comforted.

When Fafhrd eventually returned with the still giddy camel and the outraged mare, he did not interrupt, but listened gravely, his gaze occasionally straying to the dead adept, the black monolith, the stone city, or the valley's downward slope to the north. High over their heads a flock of birds was flying in the same direction. Suddenly they scattered wildly, as if an eagle had dropped among them. Fafhrd frowned. A moment later he heard a whirring in the air. The Mouser and Ahura looked up too, momentarily glimpsed something slim hurtling downward. They cringed. There was a thud as a long whitish arrow buried itself in a crack in the pavement hardly a foot from Fafhrd and stuck there vibrating.

After a moment Fafhrd touched it with shaking hand. The shaft was crusted with ice, the feathers stiff, as if, incredibly, it had sped for a long time through frigid supramundane air. There was something tied snugly around the shaft. He detached and unrolled an ice-brittle sheet of papyrus, which softened under his touch, and read, "You must go farther. Your quest is not ended. Trust in omens. Ningauble."

Still trembling, Fafhrd began to curse thunderously. He crumpled the papyrus, jerked up the arrow, broke it in two, threw the parts blindly away. "Misbegotten spawn of a eunuch, an owl, and an octopus!" he finished. "First he tries to skewer us from the skies, then he tells us our quest is not ended—when we've just ended it!"

The Mouser, well knowing these rages into which Fafhrd was apt to fall after battle, especially a battle in which he had not been able to participate, started to comment coolly. Then he saw the anger abruptly drain from Fafhrd's eyes, leaving a wild twinkle which he did not like.

"Mouser!" said Fafhrd eagerly. "Which way did I throw the arrow?"

"Why, north," said the Mouser without thinking.

"Yes, and the birds were flying north, and the arrow was coated with ice!" The wild twinkle in Fafhrd's eyes became a berserk brilliance. "Omens, he said? We'll trust in omens all right! We'll go north, north, and still north!"

The Mouser's heart sank. Now would be a particularly difficult time to combat Fafhrd's long-standing desire to take him to "that wondrously cold land where only brawny, hot-blooded men may live and they but by the killing of fierce, furry animals"—a prospect poignantly disheartening to a lover of hot baths, the sun, and southern nights.

"This is the chance of all chances," Fafhrd continued, intoning like a skald. "Ah, to rub one's naked hide with snow, to plunge like walrus into ice-garnished water. Around the Caspian and over greater mountains than these goes a way that men of my race have taken. Thor's gut, but you will love it! No wine, only hot mead and savory smoking carcasses, skin-toughening furs to wear, cold air at night to keep dreams clear and sharp, and great strong-hipped women. Then to raise sail on a winter ship and laugh at the frozen spray. Why have we so long delayed? Come! By the icy member that begot Odin, we must start at once!"

The Mouser stifled a groan. "Ah, blood brother," he intoned, not a whit less brazen-voiced, "my heart leaps even more than yours at the thought of nerve-quickening snow and all the other niceties of the manly life I have long yearned to taste. But—" Here his voice broke sadly, "—we forget this good woman, whom in any case, even if we disregard Ningauble's injunction, we must take safely back to Tyre."

He smiled inwardly.

"But I don't want to go back to Tyre," interrupted Ahura, looking up from the puppets with an impishness so like a child's that the Mouser cursed himself for ever having treated her as one. "This lonely spot seems equally far from all builded places. North is as good a way as any."

"Flesh of Freya!" bellowed Fafhrd, throwing his arms wide. "Do you hear what she says, Mouser? By Idun, that was spoken like a true snow-land woman! Not one moment must be wasted now. We shall smell mead before a year is out. By Frigg, a woman! Mouser, you good for one so small, did you not notice the pretty way she put it?"

So it was bustle about and pack and (for the present, at least, the Mouser conceded) no way out of it. The chest of aphrodisiacs, the cup, and the tattered shroud were bundled back onto the camel, which was still busy ogling the mare and smacking its great leathery lips. And Fafhrd leaped and shouted and clapped the Mouser's back as if there were not an eon-old dead stone city around them and a lifeless adept warming in the sun.

In a matter of moments they were jogging off down the valley, with Fafhrd singing tales of snowstorms and hunting and monsters big as icebergs and giants as tall as frosty mountains, and the Mouser dourly amusing himself by picturing his own death at the hands of some overly affectionate "great strong-hipped" woman.

Soon the way became less barren. Scrub trees and the valley's downward trend hid the city behind them. A surge of relief which the Mouser hardly noticed went through him as the last stony sentinel dipped out of sight, particularly the black monolith left to brood over the adept. He turned his attention to what lay ahead—a conical mountain barring the valley's mouth and wearing a high cap of mist, a lonely thunderhead which his imagination shaped into incredible towers and spires.

Suddenly his sleepy thoughts snapped awake. Fafhrd and Ahura had stopped and were staring at something wholly unexpected—a low wooden windowless house pressed back among the scrubby trees, with a couple of tilled fields behind it. The rudely carved guardian spirits at the four corners of the roof and topping the kingposts seemed Persian, but Persian purged of all southern influence—ancient Persian.

And ancient Persian too appeared the thin features, straight nose, and black-streaked beard of the aged man watching them circumspectly from the low doorway. It seemed to be Ahura's face he scanned most intently—or tried to scan, since Fafhrd mostly hid her.

"Greetings, Father," called the Mouser. "Is this not a merry day for riding, and yours good lands to pass?"

"Yes," replied the aged man dubiously, using a rusty dialect. "Though there are none, or few, who pass."

"Just as well to be far from the evil stinking cities," Fafhrd interjected heartily. "Do you know the mountain ahead, Father? Is there an easy way past it that leads north?"

At the word "mountain" the aged man cringed. He did not answer.

"Is there something wrong about the path we are taking?" the Mouser asked quickly. "Or something evil about that misty mountain?"

The aged man started to shrug his shoulders, held them contracted, looked again at the travelers. Friendliness seemed to fight with fear in his face, and to win, for he leaned forward and said hurriedly, "I warn you, sons, not to venture farther. What is the steel of your swords, the speed of your steeds, against—but remember" (he raised his voice) "I accuse no one." He looked quickly from side to side. "I have nothing at all to complain of. To me the mountain is a great benefit. My fathers returned here because the land is shunned by thief and honest man alike. There are no taxes on this land—no money taxes. I question nothing."

"Oh well, Father, I don't think we'll go farther," sighed the Mouser wilily. "We're but idle fellows who follow our noses across the world. And sometimes we smell a strange tale. And that reminds me of a matter in which you may be able to give us generous lads some help." He chinked the coins in his pouch. "We have heard a tale of a demon that inhabits here—a young demon dressed in black and silver, pale, with a black beard."

As the Mouser was saying these things the aged man was edging backward and at the finish he dodged inside and slammed the door, though not before they saw someone pluck at his sleeve. Instantly there came muffled angry expostulation in a girl's voice.

The door burst open. They heard the aged man say ". . . bring it down upon us all." Then a girl of about fifteen came running toward them. Her face was flushed, her eyes anxious and scared.

"You must turn back!" she called to them as she ran. "None but wicked things go to the mountain—or the doomed. And the mist hides a great horrible castle. And powerful, lonely demons live there. And one of them—"

She clutched at Fafhrd's stirrup. But just as her fingers were about to close on it, she looked beyond him straight at Ahura. An expression of abysmal terror came into her face. She screamed, "He! The black beard!" and crumpled to the ground.

The door slammed and they heard a bar drop into place.

They dismounted. Ahura quickly knelt by the girl, signed to them after a moment that she had only fainted. Fafhrd approached the barred door, but it would not open to any knocking, pleas, or threats. He finally solved the riddle by kicking it down. Inside he saw: the aged man cowering in a dark corner; a woman attempting to conceal a young child in a pile of straw; a very old woman sitting on a stool, obviously blind, but frightenedly peering about just the same; and a young man holding an axe in trembling hands. The family resemblance was very marked.

Fafhrd stepped out of the way of the young man's feeble axe-blow and gently took the weapon from him.

The Mouser and Ahura brought the girl inside. At sight of Ahura there were further horrified shrinkings.

They laid the girl on the straw, and Ahura fetched water and began to bathe her head.

Meanwhile, the Mouser, by playing on her family's terror and practically identifying himself as a mountain demon, got them to answer his questions. First he asked about the stone city. It was a place of ancient devil-worship, they said, a place to be shunned. Yes, they had seen the black monolith of Ahriman, but only from a distance. No, they did not worship Ahriman—see the fire-shrine they kept for his adversary Ormadz? But they dreaded Ahriman, and the stones of the devil-city had a life of their own.

Then he asked about the misty mountain, and found it harder to get satisfactory answers. The cloud always shrouded its peak, they insisted. Though once toward sunset, the young man admitted, he thought he had glimpsed crazily leaning green towers and twisted minarets. But there was danger up there, horrible danger. What danger? He could not say.

The Mouser turned to the aged man. "You told me," he said harshly, "that my brother demons exact no money tax from you for this land. What kind of tax, then, do they exact?"

"Lives," whispered the aged man, his eyes showing more white.

"Lives, eh? How many? And when do they come for them?"

"They never come. We go. Maybe every ten years, maybe every five, there comes a yellow-green light on the mountaintop at night, and a powerful calling in the air. Sometimes after such a night one of us is gone—one who was too far from the house when the green light came. To be in the house with others helps resist the calling. I never saw the light except from our door, with a fire burning bright at my back and someone holding me. My brother went when I was a boy. Then for many years afterwards the light never come, so that even I began to wonder whether it was not a boyhood legend or illusion.

"But seven years ago," he continued quaveringly, staring at the Mouser, "there came riding late one afternoon, on two gaunt and death-wearied horses, a young man and an old—or rather the semblances of a young man and an old, for, I knew without being told, knew as I crouched trembling inside the door, peering through the crack, that the masters were returning to the Castle Called Mist. The old man was bald as a vulture and had no beard. The young man had the beginnings of a silky black one. He was dressed in black and silver, and his face was very pale. His features were like—" Here his gaze flickered fearfully toward Ahura. "He rode stiffly, his lanky body rocking from side to side. He looked as if he were dead.

"They rode on toward the mountain without a sideward glance. But ever since that time the greenish-yellow light has glowed almost nightly from the mountaintop, and many of our animals have answered the call—and the wild ones too, to judge from their diminishing numbers. We have been careful, always staying near the house. It was not until three years ago that my eldest son went. He strayed too far in hunting and let darkness overtake him.

"And we have seen the black-bearded young man many times, usually at a distance, treading along the skyline or standing with head bowed upon some crag. Though once when my daughter was washing at the stream she looked up from her clothes-pounding and saw his dead eyes peering through the reeds. And once my eldest son, chasing a wounded snow-leopard into a thicket, found him talking with the beast. And once, rising early on a harvest morning, I saw him sitting by the well, staring at our doorway, although he did not seem to see me emerge. The old man we have seen too, though not so often. And for the last two years we have seen little or nothing of either, until—" And once again his gaze flickered helplessly toward Ahura.

Meanwhile the girl had come to her senses. This time her terror of Ahura was not so extreme. She could add nothing to the aged man's tale.

They prepared to depart. The Mouser noted a certain veiled vindictiveness toward the girl, especially in the eyes of the woman with the child, for having tried to warn them. So turning in the doorway he said, "If you harm one hair of the girl's head, we will return, and the black-bearded one with us, and the green light to guide us by and wreak terrible vengeance."

He tossed a few gold coins on the floor and departed.

(And so, although or rather because her family looked upon her as an ally of demons, the girl from then on led a pampered life, and came to consider her blood as superior to theirs, and played shamelessly on their fear of the Mouser and Fafhrd and Black-beard, and finally made them give her all the golden coins, and with them purchased seductive garments after fortunate passage to a faraway city, where by clever stratagem she became the wife of a satrap and lived sumptuously ever afterwards—something that is often the fate of romantic people, if only they are romantic enough.)

Emerging from the house, the Mouser found Fafhrd making a brave attempt to recapture his former berserk mood. "Hurry up, you little apprentice-demon!" he welcomed. "We've a tryst with the good land of snow and cannot lag on the way!"

As they rode off, the Mouser rejoined good-naturedly, "But what about the camel, Fafhrd? You can't very well take it to the ice country. It'll die of the phlegm."

"There's no reason why snow shouldn't be as good for camels as it is for men," Fafhrd retorted. Then, rising in his saddle and turning back, he waved toward the house and shouted, "Lad! You that held the axe! When in years to come your bones feel a strange yearning, turn your face to the north. There you will find a land where you can become a man indeed."

But in their hearts both knew that this talk was a pretense, that other planets now loomed in their horoscopes—in particular one that shone with a greenish-yellow light. As they pressed on up the valley, its silence and the absence of animal and insect life now made sinister, they felt mysteries hovering all around. Some, they knew, were locked in Ahura, but both refrained from questioning her, moved by vague apprehensions of terrifying upheavals her mind had undergone.

Finally the Mouser voiced what was in the thoughts of both of them. "Yes, I am much afraid that Anra Devadoris, who sought to make us his apprentices, was only an apprentice himself and apt, apprentice-wise, to take credit for his master's work. Black-beard is gone, but the beardless one remains. What was it Ningauble said? . . . no simple creature, but a mystery? . . . no single identity, but a mirage?"

"Well, by all the fleas that bite the Great Antiochus, and all the lice that tickle his wife!" remarked a shrill, insolent voice behind them. "You doomed gentlemen already know what's in this letter I have for you."

They whirled around. Standing beside the camel—he might conceivably have been hidden, it is true, behind a nearby boulder—was a pertly grinning brown urchin, so typically Alexandrian that he might have stepped this minute out of Rakotis with a skinny mongrel sniffing at his heels. (The Mouser half expected such a dog to appear at the next moment.)

"Who sent you, boy?" Fafhrd demanded. "How did you get here?"

"Now who and how would you expect?" replied the urchin. "Catch." He tossed the Mouser a wax tablet. "Say, you two, take my advice and get out while the getting's good. I think so far as your expedition's concerned, Ningauble's pulling up his tent pegs and scuttling home. Always a friend in need, my dear employer."

The Mouser ripped the cords, unfolded the tablet, and read:

"Greetings, my brave adventurers. You have done well, but the best remains to be done. Hark to the calling. Follow the green light. But be very cautious afterwards. I wish I could be of more assistance. Send the shroud, the cup, and the chest back with the boy as first payment."

"Loki-brat! Regin-spawn!" burst out Fafhrd. The Mouser looked up to see the urchin lurching and bobbing back toward the Lost City on the back of the eagerly fugitive camel. His impudent laughter returned shrill and faint.

"There," said the Mouser, "rides off the generosity of poor, penurious Ningauble. Now we know what to do with the camel."

"Zutt!" said Fafhrd. "Let him have the brute and the toys. Good riddance to his gossiping!"

"Not a very high mountain," said the Mouser an hour later, "but high enough. I wonder who carved this neat little path and who keeps it clear?"

As he spoke, he was winding loosely over his shoulder a long thin rope of the sort used by mountain climbers, ending in a hook.

It was sunset, with twilight creeping at their heels. The little path, which had grown out of nothing, only gradually revealing itself, now led them sinuously around great boulders and along the crests of ever steeper rock-strewn slopes. Conversation, which was only a film on wariness, had played with the methods of Ningauble and his agents—whether they communicated with one another directly, from mind to mind, or by tiny whistles that emitted a note too high for human ears to hear, but capable of producing a tremor in any brother whistle or in the ear of the bat.

It was a moment when the whole universe seemed to pause. A spectral greenish light gleamed from the cloudy top ahead—but that was surely only the sun's sky-reflected afterglow. There was a hint of all-pervading sound in the air, a mighty susurrus just below the threshold of hearing, as if an army of unseen insects were tuning up their instruments. These sensations were as intangible as the force that drew them onward, a force so feeble that they knew they could break it like a single spider-strand, yet did not choose to try.

As if in response to some unspoken word, both Fafhrd and the Mouser turned toward Ahura. Under their gaze she seemed to be changing momently, opening like a night flower, becoming ever more childlike, as if some master hypnotist were stripping away the outer, later petals of her mind, leaving only a small limpid pool, from whose unknown depths, however, dark bubbles were dimly rising.

They felt their infatuation pulse anew, but with a shy restraint on it. And their hearts fell silent as the hooded heights above, as she said, "Anra Devadoris was my twin brother."

7. Ahura Devadoris

"I never knew my father. He died before we were born. In one of her rare fits of communicativeness my mother told me, 'Your father was a Greek,

Ahura. A very kind and learned man. He laughed a great deal.' I remember how stern she looked as she said that, rather than how beautiful, the sunlight glinting from her ringletted, black-dyed hair.

"But it seemed to me that she had slightly emphasized the word 'Your.' You see, even then I wondered about Anra. So I asked Old Berenice the housekeeper about it. She told me she had seen mother bear us, both on the same night.

"Old Berenice went on to tell me how my father had died. Almost nine months before we were born, he was found one morning beaten to death in the street just outside the door. A gang of Egyptian longshoremen who were raping and robbing by night were supposed to have done it, although they were never brought to justice—that was back when the Ptolemies had Tyre. It was a horrible death. He was almost pashed to a pulp against the cobbles.

"At another time Old Berenice told me something about my mother, after making me swear by Athena and by Set and by Moloch, who would eat me if I did, never to tell. She said that mother came from a Persian family whose first daughters in the old times were all priestesses, dedicated from birth to be the wives of an evil Persian god, forbidden the embraces of mortals, doomed to spend their nights alone with the stone image of the god in a lonely temple 'half-way across the world,' she said. Mother was away that day and Old Berenice dragged me down into a little basement under Mother's bedroom and pointed out three ragged gray stones set among the bricks and told me they came from the temple. Old Berenice liked to frighten me, although she was deathly afraid of Mother.

"Of course I instantly went and told Anra, as I always did."

The little path was leading sharply upward now, along the spine of a crest. Their horses went at a walk, first Fafhrd's, then Ahura's, last the Mouser's. The lines were smoothed in Fafhrd's face, although he was still very watchful, and the Mouser looked almost like a quaint child.

Ahura continued, "It is hard to make you understand my relationship with Anra, because it was so close that even the word 'relationship' spoils it. There was a game we would play in the garden. He would close his eyes and guess what I was looking at. In other games we would change sides, but never in this one.

"He invented all sorts of versions of the game and didn't want to play any others. Sometimes I would climb up by the olive tree onto the tiled roof— Anra couldn't make it—and watch for an hour. Then I'd come down and tell him what I'd seen—some dyers spreading out wet green cloth for the sun to turn it purple, a procession of priests around the Temple of Melkarth, a galley from Pergamum setting sail, a Greek official impatiently explaining something to his Egyptian scribe, two henna-handed ladies giggling at some kilted sailors, a mysterious and lonely Jew—and he would tell me what kind of people they were and what they had been thinking and what they were planning to do. It was a very special kind of imagination, for afterwards when I began to go outside I found out that he was usually right. At the time I remember

thinking that it was as if he were looking at the pictures in my mind and seeing more than I could. I liked it. It was such a gentle feeling.

"Of course our closeness was partly because mother, especially after she
changed her way of life, wouldn't let us go out at all or mix with other children. There was more reason for that than just her strictness. Anra was very
delicate. He once broke his wrist and it was a long time healing. Mother had a
slave come in who was skilled in such things, and he told mother he was
afraid that Anra's bones were becoming too brittle. He told about children
whose muscles and sinews gradually turned to stone, so that they became
living statues. Mother struck him in the face and drove him from the house—
an action that cost her a dear friend, because he was an important slave.

"And even if Anra had been allowed to go out, he couldn't have. Once after I had begun to go outside I persuaded him to come with me. He didn't
want to, but I laughed at him, and he could never stand laughter. As soon as
we climbed over the garden wall he fell down in a faint and I couldn't rouse
him from it though I tried and tried. Finally I climbed back so I could open the
door and drag him in, and Old Berenice spotted me and I had to tell her what
had happened. She helped me carry him in, but afterwards she whipped me
because she knew I'd never dare tell mother I'd taken him outside. Anra came
to his senses while she was whipping me, but he was sick for a week afterwards. I don't think I ever laughed at him after that, until today.

"Cooped up in the house, Anra spent most of time studying. While I
watched from the roof or wheedled stories from Old Berenice and the other
slaves, or later on went out to gather information for him, he would stay in
father's library, reading, or learning some new language from father's gram-
mars and translations. Mother taught both of us to read Greek, and I picked
up a speaking knowledge of Aramaic and scraps of other tongues from the
slaves and passed them on to him. But Anra was far cleverer than I at reading. He loved letters as passionately as I did the outside. For him, they were
alive. I remember him showing me some Egyptian hieroglyphs and telling me
that they were all animals and insects. And then he showed me some Egyptian hieratics and demotics and told me those were the same animals in disguise. But Hebrew, he said, was best of all, for each letter was a magic
charm. That was before he learned Old Persian. Sometimes it was years before we found out how to pronounce the languages he learned. That was
one of my most important jobs when I started to go outside for him.

"Father's library had been kept just as it was when he died. Neatly
stacked in canisters were all the renowned philosophers, historians, poets,
rhetoricians, and grammarians. But tossed in a corner along with potsherds
and papyrus scraps like so much trash, were rolls of a very different sort.
Across the back of one of them my father had scribbled, derisively I'm sure,
in his big impulsive hand, 'Secret Wisdom!' It was those that from the first
captured Anra's curiosity. He would read the respectable books in the canisters, but chiefly so he could go back and take a brittle roll from the corner,
blow off the dust, and puzzle out a little more.

"They were very strange books that frightened and disgusted me and made me want to giggle all at once. Many of them were written in a cheap and ignorant style. Some of them told what dreams meant and gave directions for working magic—all sorts of nasty things to be cooked together. Others—Jewish rolls in Aramaic—were about the end of the world and wild adventures of evil spirits and mixed-up, messy monsters—things with ten heads and jeweled cartwheels for feet, things like that. Then there were Chaldean star-books that told how all the lights in the sky were alive and their names and what they did to you. And one jerky, half illiterate roll in Greek told about something horrible, which for a long while I couldn't understand, connected with an ear of corn and six pomegranate seeds. It was in another of those sensational Greek rolls that Anra first found out about Ahriman and his eternal empire of evil, and after that he couldn't wait until he'd mastered Old Persian. But none of the few Old Persian rolls in father's library were about Ahriman, so he had to wait until I could steal such things for him outside.

"My going outside was after mother changed her way of life. That happened when I was seven. She was always a very moody and frightening woman, though sometimes she'd be very affectionate toward me for a little while, and she always spoiled and pampered Anra, though from a distance, through the slaves, almost as if she were afraid of him.

"Now her moods became blacker and blacker. Sometimes I'd surprise her looking in horror at nothing, or beating her forehead while her eyes were closed and her beautiful face was all taut, as if she were going mad. I had the feeling she'd been backed up to the end of some underground tunnel and must find a door leading out, or lose her mind.

"Then one afternoon I peeked into her bedroom and saw her looking into her silver mirror. For a long, long while she studied her face in it and I watched her without making a sound. I knew that something important was happening. Finally she seemed to make some sort of difficult inward effort and the lines of anxiety and sternness and fear disappeared from her face, leaving it smooth and beautiful as a mask. Then she unlocked a drawer I'd never seen into before and took out all sorts of little pots and vials and brushes. With these she colored and whitened her face and carefully smeared a dark, shining powder around her eyes and painted her lips reddish-orange. All this time my heart was pounding and my throat was choking up, I didn't know why. Then she laid down her brushes and dropped her chiton and felt of her throat and breasts in a thoughtful way and took up the mirror and looked at herself with a cold satisfaction. She was very beautiful, but it was a beauty that terrified me. Until now I'd always thought of her as hard and stern outside, but soft and loving within, if only you could manage to creep into that core. But now she was all turned inside out. Strangling my sobs, I ran to tell Anra and find out what it meant. But this time his cleverness failed him. He was as puzzled and disturbed as I.

"It was right afterwards that she became even stricter with me, and although she continued to spoil Anra from a distance, kept us shut up from the world more than ever. I wasn't even allowed to speak to the new slave she'd bought, an ugly, smirking, skinny-legged girl named Phryne who used to massage her and sometimes play the flute. There were all sorts of visitors coming to the house now at night, but Anra and I were always locked in our little bedroom high up by the garden. We'd hear them yelling through the wall and sometimes screaming and bumping around the inner court to the sound of Phryne's flute. Sometimes I'd lie staring at the darkness in an inexplicable sick terror all night long. I tried every way to get Old Berenice to tell me what was happening, but for once her fear of mother's anger was too great. She'd only leer at me.

"Finally Anra worked out a plan for finding out. When he first told me about it, I refused. It terrified me. That was when I discovered the power he had over me. Up until that time the things I had done for him had been part of a game I enjoyed as much as he. I had never thought of myself as a slave obeying commands. But now when I rebelled, I found out not only that my twin had an obscure power over my limbs, so that I could hardly move them at all, or imagined I couldn't, if he were unwilling, but also that I couldn't bear the thought of him being unhappy or frustrated.

"I realize now that he had reached the first of those crises in his life when his way was blocked and he pitilessly sacrificed his dearest helper to the urgings of his insatiable curiosity.

"Night came. As soon as we were locked in I let a knotted cord out the little high window and wriggled out and climbed down. Then I climbed the olive tree to the roof. I crept over the tiles down to the square skylight of the inner court and managed to squirm over the edge—I almost fell—into a narrow, cobwebby space between the ceiling and the tiles. There was a faint murmur of talk from the dining room, but the court was empty. I lay still as a mouse and waited."

Fafhrd uttered a smothered exclamation and stopped his horse. The others did the same. A pebble rattled down the slope, but they hardly heard it. Seeming to come from the heights above them and yet to fill the whole darkening sky was something that was not entirely a sound, something that tugged at them like the Sirens' voices at fettered Odysseus. For a while they listened incredulously, then Fafhrd shrugged and started forward again, the others following.

Ahura continued, "For a long time nothing happened, except occasionally slaves hurried in and out with full and empty dishes, and there was some laughter, and I heard Phryne's flute. Then suddenly the laughter grew louder and changed to singing, and there was the sound of couches pushed back and the patter of footsteps, and there swept into the court a Dionysiac rout.

"Phryne, naked, piped the way. My mother followed, laughing, her arms linked with those of two dancing young men, but clutching to her bosom a large silver wine-bowl. The wine sloshed over and stained purple her white silk chiton around her breasts, but she only laughed and reeled more wildly. After those came many others, men and women, young and old, all singing and dancing. One limber young man skipped high, clapping his heels, and one fat old grinning fellow panted and had to be pulled by girls, but they kept it up three times around the court before they threw themselves down on the couches and cushions. Then while they chattered and laughed and kissed and embraced and played pranks and watched a naked girl prettier than Phryne dance, my mother offered the bowl around for them to dip their wine cups.

"I was astounded—and entranced. I had been almost dead with fear, expecting I don't know what cruelties and horrors. Instead, what I saw was wholly lovely and natural. The revelation burst on me, 'So this is the wonderful and important thing that people do.' My mother no longer frightened me. Though she still wore her new face, there was no longer any hardness about her, inside or out, only joy and beauty. The young men were so witty and gay I had to put my fist in my mouth to keep from screaming with laughter. Even Phryne, squatting on her heels like a skinny boy as she piped, seemed for once unmalicious and likable. I couldn't wait to tell Anra.

"There was only one disturbing note, and that was so slight I hardly noticed it. Two of the men who took the lead in the joking, a young red-haired fellow and an older chap with a face like a lean satyr, seemed to have something up their sleeves. I saw them whisper to some of the others. And once the younger grinned at mother and shouted, 'I know something about you from way back!' And once the older called at her mockingly, 'I know something about your great-grandmother, you old Persian you!' Each time mother laughed and waved her hand derisively, but I could see that she was bothered underneath. And each time some of the others paused momentarily, as if they had an inkling of something, but didn't want to let on. Eventually the two men drifted out, and from then on there was nothing to mar the fun.

"The dancing became wilder and staggering, the laughter louder, more wine was spilt than drank. Then Phryne threw away her flute and ran and landed in the fat man's lap with a jounce that almost knocked the wind out of him. Four or five of the others tumbled down.

"Just at that moment there came a crashing and a loud rending of wood, as if a door were being broken in. Instantly everyone was as still as death. Someone jerked around and a lamp snuffed out, throwing half the court into shadow.

"Then loud, shaking footsteps, like two paving blocks walking, sounded through the house, coming nearer and nearer.

"Everyone was frozen, staring at the doorway. Phryne still had her arm around the fat man's neck. But it was in mother's face that the truly unbearable terror showed. She had retreated to the remaining lamp and dropped to her knees there. The whites showed around her eyes. She began to utter short, rapid screams, like a trapped dog.

"Then through the doorway clomped a great ragged-edged, square-limbed, naked stone man fully seven feet high. His face was just expressionless black gashes in a flat surface, and before him was thrust a mortary stone member. I couldn't bear to look at him, but I had to. He tramped echoingly across the room to mother, jerked her up, still screaming, by the hair, and with the other hand ripped down her wine-stained chiton. I fainted.

"But it must have ended about there, for when I came to, sick with terror, it was to hear everyone laughing uproariously. Several of them were bending over mother, at once reassuring and mocking her, the two men who had gone out among them, and to one side was a jumbled heap of cloth and thin boards, both crusted with mortar. From what they said I understood that the red-haired one had worn the horrible disguise, while satyr-face had made the footsteps by rhythmically clomping on the floor with a brick, and had simulated the breaking door by jumping on a propped-up board.

"'Now tell us your great-grandmother wasn't married to a stupid old stone demon back in Persia!' he jeered pleasantly, wagging his finger.

"Then came something that tortured me like a rusty dagger and terrified me, in a very quiet way, as much as the image. Although she was white as milk and barely able to totter, mother did her best to pretend that the loathsome trick they'd played on her was just a clever joke. I knew why. She was horribly afraid of losing their friendship and would have done anything rather than be left alone.

"Her pretence worked. Although some of them left, the rest yielded to her laughing entreaties. They drank until they sprawled out snoring. I waited until almost dawn, then summoned all my courage, made my stiff muscles pull me up onto the tiles, cold and slippery with dew, and with what seemed the last of my strength, dragged myself back to our room.

"But not to sleep. Anra was awake and avid to hear what had happened. I begged him not to make me, but he insisted. I had to tell him everything. The pictures of what I'd seen kept bobbing up in my wretchedly tired mind so vividly that it seemed to be happening all over again. He asked all sorts of questions, wouldn't let me miss a single detail. I had to relive that first thrilling revelation of joy, tainted now by the knowledge that the people were mostly sly and cruel.

"When I got to the part about the stone image, Anra became terribly excited. But when I told him about it all being a nasty joke, he seemed disappointed. He became angry, as if he suspected me of lying.

"Finally he let me sleep.

"The next night I went back to my cubbyhole under the tiles."

Again Fafhrd stopped his horse. The mist masking the mountaintop had suddenly begun to glow, as if a green moon were rising, or as if it were a volcano spouting green flames. The hue tinged their upturned faces. It lured like some vast cloudy jewel. Fafhrd and the Mouser exchanged a glance of fatalistic wonder. Then all three proceeded up the narrowing ridge.

Ahura continued, "I'd sworn by all the gods I'd never do it. I'd told myself I'd rather die. But . . . Anra made me.

"Daytimes I wandered around like a stupefied little ghost-slave. Old Berenice was puzzled and suspicious and once or twice I thought Phryne grimaced knowingly. Finally even mother noticed and questioned me and had a physician in.

"I think I would have gotten really sick and died, or gone mad, except that then, in desperation at first, I started to go outside, and a whole new world opened to me."

As she spoke on, her voice rising in hushed excitement at the memory of it, there was painted in the minds of Fafhrd and the Mouser a picture of the magic city that Tyre must have seemed to the child—the waterfront, the riches, the bustle of trade, the hum of gossip and laughter, the ships and strangers from foreign lands.

"Those people I had watched from the roof—I could touch them now, follow them around corners, make friends with them—and I soon found that I could make friends almost anywhere. Every person I met seemed a wonderful mystery, something to be smiled and chattered at. I dressed as a slave-child, and all sorts of folk got to know me and expect my coming—other slaves, tavern wenches and sellers of sweetmeats, street merchants and scribes, errand boys and boatmen, seamstresses and cooks. I made myself useful, ran errands myself, listened delightedly to their endless talk, passed on gossip I'd heard, gave away bits of food I'd stolen at home, became a favorite. It seemed to me I could never get enough of Tyre. I scampered from morning to night. It was generally twilight before I climbed back over the garden wall.

"I couldn't fool Old Berenice, but after a while I found a way to escape her whippings. I threatened to tell mother it was she who had told red-hair and satyr-face about the stone image. I don't know if I guessed right or not, but the threat worked. After that, she would only mumble venomously whenever I sneaked in after sunset. As for mother, she was getting farther away from us all the time, alive only by night, lost by day in frightened brooding.

"Then, each evening, came another delight. I would tell Anra everything I had heard and seen, each new adventure, each little triumph. Like a magpie I brought home for him all the bright colors, sounds, and odors. Like a magpie I repeated for him the babble of strange languages I'd heard, the scraps of learned talk I'd caught from priests and scholars. I forgot what he'd done to me. We were playing the game again, the most wonderful version of all. Often he helped me, suggesting new places to go, new things to watch for, and once he even saved me from being kidnapped by a couple of ingratiating Alexandrian slave-dealers whom anyone but I would have suspected.

"It was odd how that happened. The two had made much of me, were promising me sweetmeats if I would go somewhere nearby with them, when I thought I heard Anra's voice whisper 'Don't.' I became cold with terror and darted down an alley.

"It seemed as though Anra were now able sometimes to see the pictures in my mind even when I was away from him. I felt ever so close to him.

"I was wild for him to come out with me, but I've told you what happened the one time he tried. And as the years passed, he seemed to become tied even tighter to the house. Once when mother vaguely talked of moving to Antioch, he fell ill and did not recover until she had promised we would never, never go.

"Meanwhile he was growing up into a slim and darkly handsome youth. Phryne began to make eyes at him and sought excuses to go to his room. But he was frightened and rebuffed her. However, he coaxed me to make friends with her, although mother had forbidden it, to go to her room, talk to her, be near her, even share her bed those nights when mother did not want her. He seemed to like that.

"You know the restlessness that comes to a maturing child, when he seeks love, or adventure, or the gods, or all three. That restlessness had come to Anra, but his only gods were in those dusty, dubious rolls my father had labeled 'Secret Wisdom!' I hardly knew what he did by day any more except that there were odd ceremonies and experiments mixed with his studies. Some of them he conducted in the little basement where the three gray stones were. At such times he had me keep watch. He no longer told me what he was reading or thinking, and I was so busy in my new world that I hardly noticed the difference.

"And yet I could see the restlessness growing. He sent me on longer and more difficult missions, had me inquire after books the scribes had never heard of, seek out all manner of astrologers and wise-women, required me to steal or buy stranger and stranger ingredients from the herb doctors. And when I did win such treasures for him, he would only snatch them from me unjoyfully and be twice as gloomy the evening after. Gone were such days of rejoicing as when I had brought him the first Persian rolls about Ahriman, the first lodestone, or repeated every syllable I had overheard of the words of a famous philosopher from Athens. He was beyond all that now. He sometimes hardly listened to my detailed reports, as if he had already glanced through them and knew they contained nothing to interest him.

" He grew haggard and sick. His restlessness took the form of a frantic pacing. I was reminded of my mother trapped in that blocked-off, underground corridor. It made my heart hurt to watch him. I longed to help him, to share with him my new exciting life, to give him the thing he so desperately wanted.

"But it was not my help he needed. He had embarked on a dark, mysterious quest I did not understand, and he had reached a bitter, corroding impasse where of his own experience he could go no farther.

"He needed a teacher."

8. The Old Man Without a Beard

"I was fifteen when I met the Old Man Without a Beard. I called him that then and I still call him that, for there is no other distinguishing characteristic my mind can seize and hold. Whenever I think of him, even whenever I look at him, his face melts into the mob. It is as if a master actor, after portraying every sort of character in the world, should have hit on the simplest and most perfect of disguises.

"As to what lies behind that too-ordinary face—the something you can sometimes sense but hardly grasp—all I can say is a satiety and an emptiness that are not of this world."

Fafhrd caught his breath. They had reached the end of the ridge. The leftward slope had suddenly tilted upward, become the core of the mountain, while the rightward slope had swung downward and out of sight, leaving an unfathomable black abyss. Between, the path continued upward, a stony strip only a few feet wide. The Mouser touched reassuringly the coil of rope over his shoulder. For a moment their horses hung back. Then, as if the faint green glow and the ceaseless murmuring that bathed them were an intangible net, they were drawn on.

"I was in a wine shop. I had just carried a message to one of the men-friends of the Greek girl Chloe, hardly older than myself, when I noticed him sitting in a corner. I asked Chloe about him. She said he was a Greek chorister and commercial poet down on his luck, or, no, that he was an Egyptian fortuneteller, changed her mind again, tried to remember what a Samian pander had told her about him, gave him a quick puzzled look, decided that she didn't really know him at all and that it didn't matter.

"But his very emptiness intrigued me. Here was a new kind of mystery. After I had been watching him for some time, he turned around and looked at me. I had the impression that he had been aware of my inquiring gaze from the beginning, but had ignored it as a sleepy man a buzzing fly.

"After that one glance he slumped back into his former position, but when I left the shop he walked at my side.

"'You're not the only one who looks through your eyes, are you?' he said quietly.

"I was so startled by his question that I didn't know how to reply, but he didn't require me to. His face brightened without becoming any more individualized and he immediately began to talk to me in the most charming and humorous way, though his words gave no clue as to who he was or what he did.

"However, I gathered from hints he let fall that he possessed some knowledge of those odd sorts of things that always interested Anra and so I followed him willingly, my hand in his.

"But not for long. Our way led up a narrow twisting alley, and I saw a sideways glint in his eye, and felt his hand tighten on mine in a way I did not like. I became somewhat frightened and expected at any minute the danger warning from Anra.

"We passed a lowering tenement and stopped at a rickety three-story shack leaning against it. He said his dwelling was at the top. He was drawing me toward the ladder that served for stairs, and still the danger warning did not come.

"Then his hand crept toward my wrist and I did not wait any longer, but jerked away and ran, my fear growing greater with every step.

"When I reached home, Anra was pacing like a leopard. I was eager to tell him all about my narrow escape, but he kept interrupting me to demand details of the Old Man and angrily flirting his head because I could tell him so little. Then, when I came to the part about my running away, an astounding look of tortured betrayal contorted his features, he raised his hands as if to strike me, then threw himself down on the couch, sobbing.

"But as I leaned over him anxiously, his sobs stopped. He looked around at me, over his shoulder, his face white but composed, and said, 'Ahura, I must know everything about him.'

"In that one moment I realized all that I had overlooked for years—that my delightful airy freedom was a sham—that it was not Anra, but I, that was tethered—that the game was not a game, but a bondage—that while I had gone about so open and eager, intent only on sound and color, form and movement, he had been developing the side I had no time for, the intellect, the purpose, the will—that I was only a tool to him, a slave to be sent on errands, an unfeeling extension of his own body, a tentacle he could lose and grow again, like an octopus—that even my misery at his frantic disappointment, my willingness to do anything to please him, was only another lever to be coldly used against me—that our very closeness, so that we were only two halves of one mind, was to him only another tactical advantage.

"He had reached the second great crisis of his life, and again he unhesitatingly sacrificed his nearest.

"There was something uglier to it even than that, as I could see in his eyes as soon as he was sure he had me. We were like brother and sister kings in Alexandria or Antioch, playmates from infancy, destined for each other, but unknowingly, and the boy crippled and impotent—and now, too soon and horridly had come the bridal night.

"The end was that I went back to the narrow alley, the lowering tenement, the rickety shack, the ladder, the third story, and the Old Man Without a Beard.

"I didn't give in without a struggle. Once I was out of the house I fought every inch of the way. Up until now, even in the cubbyhole under the tiles, I had only to spy and observe for Anra. I had not to do things.

"But in the end it was the same. I dragged myself up the last rung and knocked on the warped door. It swung open at my touch. Inside, across a fumy room, behind a large empty table, by the light of a single ill-burning lamp, his eyes as unwinking as a fish's, and upon me, sat the Old Man Without a Beard."

Ahura paused, and Fafhrd and the Mouser felt a clamminess descend upon their skins. Looking up, they saw uncoiling downward from dizzy heights, like the ghosts of constrictive snakes or jungle vines, thin tendrils of green mist.

"Yes," said Ahura, "there is always mist or smokiness of some sort where he is.

"Three days later I returned to Anra and told him everything—a corpse giving testimony as to its murderer. But in this instance the judge relished the testimony, and when I told him of a certain plan the Old Man had in mind, an unearthly joy shimmered on his face.

"The Old Man was to be hired as a tutor and physician for Anra. This was easily arranged, as mother always acceded to Anra's wishes and perhaps still had some hope of seeing him stirred from his seclusion. Moreover, the Old Man had a mixture of unobtrusiveness and power that I am sure would have won him entry everywhere. Within a matter of weeks he had quietly established a mastery over everyone in the house—some, like mother, merely to be ignored; others, like Phryne, ultimately to be used.

"I will always remember Anra on the day the Old Man came. This was to be his first contact with the reality beyond the garden wall, and I could see that he was terribly frightened. As the hours of waiting passed, he retreated to his room, and I think it was mainly pride that kept him from calling the whole thing off. We did not hear the Old Man coming—only Old Berenice, who was counting the silver outside, stopped her muttering. Anra threw himself back on the couch in the farthest corner of the room, his hands gripping its edge, his eyes fixed on the doorway. A shadow lurched into sight there, grew darker and more definite. Then the Old Man put down on the threshold the two bags he was carrying and looked beyond me at Anra. A moment later my twin's painful gasps died in a faint hiss of expired breath. He had fainted.

"That evening his new education began. Everything that had happened was, as it were, repeated on a deeper, stranger level. There were languages to be learned, but not any languages to be found in human books; rituals to be intoned, but not to any gods that ordinary men have worshipped; magic to be brewed, but not with herbs that I could buy or steal. Daily Anra was instructed in the ways of inner darkness, the sicknesses and unknown powers of the mind, the eon-buried emotions that must be due to insidious impurities the gods overlooked in the earth from which they made man. By silent stages our home became a temple of the abominable, a monastery of the unclean.

"Yet there was nothing of tainted orgy, of vicious excess about their actions. Whatever they did, was done with strict self-discipline and mystic concentration. There was no looseness anywhere about them. They aimed at a knowledge and a power, born of darkness, true, but one which they were willing to make any self-sacrifice to obtain. They were religious, with this difference: their ritual was degradation, their aim a world chaos played upon like a broken lyre by their master minds, their god the quintessence of evil, Ahriman, the ultimate pit.

"As if performed by sleepwalkers, the ordinary routine of our home, went on. Indeed, I sometimes felt that we were all of us, except Anra, merely dreams behind the Old Man's empty eyes—actors in a deliberate nightmare where men portrayed beasts; beasts, worms; worms, slime.

"Each morning I went out and made my customary way through Tyre, chattering and laughing as before, but emptily, knowing that I was no more free than if visible chains leashed me to the house, a puppet dangled over the garden wall. Only at the periphery of my masters' intentions did I dare oppose them even passively—once I smuggled the girl Chloe a protective amulet because I fancied they were considering her as a subject for such experiments as they had tried on Phryne. And daily the periphery of their intentions widened—indeed, they would long since have left the house themselves, except for Anra's bondage to it.

"It was to the problem of breaking that bondage that they now devoted themselves. I was not told how they hoped to manage it, but I soon realized that I was to play a part.

"They would shine glittering lights into my eyes and Anra would chant until I slept. Hours or even days later I would awake to find that I had gone unconsciously about my daily business, my body a slave to Anra's commands. At other times Anra would wear a thin leather mask which covered all his features, so that he could only see, if at all, through my eyes. My sense of oneness with my twin grew steadily with my fear of him.

"Then came a period in which I was kept closely pent up, as if in some savage prelude to maturity or death or birth, or all three. The Old Man said something about 'not to see the sun or touch the earth.' Again I crouched for hours in the cubbyhole under the tiles or on reed mats in the little basement. And now it was my eyes and ears that were covered rather than Anra's. For hours I, whom sights and sounds had nourished more than food, could see nothing but fragmentary memories of the child-Anra sick, or the Old Man across the fumy room, or Phryne writhing on her belly and hissing like a snake. But worst of all was my separation from Anra. For the first time since our birth I could not see his face, hear his voice, feel his mind. I withered like a tree from which the sap is withdrawn, an animal in which the nerves have been killed.

"Finally came a day or night, I know not which, when the Old Man loosened the mask from my face. There could hardly have been more than a glimmer of light, but my long-blindfolded eyes made out every detail of the little basement with a painful clarity. The three gray stones had been dug out of the pavement. Supine beside them lay Anra, emaciated, pale, hardly breathing, looking as though he were about to die."

The three climbers stopped, confronted by a ghostly green wall. The narrow path had emerged onto what must be the mountain's tablelike top. Ahead stretched a level expanse of dark rock, mist-masked after the first few yards. Without a word they dismounted and led their trembling horses forward into a moist realm which, save that the water was weightless, most resembled a faintly phosphorescent sea-bottom.

"My heart leaped out toward my twin in pity and horror. I realized that despite all tyranny and torment I still loved him more than anything in the world, loved him as a slave loves the weak, cruel master who depends for everything on that slave, loved him as the ill-used body loves the despot mind. And I felt more closely linked to him, our lives and deaths interdependent, than if we had been linked by bonds of flesh and blood, as some rare twins are.

"The Old Man told me I could save him from death if I chose. For the present I must merely talk to him in my usual fashion. This I did, with an eagerness born of days without him. Save for an occasional faint fluttering of his sallow eyelids, Anra did not move, yet I felt that never before had he listened as intently, never before had he understood me as well. It seemed to me that all my previous speech with him had been crude by contrast. Now I remembered and told him all sorts of things that had escaped my memory or seemed too subtle for language. I talked on and on, haphazardly, chaotically, ranging swiftly from local gossip to world history, delving into myriad experiences and feelings, not all of them my own.

"Hours, perhaps days passed—the Old Man may have put some spill of slumber or deafness on the other inmates of the house to guard against interruption. At times my throat grew dry and he gave me drink, but I hardly dared pause for that, since I was appalled at the slight but unremitting change for the worse that was taking place in my twin and I had become possessed with the idea that my talking was the cord between life and Anra, that it created a channel between our bodies, across which my strength could flow to revive him.

"My eyes swam and blurred, my body shook, my voice ran the gamut of hoarseness down to an almost inaudible whisper. Despite my resolve I would have fainted, save that the Old Man held to my face burning aromatic herbs which caused me to come shudderingly awake.

"Finally I could no longer speak, but that was no release, as I continued to twitch my cracked lips and think on and on in a rushing feverish stream. It was as if I jerked and flung from the depths of my mind scraps of ideas from which Anra sucked the tiny life that remained to him.

"There was one persistent image—of a dying Hermaphroditus approaching Salmacis' pool, in which he would become one with the nymph.

"Farther and farther I ventured out along the talk-created channel between us, nearer and nearer I came to Anra's pale, delicate, cadaverous face, until, as with a despairing burst of effort I hurled my last strength to him, it loomed large as a green-shadowed ivory cliff falling to engulf me—"

Ahura's words broke off in a gasp of horror. All three stood still and stared ahead. For rearing up before them in the thickening mist, so near that they felt they had been ambushed, was a great chaotic structure of whitish, faintly yellowed stone, through whose narrow windows and wide-open door streamed a baleful greenish light, source of the mist's phosphorescent glow. Fafhrd and the Mouser thought of Karnak and its obelisks, of the Pharos lighthouse, of the Acropolis, of the Ishtar Gate in Babylon, of the ruins of Khatti, of the Lost City of Ahriman, of those doomful mirage-towers that seamen see where are Scylla and Charybdis. Of a truth, the architecture of the strange structure varied so swiftly and to such unearthly extremes that it was lifted into an insane stylistic realm all its own. Mist-magnified, its twisted ramps and pinnacles, like a fluid face in a nightmare, pushed upward toward where the stars should have been.

9. The Castle Called Mist

"What happened next was so strange that I felt sure I had plunged from feverish consciousness into the cool retreat of a fanciful dream," Ahura continued as, having tethered their horses, they mounted a wide stairway toward that open door which mocked alike sudden rush and cautious reconnoitering. Her story went on with as calm and drugged a fatalism as their step-by-step advance. "I was lying on my back beside the three stones and watching my body move around the little basement. I was terribly weak, I could not stir a muscle, and yet I felt delightfully refreshed—all the dry burning and aching in my throat was gone. Idly, as one will in a dream, I studied my face. It seemed to be smiling in triumph, very foolishly I thought. But as I continued to study it, fear began to intrude into my pleasant dream. The face was mine, but there were unfamiliar quirks of expression. Then, becoming aware of my gaze, it grimaced contemptuously and turned and said something to the Old Man, who nodded matter-of-factly. The intruding fear engulfed me. With a tremendous effort I managed to roll my eyes downward and look at my real body, the one lying on the floor.

"It was Anra's."

They entered the doorway and found themselves in a huge, many-nooked and niched stone room—though seemingly no nearer the ultimate source of the green glow, except that here the misty air was bright with it. There were stone tables and benches and chairs scattered about, but the chief feature of the place was the mighty archway ahead, from which stone groinings curved upward in baffling profusion. Fafhrd's and the Mouser's eyes momentarily sought the keystone of the arch, both because of its great size and because there was an odd dark recess toward its top.

The silence was portentous, making them feel uneasily for their swords. It was not merely that the luring music had ceased—here in the Castle Called Mist there was literally no sound, save what rippled out futilely from their own beating hearts. There was instead a fogbound concentration that froze into the senses, as though they were inside the mind of a titanic thinker, or as if the stones themselves were entranced.

Then, since it seemed as unthinkable to wait in that silence as for lost hunters to stand motionless in deep winter cold, they passed under the archway and took at random an upward-leading ramp.

Ahura continued, "Helplessly I watched them make certain preparations. While Anra gathered some small bundles of manuscripts and clothing, the Old Man lashed together the three mortar-crusted stones.

"It may have been that in the moment of victory he relaxed habitual precautions. At all events, while he was still bending over the stones, my mother entered the room. Crying out, 'What have you done to him?' she threw herself down beside me and felt at me anxiously. But that was not to the Old Man's liking. He grabbed her by shoulders and roughly jerked her back. She lay huddled against the wall, her eyes wide, her teeth chattering—especially when she saw Anra, in my body, grotesquely lift the lashed stones. Meanwhile the Old Man hoisted me, in my new, wasted form, to his shoulder, picked up the bundles, and ascended the short stair.

"We walked through the inner court, rose-strewn and filled with mother's perfumed, wine-splashed friends, who stared at us in befuddled astonishment, and so out of the house. It was night. Five slaves waited with a curtained litter in which the Old Man placed me. My last glimpse was of mother's face, its paint tracked by tears, peering horrifiedly through the half open door."

The ramp issued onto an upper level and they found themselves wandering aimlessly through a mazy series of rooms. Of little use to record here the things they thought they saw through shadowy doorways, or thought they heard through metal doors with massy complex bolts whose drawing they dared not fathom. There was a disordered, high-shelved library, certain of the rolls seeming to smoke and fume as though they held in their papyrus and ink the seeds of a holocaust; the corners were piled with sealed canisters of greenish stone and age-verdigrised brass tablets. There were instruments that Fafhrd did not even bother to warn the Mouser against touching. Another room exuded a fearful animal stench; upon its slippery floor they noted a sprinkling of short, incredibly thick black bristles. But the only living creature they saw at any time was a little hairless thing that looked as if it had once sought to become a bear cub; when Fafhrd stooped to pet it, it flopped away whimpering. There was a door that was thrice as broad as it was high, and its height hardly that of a man's knee. There was a window that let upon a blackness that was neither of mist nor of night, and yet seemed infinite; peering in, Fafhrd could faintly see rusted iron handholds leading upward. The Mouser uncoiled his climbing rope to its full length and swung it around inside the window, without the hook striking anything.

Yet the strangest impression this ominously empty stronghold begot in them was also the subtlest, and one which each new room or twisting corridor heightened—a feeling of architectural inadequacy. It seemed impossible that the supports were equal to the vast weights of the great stone floors and ceilings, so impossible that they almost became convinced that there were buttresses and retaining walls they could not see, either invisible or existing in some other world altogether, as if the Castle Called Mist had only partially emerged from some unthinkable outside. That certain bolted doors seemed to lead where no space could be, added to this hinting.

They wandered through passages so distorted that, though they retained a precise memory of landmarks, they lost all sense of direction.

Finally Fafhrd said, "This gets us nowhere. Whatever we seek, whomever we wait for—Old Man or demon—it might as well be in that first room of the great archway."

The Mouser nodded as they turned back, and Ahura said, "At least we'll be at no greater disadvantage there. Ishtar, but the Old Man's rhyme is true! 'Each chamber is a slavering maw, each arch a toothy jaw.' I always greatly feared this place, but never thought to find a mazy den that sure as death has stony mind and stony claws.

"They never chose to bring me here, you see, and from the night I left our home in Anra's body, I was a living corpse, to be left or taken where they wished. They would have killed me, I think, at least there came a time when Anra would, except it was necessary that Anra's body have an occupant—or my rightful body when he was out of it, for Anra was able to re-enter his own body and walk about in it in this region of Ahriman. At such times I was kept drugged and helpless at the Lost City. I believe that something was done to his body at that time—the Old Man talked of making it invulnerable—for after I returned to it, I found it seeming both emptier and stonier than before."

Staring back down the ramp, the Mouser thought he heard from somewhere ahead, against the terrible silence, the faintest of windy groans.

"I grew to know my twin's body very well, for I was in it most of seven years in the tomb. Somewhere during that black period all fear and horror vanished—I had become habituated to death. For the first time in my life my will, my cold intelligence, had time to grow. Physically fettered, existing almost without sensation, I gained inward power. I began to see what I could never see before—Anra's weaknesses.

"For he could never cut me wholly off from him. The chain he had forged between our minds was too strong for that. No matter how far away he went, no matter what screens he raised up, I could always see into some sector of his mind, dimly, like a scene at the end of a long, narrow, shadowy corridor.

"I saw his pride—a silver-armored wound. I watched his ambition stalk among the stars as if they were jewels set on black velvet in his treasure house to be. I felt, almost as if it were my own, his choking hatred of the bland, miserly gods—almighty fathers who lock up the secrets of the universe, smile at our pleas, frown, shake their heads, forbid, chastise; and his groaning rage at the bonds of space and time, as if each cubit he could not see and tread upon were a silver manacle on his wrist, as if each moment before or after his own life were a silver crucifying nail. I walked through the gale-blown halls of his loneliness and glimpsed the beauty that he cherished—shadowy, glittering forms that cut the soul like knives—and once I came upon the dungeon of his love, where no light came to show it was corpses that were fondled and bones kissed. I grew familiar with his desires, which demanded a universe of miracles peopled by unveiled gods. And his lust, which quivered at the world as at a woman, frantic to know each hidden part.

"Happily, for I was learning at long last to hate him, I noted how, though he possessed my body, he could not use it easily and bravely as I had. He could not laugh, or love, or dare. He must instead hang back, peer, purse his lips, withdraw."

More than halfway down the ramp, it seemed to the Mouser that the groan was repeated, louder, more whistlingly.

"He and the Old Man started on a new cycle of study and experience that took them, I think, to all corners of the world and that they were confident, I'm sure, would open to them those black realms wherein their powers would become infinite. Anxiously from my cramped vantage-point I watched their quest ripen and then, to my delight, rot. Their outstretched fingers just missed the next handhold in the dark. There was something that both of them lacked. Anra became bitter, blamed the Old Man for their lack of success. They quarreled.

"When I saw Anra's failure become final, I mocked him with my laughter, not of lips but of mind. From here to the stars he could not have escaped it—it was then he would have killed me. But he dared not while I was in his own body, and I now had the power to bar him from that.

"Perhaps it was my faint thought-laughter that turned his desperate mind to you and to the secret of the laughter of the Elder Gods—that, and his need of magical aid in regaining his body. For a while then I almost feared he had found a new avenue of escape—or advance—until this morning before the tomb, with sheer cruel joy, I saw you spit on his offers, challenge, and, helped by my laughter, kill him. Now there is only the Old Man to fear."

Passing again under the massive multiple archway with its oddly recessed keystone, they heard the whistling groan once more repeated, and this time there was no mistaking its reality, its nearness, its direction. Hastening to a shadowy and particularly misty corner of the chamber, they made out an inner window set level with the floor, and in that window they saw a face that seemed to float bodyless on the thick fog. Its features defied recognition—it might have been a distillation of all the ancient, disillusioned faces in the world. There was no beard below the sunken cheeks.

Coming close as they dared, they saw that it was perhaps not entirely bodyless or without support. There was the ghostly suggestion of tatters of clothing or flesh trailing off, a pulsating sack that might have been a lung, and silver chains with hooks or claws.

Then the one eye remaining to that shameful fragment opened and fixed upon Ahura, and the shrunken lips twisted themselves into the caricature of a smile.

"Like you, Ahura," the fragment murmured in the highest of falsettos, "he sent me on an errand I did not want to run."

As one, moved by a fear they dared not formulate, Fafhrd and the Mouser and Ahura half turned round and peered over their shoulders at the mist-clogged doorway leading outside. For three, four heartbeats they peered. Then, faintly, they heard one of the horses whinny. Whereupon they turned fully round, but not before a dagger, sped by the yet unshaking hand of Fafhrd, had buried itself in the open eye of the tortured thing in the inner window.

Side by side they stood, Fafhrd wild-eyed, the Mouser taut, Ahura with the look of someone who, having successfully climbed a precipice, slips at the very summit.

A slim shadowy- bulk mounted into the glow outside the doorway.

"Laugh!" Fafhrd hoarsely commanded Ahura. "Laugh!" He shook her, repeating the command.

Her head flopped from side to side, the cords in her neck jerked, her lips twitched, but from them came only a dry croaking. She grimaced despairingly.

"Yes," remarked a voice they all recognized, "there are times and places where laughter is an easily-blunted weapon—as harmless as the sword which this morning pierced me through."

Death-pale as always, the tiny blood-clot over his heart, his forehead crumpled in, his black garb travel-dusted, Anra Devadoris faced them.

"And so we come back to the beginning," he said slowly, "but now a wider circle looms ahead."

Fafhrd tried to speak, to laugh, but the words and laughter choked in his throat.

"Now you have learned something of my history and my power, as I intended you should," the adept continued. "You have had time to weigh and reconsider. I still await your answer."

This time it was the Mouser who sought to speak or laugh and failed.

For a moment the adept continued to regard them, smiling confidently. Then his gaze wandered beyond them. He frowned suddenly and strode forward, pushed past them, knelt by the inner window.

As soon as his back was turned Ahura tugged at the Mouser's sleeve, tried to whisper something—with no more success than one deaf and dumb.

They heard the adept sob, "He was my nicest."

The Mouser drew a dagger, prepared to steal on him from behind, but Ahura dragged him back, pointing in a very different direction.

The adept whirled on them. "Fools!" he cried, "have you no inner eye for the wonders of darkness, no sense of the grandeur of horror, no feeling for a quest beside which all other adventurings fade in nothingness, that you should destroy my greatest miracle—slay my dearest oracle? I let you come here to Mist, confident its mighty music and glorious vistas would win you to my view—and thus I am repaid. The jealous, ignorant powers ring me round—you are my great hope fallen. There were unfavorable portents as I walked from the Lost City. The white, idiot glow of Ormadz faintly dirtied the black sky. I heard in the wind the senile clucking of the Elder Gods. There was a fumbling abroad, as if even incompetent Ningauble, last and stupidest of the hunting pack, were catching up. I had a charm in reserve to thwart them, but it needed the Old Man to carry it. Now they close in for the kill. But there are still some moments of power left me and I am not wholly yet without allies. Though I am doomed, there are still those bound to me by such ties that they must answer me if I call upon them. You shall not see the end, if end there be." With that he lifted his voice in a great eerie shout, "Father! Father!"

The echoes had not died before Fafhrd rushed at him, his great sword singing.

The Mouser would have followed suit except that, just as he shook Ahura off, he realized at what she was so insistently pointing.

The recess in the keystone above the mighty archway.

Without hesitation he unslipped his climbing rope, and running lightly across the chamber, made a whistling cast.

The hook caught in the recess.

Hand over hand he climbed up.

Behind him he heard the desperate skirl of swords, heard also another sound, far more distant and profound.

His hand gripped the lip of the recess, he pulled himself up and thrust in head and shoulders, steadying himself on hip and elbow. After a moment, with his free hand, he whipped out his dagger.

Inside, the recess was hollowed like a bowl. It was filled with a foul greenish liquid and incrusted with glowing minerals. At the bottom, covered by the liquid, were several objects—three of them rectangular, the others irregularly round and rhythmically pulsating.

He raised his dagger, but for the moment did not, could not, strike. There was too crushing a weight of things to be realized and remembered— what Ahura had told about the ritual marriage in her mother's family—her suspicion that, although she and Anra were born together, they were not children of the same father—how her Greek father had died (and now the Mouser guessed at the hands of what)—the strange affinity for stone the slave-physician had noted in Anra's body—what she had said about an operation performed on him—why a heart-thrust had not killed him—why his skull had cracked so hollowly and egg-shell easy—how he had never seemed to breathe—old legends of other sorcerers who had made themselves invulnerable by hiding their hearts—above all, the deep kinship all of them had sensed between Anra and this half-living castle—the black, man-shaped monolith in the Lost City—

As if pinioned by a nightmare, he helplessly heard the clash of swords rise toward a climax, heard it blotted out by the other sound—a gargantuan stony clomping that seemed to be following their course up the mountain, like a pursuing earthquake—

The Castle Called Mist began to tremble, and still he could not strike—

Then, as if surging across infinity from that utmost rim beyond which the Elder Gods had retreated, relinquishing the world to younger deities, he heard a mighty, star-shaking laughter that laughed at all things, even at this; and there was power in the laughter, and he knew the power was his to use.

With a downward sweep of his arm he sent his dagger plunging into the green liquid and tearing through the stone-crusted heart and brain and lungs and guts of Anra Devadoris.

The liquid foamed and boiled, the castle rocked until he was almost shaken from the niche, the laughter and stony clomping rose to a pandemonium.

Then, in an instant it seemed, all sound and movement ceased. The Mouser's muscles went weak. He half fell, half slid, to the floor. Looking about dazedly, making no attempt to rise, he saw Fafhrd wrench his sword from the fallen adept and totter back until his groping hand found the support of a table-edge, saw Ahura, still gasping from the laughter that had possessed her, go up and kneel beside her brother and cradle his crushed head on her knees.

No word was spoken. Time passed. The green mist seemed to be slowly thinning.

Then a small black shape swooped into the room through a high window and the Mouser grinned.

"Hugin," he called luringly.

The shape swooped obediently to his sleeve and clung there, head down. He detached from the bat's leg a tiny parchment.

"Fancy, Fafhrd, it's from the commander of our rear guard," he announced gayly. "Listen:

"'To my agents Fafhrd and the Gray Mouser, funeral greetings! I have regretfully given up all hope for you, and yet—token of my great affection—I risk my own dear Hugin in order to get this last message through. Incidentally, Hugin, if given opportunity, will return to me from Mist—something I am afraid you will not be able to do. So if, before you die, you see anything interesting—and I am sure you will—kindly scribble me a memorandum. Remember the proverb: Knowledge takes precedence over death. Farewell for two thousand years, dearest friends. Ningauble.'"

"That demands drink," said Fafhrd, and walked out into the darkness. The Mouser yawned and stretched himself, Ahura stirred, printed a kiss on the waxen face of her brother, lifted the trifling weight of his head from her lap, and laid it gently on the stone floor. From somewhere in the upper reaches of the castle they heard a faint crackling.

Presently Fafhrd returned, striding more briskly, with two jars of wine under his arm.

"Friends," he announced, "the moon's come out, and by its light this castle begins to look remarkably small. I think the mist must have been dusted with some green drug that made us see sizes wrong. We must have been drugged, I'll swear, for we never saw something that's standing plain as day at the bottom of the stairs with its foot on the first step—a black statue that's twin brother to the one in the Lost City."

The Mouser lifted his eyebrows. "And if we went back to the Lost City . . . ?" he asked.

"Why," said Fafhrd, "we might find that those fool Persian farmers, who admitted hating the thing, had knocked down the statue there, and broken it up, and hidden the pieces." He was silent for a moment. Then, "Here's wine," he rumbled, "to sluice the green drug from our throats."

The Mouser smiled. He knew that hereafter Fafhrd would refer to their present adventure as "the time we were drugged on a mountaintop."

They all three sat on a table-edge and passed the two jars endlessly round. The green mist faded to such a degree that Fafhrd, ignoring his claims about the drug, began to argue that even it was an illusion. The crackling from above increased in volume; the Mouser guessed that the impious rolls in the library, no longer shielded by the damp, were bursting into flame. Some proof of this was given when the abortive bear cub, which they had completely forgotten, came waddling frightenedly down the ramp. A trace of decorous down was already sprouting from its naked hide. Fafhrd dribbled some wine on its snout and held it up to the Mouser.

"It wants to be kissed," he rumbled.

"Kiss it yourself, in memory of pig-trickery," replied the Mouser.

This talk of kissing turned their thoughts to Ahura. Their rivalry forgotten, at least for the present, they persuaded her to help them determine whether her brother's spells were altogether broken. A moderate number of hugs demonstrated this clearly.

"Which reminds me," said the Mouser brightly, "now that our business here is over, isn't it time we started, Fafhrd, for your lusty Northland and all that bracing snow?"

Fafhrd drained one jar dry and picked up the other.

"The Northland?" he ruminated. "What is it but a stamping ground of petty, frost-whiskered kinglets who know not the amenities of life. That's why I left the place. Go back? By Thor's smelly jerkin, not now!"

The Mouser smiled knowingly and sipped from the remaining jar. Then, noticing the bat still clinging to his sleeve, he took stylus, ink, and a scrap of parchment from his pouch, and, with Ahura giggling over his shoulder, wrote:

"To my aged brother in petty abominations, greetings! It is with the deepest regret that I must report the outrageously lucky and completely unforeseen escape of two rude and unsympathetic fellows from the Castle Called Mist. Before leaving, they expressed to me the intention of returning to someone called Ningauble—you are Ningauble, master, are you not?— and lopping off six of his seven eyes for souvenirs. So I think it only fair to warn you. Believe me, I am your friend. One of the fellows was very tall and at times his bellowings seemed to resemble speech. Do you know him? The other fancied a gray garb and was of extreme wit and personal beauty, given to . . ."

Had any of them been watching the corpse of Anra Devadoris at this moment, they would have seen a slight twitching of the lower jaw. At last the mouth came open, and out leapt a tiny black mouse. The cub-like creature, to whom Fafhrd's fondling and the wine had imparted the seeds of self-confidence, lurched drunkenly at it, and the mouse began a squeaking scurry toward the wall. A wine jar, hurled by Fafhrd, shattered on the crack into which it shot; Fafhrd had seen, or thought he had seen, the untoward place from which the mouse had come.

"Mice in his mouth," he hiccupped. "What dirty habits for a pleasant young man! A nasty, degrading business, this thinking oneself an adept."

"I am reminded," said the Mouser, "of what a witch told me about adepts. She said that, if an adept chances to die, his soul is reincarnated in a mouse. If, as a mouse, he managed to kill a rat, his soul passes over into a rat. As a rat, he must kill a cat; as a cat, a wolf; as a wolf, a panther; and, as a panther, a man. Then he can recommence his adeptry. Of course, it seldom happens that anyone gets all the way through the sequence and in any case it takes a very long time. Trying to kill a rat is enough to satisfy a mouse with mousedom."

Fafhrd solemnly denied the possibility of any such foolery, and Ahura cried until she decided that being a mouse would interest rather than dishearten her peculiar brother. More wine was drunk from the remaining jar. The crackling from the rooms above had become a roar, and a bright red glow consumed the dark shadows. The three adventurers prepared to leave the place.

Meantime the mouse, or another very much like it, thrust its head from the crack and began to lick the wine-damp shards, keeping a fearful eye upon those in the great room, but especially upon the strutting little would-be bear.

A great blast of wind, cold and pure, blew away the last lingering of Mist. As they went through the doorway they saw, outspread above them, the self-consistent stars.

[*Night's Black Agents* (Arkham House, 1947)]

THE DEMONS OF THE UPPER AIR

I.

There is a whispering outside the walls,
A thing upon the roof,
Come from the shadows, most like a shadow,
But a shadow with teeth and hooking claws,
A whispering shadow.
The hearts that hug the fire within
Beat faster, move closer,
Snuggle down in their pocket of safety,
Opposing the threat from the alien reaches,
Holding their ears against the voice
Of the thing from the thin, high air.
It whispers of conflicts behind the low clouds,
Of creatures nearer and creatures stranger
Than those in the shielding house would wish;
In penetrant treble it whispering sings
The challenging song of those who ride
Where the air thins out to emptiness;
And its voice goes low again to tell
Of the terrible insecurity
Of the whirling, plunging earth.
Let the dwellers within shut their ears,
Stuff cranny and crack, bolt shutter and door and inner door—
There still comes a murmuring down past the fire,
Against the smoke and the pushing heat,
Tainting even the roaring of the fire:
A whispering outside the walls,
A thing upon the roof.

II.

Solomon sought to seal us up,
Thinking we were a book a man might seal,
Thinking we were strange pictures
And our racing thoughts
But dimming words upon a yellowed page.

Lo, Solomon is dead
And we still ride the upper air
Above a newer Babylon.

Upon the cold moon's spaceward side
Our fortress stands, the gates rust not;
Out on the last, unknown sphere
That rings the sun our pennon flies;
And men still hear above their heads
Our whistling cries, our trumpet calls,
And see, gigantic, menacing,
Our shadows on their tallest walls.

True, true indeed, a book are we,
A book that was penned by the elder gods,
A book that never a man may seal.

III.

Above, above
The air is thin, the sky is bright;
Come up, soft sister, through the night.
Around, around
The far stars wheel, the space winds surge
Against the dwellers on the verge;
The sky is black, the sky is bright;
Leave dreaming to the lower night.
Leave, leave
Your body to the earth,
Small sins to hell, small plans to mirth;
Cast, cast away
All lesser fear
To cumber still the cumbered sphere;
Slip, slip
Your silky, soft cocoon
And rise through madness to our noon.
Your soul is steel: hard, slim, and bright;
Thrust it, o sister, through the night.

IV.

Signs? Signs? You ask for a sign?
These be the false signs that yet stir the mind
To spy for the true!
The eye of the cat and the words of the madman,
Sudden, forsaken, meaningless words;

The cries of the screech owl, of shells, and far lightning,
Only seeming to come from the haunts of far souls;
The symbols bizarre of the mathematician,
Clear thought to him, a mad whisper to most;
The stones and the streets of dead, desert-hid cities,
Walked once by men commercial and civil,
Men up to the minute, by such and no others;
The brooding of mountains, the anger of oceans,
The lean wind, the cold spaces, the black suns beyond suns,
The howl of the wolf and the wing of the raven—
Those be the false signs,
Those be type of the thousand hints,
Which, sought for themselves, yield less than they seemed.

These be the true signs, if true signs there be:
The far darting of vision that comes with creation,
The quip of the great man sharp-tweaked by fate's fingers,
The last, doubtful hints on the great heap of knowledge,
Perched like strange birds that plot a strange flight;
The certainty born of practice and labour
But by what father none may know;
The slipping of meditant souls from earth bodies,
The pantherlike leap of imagination,
Second sight, far sight, beyond all suns seeing—
Those be the true signs, the signs of dark power,
The signs of the far way, if such signs there be.

V.

Since light first fought with darkness
And the first created cat wailed down
The cry of chaos, now coherent,
From the new-risen, inky walls of Niffleheim,
We have been.

Old are we as the elder gods,
Yet not as they.
We strive not, boisterous,
To raise firmaments
But fly, black-winged, above;
They make the hearty music of the spheres—
We, the shrill, soaring overtones.

The windswept, icy mountaintops of mind
Show tracks of our sharp claws.

Both over raging war and striving peace
Our wing beat sounds;
Ultima Thule is our perching place,
For to the uttermost black bound of things
Our squadrons strive.

Ghosts are we but with skeletons of steel.
As mists are we, yet in our loins a seed
That laughs at barrenness.

The present grips the future with our claws,
Forgotten facts ride forward on our wings,
And inspiration's first faint harmonies
Sound in our songs, while eerie, far-off things
Call out to beg us bring them down to earth.

No one so deaf to miss our whispering,
No realm so lightless but our shadows fall;
Ho, wild, unrul'd allies upon the earth,
We are your friends who ride the icy nights,
We are the demons of the upper air.

VI.

Ho, tramper on the road below,
I spy the end toward which you go;
A little inn's across the hill,
Girls to sport with, wine to swill;
Chill is the way here in the air
And chill the part of you I bear.

Beyond the inn's a mountain tall,
Guarded by bastion and by wall,
Towers lift there from the snow,
Grimly gaze on those below;
Though manned by things with axe and mace,
Those towers are my perching place.

Beyond, a factory city's found
With costly suburbs snuggled round
And rich, sweet stench of luxury;
A mighty marching there I see,
Tuned to strong metal's martial din—
     When I grin down on those rich things
     I must beat swift my black bat wings—
For o'er that town the air is thin.

And still beyond's a dimmer way,
A castle dubious and dark,
A pit too deep for any day
To penetrate, and yet some spark
Lets me glimpse through the looming veil
An eyrie set above a dale.

Ho, tramper on the road below,
The way's not bad that you must go
And there is always enough air
To bear that part of you I bear;
But do not linger by the way,
Remember, I'm not in your pay.

VII.

Be these my words
To that which is higher,
To that which is darker,
To that which is swifter.
Be token, not worship,
Be spying, not trusting
The spirits of night
And the upper air riders.
Prayer-saken, ghost-ridden,
By earth-gods fear-shaken,
By elder things bidden,
I may not house with you
And yet I must seek you,
I may not school with you
And yet I must cry you.
Black loving and longing
To you be my token;
My soul has rid with you,
Its charger mistrusting;
My spirit has cried out
Your thin cries, dark lusting;
With you I have charged
In terror and pride
To riddle all riddles
In Asgardsride.
My words be a token
To lean souls swift riding;
My cry be a challenge
To evils time-biding.

VIII.

Out the frost-rimmed windows peer,
You who have arisen early,
Mind not cold for you may hear
A fanfare from the stratosphere.

"Ho, Brother! Is the way past Neptune clear?
And those strange beasts on the galactic rim—
Do they claw still the elder gods' last gate?
News of the airless monster whom kind fate
Drove once across the river none may swim?
What of the other creatures that we fear?
What stars tow now the planets they ruled late?
And he who went beyond—say, what of him?"

Eldritch words like these are flying,
Voices through the high air crying,
You whose sleep was too uneasy,
You may hear them, rising, dying.

[*Leaves,* 1938]

THE SUNKEN LAND

"I was born with luck as a twin!" roared Fafhrd the Northerner jovially, leaping up so swiftly that the cranky sloop rocked a little in spite of its outriggers. "I catch a fish in the middle of the ocean. I rip up its belly. And look, little man, what I find!"

The Gray Mouser drew back from the fish-bloodied hand thrust almost into his face, wrinkled his nose with sneering fastidiousness, raised his left eyebrow and peered. The object did not seem very small even on Fafhrd's broad palm, and although slimed-over a little, was indubitably gold. It was both a ring and a key, the key part set at a right angle, so that it would lie along the finger when worn. There were carvings of some sort. Instinctively the Gray Mouser did not like the object. It somehow focused the vague uneasiness he had felt now for several days.

To begin with, he did not like the huge, salty ocean, and only Fafhrd's bold enthusiasm and his own longing for the land of Lankhmar had impelled him to embark on this long, admittedly risky voyage across unchartered deeps. He did not like the fact that a school of fish was making the boil at such a great distance from any land. Even the uniformly stormless weather and favorable winds disturbed him, seeming to indicate correspondingly great misfortunes held in store, like a growing thundercloud in quiet air. Too much good luck was always dangerous. And now this ring, acquired without effort by an astonishingly lucky chance.

They peered at it more closely, Fafhrd slowly turning it round. The carving on the ring part, as far as one could make out, represented a sea monster dragging down a ship. It was highly stylized, however, and there was little detail. One might be mistaken. What puzzled the Mouser most, since he had traveled to far places and knew much of the world, was that he did not recognize the style.

But in Fafhrd it roused strange memories. Recollections of certain legends told round flickering driftwood fires through the long northern night; tales of great seafarings and distant raids made in ancient days; firelight glimpses of certain bits of loot taken by some uncountably distant ancestor and considered too traditionally significant to barter or sell or even give away; ominously vague warnings used to frighten little boys who were inclined to swim or sail too far out. For a moment his green eyes clouded and his windburned face became serious, but only for a moment.

"A pretty enough thing, you'll agree," he said, laughing. "Whose door do you think it unlocks? Some king's mistress', I'd say. It's big enough for a king's finger." He tossed it up, caught it, and wiped it on the rough cloth of his tunic.

"I wouldn't wear it," said the Mouser. "It was probably eaten from a drowned man's hand and sucked poison from the sea ooze. Throw it back."

"And fish for a bigger one?" asked Fafhrd, grinning. "No, I'm content with this." He thrust it down on the middle finger of his left hand, doubled up his fist, and surveyed it critically. "Good for bashing people with, too," he remarked.

Then, seeing a big fish flash out of the water and almost flop into the cockpit, he snatched up his bow, fitted to the string a featherless arrow whose head was barbed and heavily weighted, and stared down over the side, foot extended along the outrigger. A light, waxed line was attached to the arrow.

The Mouser watched him, not without envy. Fafhrd, big rangy man that he was, seemed to acquire an altogether new litheness and sureness of movement whenever they were on shipboard. He became as nimble as the Mouser was on shore. The Mouser was no landlubber and could swim as well as Fafhrd, but he always felt a trifle uneasy when there was only water in sight, day in and day out, just as Fafhrd felt uneasy in cities, though relishing taverns and street fights. On shipboard the Mouser became cautious and apprehensive; he made a point of watching for slow leaks, creeping fires, tainted food and rotten cordage. He disapproved of Fafhrd's constant trying out of new rigs and waiting until the last moment before reefing sail. It irked him a little that he couldn't quite call it foolhardy.

Fafhrd continued to scan intently the swelling, sliding waters. His long, copper-red hair was shoved back over his ears and knotted securely. He was clothed in rough, brownish tunic and trousers. Light leather slippers, easily kicked off, were on his feet. Belt, longsword, and other weapons were, of course, absent, wrapped away in oiled cloth against the rust. And there were no jewels or ornaments, save for the ring.

The Mouser's gaze shifted past him to where clouds were piling up a little on the horizon off the bow to starboard. He wondered, almost with relief, whether this mightn't be the dirty weather due them. He pulled his thin gray tunic closer at his throat, and shifted the tiller a little. The sun, near setting, projected his crouching shadow against the brownish sail.

Fafhrd's bow twanged and the arrow plummeted. Line hissed from the reel he held in his arrow hand. He checked it with his thumb. It slackened a trifle, then jerked off toward the stern. Fafhrd's foot slid along the outrigger until it stopped against the pontoon, a good three arm's lengths from the side. He let the other foot slide after it and lay them effortlessly braced, sea drenching his legs, playing the fish carefully, laughing and grunting satisfiedly.

"And what was your luck this time?" the Mouser asked afterward, as Fafhrd served them smoking-hot, white tender flesh broiled over the firebox in the snug cabin forward. "Did you get a bracelet and necklace to match the ring?"

Fafhrd grinned with his mouth full and did not answer, as if there were nothing in the world to do but eat. But when they stretched themselves out later in the starry, cloud-broken darkness alive with a racing wind from starboard that drove their craft along at an increasing speed, he began to talk.

"I think they called the land Simorgya. It sank under the sea ages ago. Yet even then my people had gone raiding against it, though it was a long sail out and a weary beat homeward. My memory's uncertain. I only heard scraps of talk about it when I was a little child. But I did see a few trinkets carved somewhat like this ring; just a very few. The legends, I think, told that the men of far Simorgya were mighty magicians, claiming power over wind and wave and the creatures below. Yet the sea gulped them down for all that. Now they're there." He rotated his hand until his thumb pointed at the bottom of the boat. "My people, the legends say, went raiding against them one summer, and none of the boats returned, save one, which came back after hope had been lost, its men almost dead from thirst. They told of sailing on and on, and never reaching Simorgya, never sighting its rocky coast and squat, many-windowed towers. Only the empty sea. More raiders went out the next summer and the next, yet none ever found Simorgya."

"But in that case," questioned the Mouser sharply, "may we not even now be sailing over that sunken land? May not that very fish you caught have swum in and out the windows of those towers?"

"Who can say?" answered Fafhrd, a little dreamily. "The ocean's big. If we're where we think we are—that is, halfway home—it might be the case. Or not. I do not know if there ever really was a Simorgya. The legend-makers are great liars. In any case, that fish could hardly have been so ancient as to have eaten the flesh of a man of Simorgya."

"Nevertheless," said the Mouser in a small, flat voice, "I'd throw that ring away."

Fafhrd chuckled. His imagination was stirred, so that he saw the fabled land of Simorgya, not lightless and covered with great drifts of sea ooze, but as it once might have been, alive with ancient industry and commerce, strong with alien wizardry. Then the picture changed and he saw a long, narrow, twenty-oared galley, such as his people made, driving ahead into a stormy sea. There was the glint of gold and steel about the captain on the poop, and the muscles of the steersman cracked as he strained at the steering oar. The faces of the warrior-rowers were exultantly eager, dominated by the urge to rape the unknown. The whole ship was like a thirsty spearhead. He marveled at the vividness of the picture. Old longings vibrated faintly in his flesh. He felt the ring, ran his finger over the carving of the ship and monster, and again chuckled.

The Mouser fetched a stubby, heavy-wicked candle from the cabin and fixed it in a small horn lantern that was proof against wind. Hanging at the stern it pushed back the darkness a little, not much. Until midnight it was the Mouser's watch. After a while Fafhrd slumbered.

He awoke with the feeling that the weather had changed and quick work was wanted. The Mouser was calling him. The sloop was heeled over so that the starboard pontoon rode the crests of the waves. There was chilly spray in the wind. The lantern swung wildly. Only astern were stars visible. The Mouser brought the sloop into the wind, and Fafhrd took a triple reef in the sail, while waves hammered at the bow, an occasional light crest breaking over.

When they were on their course again, he did not immediately join the Mouser, but stood wondering, for almost the first time, how the sloop would stand heavy seas. It was not the sort of boat he would have built in his northern homeland, but it was the best that could be gotten under the circumstances. He had caulked and tarred it meticulously, replaced any wood that looked too weak, substituted a triangular sail for the square one, and increased the height of the bow a trifle. To offset a tendency to capsize, he had added outriggers a little astern of the mast, getting the strongest, truest wood for the long cross pieces, carefully steaming them into the proper shape. It was a good job, he knew, but that didn't change the fact that the boat had a clumsy skeleton and many hidden weaknesses. He sniffed the raw, salt air and peered to windward through narrowed eyes, trying to gauge the weather. The Mouser was saying something, he realized, and he turned his head to listen.

"Throw the ring away before she blows a hurricane!"

He smiled and made a wide gesture that meant "No." Then he turned back to gaze at the wild glimmering chaos of darkness and waves to wind-ward. Thoughts of the boat and the weather dropped away, and he was con-tent to drink in the awesome, age-old scene, swaying to keep balance, feeling each movement of the boat and at the same time sensing, almost as if it were something akin to himself, the godless force of the elements.

It was then the thing happened that took away his power to react and held him, as it were, in a spell. Out of the surging wall of darkness emerged the dragon-headed prow of a galley. He saw the black wood of the sides, the light wood of the oars, the glint of wet metal. It was so like the ship of his imaginings that he was struck dumb with wonder as to whether it was only another vision, or whether he had had a foreglimpse of it by second sight, or whether he had actually summoned it across the deeps by his thoughts. It loomed higher, higher, higher.

The Mouser cried out and pushed over the tiller, his body arched with the mighty effort. Almost too late the sloop came out of the path of the dragon-headed prow. And still Fafhrd stared as at an apparition. He did not hear the Mouser's warning shout as the sloop's sail filled from the other side and slammed across with a rush. The boom caught him in the back of the knees and hurled him outward, but not into the sea, for his feet found the narrow pontoon and he balanced there precariously. In that instant an oar of the galley swung down at him and he toppled sideways, instinctively grasp-ing the blade as he fell. The sea drenched him and wrenched at him, but he clung tightly and began to pull himself up the oar, hand over hand.

His legs were numb; he feared he would be unable to swim. And he was still bewitched by what he saw. For the moment he forgot the Mouser and the sloop entirely. He shook off the greedy waves, reached the side of the galley, caught hold of the oarhole. Then he looked back and saw, in a kind of stupid surprise, the disappearing stern of the sloop and the Mouser's gray-capped face, revealed by a close swing of the lantern staring at him in blank helplessness.

What happened next ended whatever spell had held him. A hand that carried steel struck. He twisted to one side and caught the wrist, then grasped the side of the galley, got his foot in the oarhole, on top of the oar, and heaved. The man dropped the knife too late, clawed at the side, failed to get a secure hold, and was dragged overboard, spitting, and snapping his jaws in futile panic. Fafhrd, instinctively taking the offensive, sprang down onto the oarbench, which was the last of ten and half under the poop deck. His questioning eyes spied a rack of swords and he whirled one out, menacing the two shadowy figures hastening toward him, one from the forward oarbenches, one from the poop. They attacked with a rush, but silently, which was strange. The spray-wet weapons sparkled as they clashed.

Fafhrd fought warily, on guard for a blow from above, timing his lunges to the roll of the galley. He dodged a swashing blow and parried an unexpected backhanded slash from the same weapon. Stale, sour wine fumes puffed into his face. Someone dragged out an oar and thrust it like a huge lance; it came between Fafhrd and the two swordsmen, crashing heavily into the sword rack. Fafhrd glimpsed a ratlike, beady-eyed, toothy face peering up at him from the deeper darkness under the poop. One of the swordsmen lunged wildly, slipped and fell. The other gave ground, then gathered himself for a rush. But he paused with his sword in midair, looking over Fafhrd's head as if at a new adversary. The crest of a great wave struck him in the chest, obscuring him.

Fafhrd felt the weight of the water on his shoulders and clutched at the poop for support. The deck was at a perilous tilt. Water gushed up through the opposite oarholes. In the confusion, he realized, the galley had gotten into the troughs and was beginning to take the seas broadside. She wasn't built to stand that. He vaulted up out of another breaking wave onto the poop and added his strength to that of the lone struggling steersman. Together they strained at the great oar, which seemed to be set in stone instead of water. Inch by inch they fought their way across the narrow deck. None the less, the galley seemed doomed.

Then something—a momentary lessening of the wind and waves or perhaps a lucky pull by a forward oarsman—decided the issue. As slowly and laboriously as a waterlogged hulk the galley lifted and began to edge back into the proper course. Fafhrd and steersman strained prodigiously to hold each foot gained. Only when the galley was riding safe before the wind did they look up. Fafhrd saw two swords leveled steadily at his chest. He calculated his chances and did not move.

It was not easy to believe that fire had been preserved through that tremendous wetting, but one of them nevertheless carried a sputtering tarry torch. By its light Fafhrd saw that they were Northerners akin to himself. Big rawboned fellows, so blond they seemed almost to lack eyebrows. They wore metal-studded war gear and close-fitting bronze helmets. Their expressions were frozen halfway between a glare and a grin. Again he smelled stale wine. His glance strayed forward. Three oarsmen were bailing with bucket and hand crane.

Somebody was striding toward the poop—the leader, if one could guess from gold and jewels and an air of assurance. He sprang up the short ladder, his limbs supple as a cat's. He seemed younger than the rest and his features were almost delicate. Fine, silky blond hair was plastered wetly against his cheeks. But there was feline rapacity in his tight, smiling lips, and there was craziness in his jewel-blue eyes. Fafhrd hardened his own face against their inspection. One question kept nagging him. Why, even at the height of the confusion, had there been no cries, no shouts, no bellowed orders? Since he had come aboard, there had not been a word uttered.

The young leader seemed to come to a conclusion about Fafhrd, for his thin smile widened a trifle and he motioned toward the oar deck. Then Fafhrd broke silence and said in a voice that sounded unnatural and hoarse. "What do you intend? Weigh well the fact that I saved your ship."

He tensed himself, noting with some satisfaction that the steersman stayed close beside him, as if their shared task had forged a bond between them. The smile left the leader's face. He laid his finger to his lips and then impatiently repeated his first gesture. This time Fafhrd understood. He was to replace the oarsman he had pulled overboard. He could not but admit there was a certain ironic justice to the idea. It was borne in on him that swift death would be his lot if he renewed the fight at such a disadvantage; slow death, if he leaped overboard in the mad hope of finding the sloop in the howling, heaving darkness. The arms holding the swords became taut. He curtly nodded his head in submission. At least they were his own people.

With the first feel of the heavy, rebellious water against the blade of his oar, a new feeling took hold of Fafhrd—a feeling with which he was not unfamiliar. He seemed to become part of the ship, to share its purposes, whatever they might be. It was the age-old spirit of the oarbench. When his muscles had warmed to the task and his nerves became accustomed to the rhythm, he found himself stealing glances at the men around him, as if he had known them before; trying to penetrate and share the eager, set look on their faces.

Something huddled in many folds of ragged cloth shuffled out from the little cabin far back under the poop and held a leather flask to the lips of the opposite oarsman. The creature looked absurdly squat among such tall men. When it turned, Fafhrd recognized the beady eyes he had glimpsed before, and as it came nearer, distinguished under the heavy cowl the wrinkled, subtle, ochre face of an aged Mingol.

"So you're the new one," the Mingol croaked jeeringly. "I liked your swordplay. Drink deep now, for Lavas Laerk may decide to sacrifice you to the sea gods before morning. But, mind you, don't dribble any."

Fafhrd sucked greedily, then almost coughed and spat when a rush of strong wine seared his throat. After a while the Mingol jerked the flask away.

"Now you know what Lavas Laerk feeds his oarsmen. There are few crews in this world or the next that row on wine." He chuckled humorously, but with a certain glee, then said, "But you're wondering why I talk aloud. Well, young Lavas Laerk may put a vow of silence on all his men, but he may not do the same to me, who am only a slave. For I tend the fire—how carefully you know—and serve out the wine and cook the meat, and recite incantations for the good of the ship. There are certain things that neither Lavas Laerk nor any other man, nor any other demon, may demand of me."

"But what does Lavas Laerk—"

The Mingol's leathery palm clapped over Fafhrd's mouth and shut off the whispered question.

"Sh! Do you care so little for life? Remember, you are Lavas Laerk's henchman. But I will tell you what you would know." He sat down on the wet bench beside Fafhrd, looking like a bundle of black rags someone had dropped there. "Lavas Laerk has sworn to raid far Simorgya, and he has put a vow of silence upon himself and his men until they sight the coast. Sh! Sh! I know they say Simorgya is under the waves, or that there never was such a place. But Lavas Laerk swore a great oath before his mother, whom he hates worse than he hates his friends, and he killed a man who thought to question his decision. So it's Simorgya we seek, if only to steal pearls from the oysters and ravish the fishes. Lean down and row more easily for a space, and I will tell you a secret that's no secret and make a prophecy that's no prophecy." He crowded closer. "Lavas Laerk hates all men who are sober, for he believes—and rightly—that only drunken men are even a little like himself. Tonight the crew will row well, though it's a day since they've had meat. Tonight the wine will make them see at least the glow of the visions that Lavas Laerk sees. But next morning there will be aching backs and sick guts and pain-hammered skulls. And then there will be mutiny and not even Lavas Laerk's madness will save him."

Fafhrd wondered why the Mingol shuddered, coughed weakly and made a gargling sound. He reached over and a warm fluid drenched his naked hand. Then Lavas Laerk pulled his dirk from the Mingol's neck and the Mingol rolled forward off the bench.

No word was spoken, but knowledge that some abominable deed had been committed passed from oarsman to oarsman through the stormy darkness until it reached the bench in the bow. Then gradually there began a kind of pent-up commotion, which increased markedly as there slowly percolated forward an awareness of the specially heinous nature of the deed—the murder of the slave who tended the fire and whose magical powers, though often scoffed at, were entwined with the destiny of the ship itself.

Still no completely intelligible words, but low grunts and snarls and mutterings, the scrape of oars being drawn in and rested, a growing murmur in which consternation and fear and anger were mixed, and which washed back and forth between bow and poop like a wave in a tub. Half caught up by it, Fafhrd readied himself for a spring, though whether at the apprehensively motionless figure of Lavas Laerk or back toward the comparative safety of the poop cabin, he could not say. Certainly Lavas Laerk was doomed; or rather he would have been doomed, had not the steersman screamed from the poop in a great shaky voice, "Land ho! Simorgya! Simorgya!"

That wild cry, like a clawed skeletal hand, seized upon the agitation of the crew and wrenched it to an almost unbearable climax. A shuddering inhalation of breath swept the ship. Then came shouts of wonder, cries of fear, curses that were half prayers. Two oarsmen started to fight together for no other reason than that the sudden, painful upgush of feeling demanded action of some sort, any sort. Another pushed wildly at his oar, screeching at the rest to follow his example and reverse the galley's course and so escape. Fafhrd vaulted upon his bench and stared ahead.

It loomed up vast as a mountain and perilously close. A great black blot vaguely outlined by the lesser darkness of the night, partly obscured by trailings of mist and scud, yet showing in various places and at varying distances squares of dim light which by their regular arrangement could be nothing but windows. And with each pounding heartbeat the roar of surf and the thunder of breaking waves grew louder.

All at once it was upon them. Fafhrd saw a great overhanging crag slide by, so close it snapped the last oar on the opposite side. As the galley lifted on a wave he looked awestruck into three windows in the crag—if it was a crag and not a half submerged tower—but saw nothing save a ghostly yellow luminescence. Then he heard Lavas Laerk bellowing commands in a harsh, high-pitched voice. A few of the men worked frantically at the oars, but it was too late for that, although the galley seemed to have gotten behind some protecting wall of rock into slightly calmer waters. A terrible rasping noise went the length of the keel. Timbers groaned and cracked. A last wave lifted them and a great grinding crash sent men reeling and tumbling. Then the galley stopped moving altogether and the only sound was the roar of the surf, until Lavas Laerk cried exultantly, "Serve out weapons and wine! Make ready for a raid!"

The words seemed incredible in this more than dangerous situation, with the galley broken beyond repair, gutted by the rocks. Yet the men rallied and seemed even to catch something of the wild eagerness of their master, who had proven to them that the world was no more sane than he.

Fafhrd watched them fetch torch after torch from the poop cabin, until the whole stem of the wreck smoked and flared. He watched them snatch and suck at the wineskins and heft the swords and dirks given out, comparing them and cleaving at the air to get the feel. Then some of them grabbed hold of him and hustled him to the sword rack, saying, "Here, Red Hair, you must have a weapon, too." Fafhrd went along unresisting, yet he felt that something would prevent them from arming one who so late had been their enemy. And he was right in this, for Lavas Laerk stopped the lieutenant who was about to hand Fafhrd a sword, and stared with growing intentness at Fafhrd's left hand.

Puzzled, Fafhrd raised it, and Lavas Laerk cried, "Seize him!" and at the same instant jerked something from Fafhrd's middle finger. Then Fafhrd remembered. It was the ring.

"There can be no doubt about the workmanship," said Lavas Laerk, peering cunningly at Fafhrd, his bright blue eyes giving the impression of being out of focus or slightly crossed. "This man is a Simorgyan spy, or perhaps a Simorgyan demon who has taken the form of a Northerner to allay our suspicions. He climbed out of the sea in the teeth of a roaring storm, did he not? What man among you saw any boat?"

"I saw a boat," ventured the steersman hurriedly. "A queer sloop with triangular sail—" But Lavas Laerk shut him up with a sidewise glance.

Fafhrd felt the point of a dirk at his back and checked his tightening muscles.

"Shall we kill him?" The question came from close behind Fafhrd's ear.

Lavas Laerk smiled crookedly up at the darkness and paused, as if listening to the advice of some invisible storm wraith. Then he shook his head. "Let him live for the present. He can show us where loot is hid. Guard him with naked swords."

Whereupon they all left the galley, clambering down ropes hung from the prow onto rocks which the surf alternately covered and uncovered. One or two laughed and jumped. A dropped torch hissed out in the brine. There was much shouting. Someone began to sing in a drunken voice that had an edge like a rusty knife. Then Lavas Laerk got them into a sort of order and they marched away, half of them carrying torches, a few still hugging wineskins, sliding and slipping, cursing the sharp rocks and barnacles which cut them when they fell, hurling exaggerated threats at the darkness ahead, where strange windows glowed, Behind them the long galley lay like a dead beetle, the oars sprawled out from the ports all askew.

They had marched for some little distance, and the sound of the breakers was less thunderous, when their torchlight helped reveal a portal in a great wall of black rock that might or might not have been a castle rather than a caverned cliff. The portal was square and high as an oar. Three worn stone steps drifted with wet sand led up to it. Dimly they could discern on the pillars, and on the heavy lintel overhead, carvings partly obliterated by slime and incrustations of some sort, but unmistakably Simorgyan in their obscure symbolism.

The crew, staring silently now, drew closer together. The ragged procession became a tight knot. Then Lavas Laerk called mockingly, "Where are your guards, Simorgya? Where are your fighting men?" and walked straight up the stone steps. After a moment of uncertainty, the knot broke and the men followed him.

On the massive threshold Fafhrd involuntarily halted, dumbstruck by realization of the source of the faint yellow light he had earlier noticed in the high windows. For the source was everywhere: ceiling, walls, and slimy floor all glowed with a wavering phosphorescence. Even the carvings glimmered. Mixed awe and repugnance gripped him. But the men pressed around and against him, and carried him forward. Wine and leadership had dulled their sensibilities and as they strode down the long corridor they seemed little aware of the abysmal scene.

At first some held their weapons ready to meet a possible foray or ambush, but soon they lowered them negligently, and even sucked at the wineskins and jested. A hulking oarsman, whose blond beard was patched with yellow scud from the surf, struck up a chanty and others joined in, until the dank walls roared. Deeper and deeper they penetrated into the cave or castle, along the wide, winding, ooze-carpeted corridor.

Fafhrd was carried along as by a current. When he moved too slowly, the others jostled him and he quickened his pace, but it was all involuntary. Only his eyes responded to his will, turning from side to side, drinking in details with fearful curiosity. The endless series of vague carvings, wherein sea monsters and unwholesome manlike figures and vaguely anthropomorphic giant skates or rays seemed to come alive and stir as the phosphorescence fluctuated. A group of highest windows or openings of some sort, from which dark slippery weeds trailed down. The pools of water here and there. The still-alive, gasping fish which the others trod or kicked aside. The clumps of bearded shells clinging to the corners. The impression of things scuttling out of the way ahead. Louder and louder the thought drummed in his skull: Surely the others must realize where they were. Surely they must know the phosphorescence was that of the sea. Surely they must know that this was the retreat of the more secret creatures of the deep. Surely, surely they must know that Simorgya had indeed sunk under the sea and only risen up yesterday—or yester-hour.

But on they marched after Lavas Laerk, and still sang and shouted and swilled wine in quick gulps, throwing back their heads and lifting up the sacks as they strode. And Fafhrd could not speak. His shoulder muscles were contracted as if the weight of the sea were already pressing them down. His mind was engulfed and oppressed by the ominous presence of sunken Simorgya. Memories of the legends. Thoughts of the black centuries during which sea life had slowly crept and wriggled and swum through the mazes of rooms and corridors until it had a lair in every crack and cranny and Simorgya was one with the mysteries of the ocean. In a deep grotto that opened on the corridor he made out a thick table of stone, with a great stone chair behind it; and though he could not be sure, he thought he distinguished an octopus shape slouched there in a travesty of a human occupant, tentacles coiling the chair, unblinking eyes staring glisteningly.

Gradually the flare of the smoky torches paled, as the phosphorescence grew stronger. And when the men broke off singing, the sound of the surf was no longer audible.

Then Lavas Laerk, from around a sharp turn in the corridor, uttered a triumphant cry. The others hastened after, stumbling, lurching, calling out eagerly.

"Oh, Simorgya!" crew Lavas Laerk, "we have found your treasure house!"

The room in which the corridor ended was square and considerably lower-ceilinged than the corridor. Standing here and there were a number of black, soggy-looking, heavily bound chests. The stuff underfoot was muckier. There were more pools of water. The phosphorescence was stronger.

The blond-bearded oarsman leaped ahead as the others hesitated, and wrenched at the cover of the nearest chest. A corner came away in his hands, the wood soft as cheese, the seeming metal a black, smeary ooze. He grasped at it again and pulled off most of the top, revealing a layer of dully-gleaming gold and slime-misted gems. Over that jeweled surface a crablike creature scuttled, escaping through a hole in the back.

With a great, greedy shout, the others rushed at the chests, jerking, gouging, even smiting with their swords at the spongy wood. Two, fighting as to which should break open a chest, fell against it and it went to pieces under them, leaving them struggling in jewels and muck.

All this while Lavas Laerk stood on the same spot from which he had uttered his first taunting cry. To Fafhrd, who stood forgotten beside him, it seemed that Lavas Laerk was distraught that his quest should come to any end, that Lavas Laerk was desperately searching for something further, something more than jewels and gold to sate his mad willfulness. Then he noted that Lavas Laerk was looking at something intently—a square, slime-filmed, but apparently golden door across the room from the mouth of the corridor; upon it was the carving of some strange, undulant blanketlike sea monster. He heard Lavas Laerk laugh throatily and watched him stride unswervingly toward the door. He saw that Lavas Laerk had something in his hand. With a shock of surprise he recognized it as the ring Lavas Laerk had taken from him. He saw Lavas Laerk shove at the door without budging it. He saw Lavas Laerk fumble with the ring and fit the key part into the golden door and turn it. He saw the door give a little to Lavas Laerk's next push.

Then he realized—and the realization came with an impact like a rushing wall of water—that nothing had happened accidentally, that everything from the moment his arrow struck the fish had been intended by someone or something—something that wanted a door unlocked—and he turned and fled down the corridor as if a tidal wave were sucking at his heels.

The corridor, without torchlight, was pale and shifty as a nightmare. The phosphorescence seemed to crawl as if alive, revealing previously unspied creatures in every niche. Fafhrd stumbled, sprawled at full length, raced on. His fastest bursts of speed seemed slow as in a bad dream. He tried to look only ahead, but still glimpsed from the corners of his eyes every detail he had seen before: the trailing weeds, the monstrous carvings, the bearded shells, the sombrely staring octopus eyes. He noted without surprise that his feet and body glowed wherever the slime had splashed or smeared. He saw a small square of darkness in the omnipresent phosphorescence and sprinted toward it. It grew in size. It was the cavern's portal. He plunged across the threshold into the night. He heard a voice calling his name.

It was the Gray Mouser's voice. It came from the opposite direction to the wrecked galley. He ran toward it across treacherous ledges. Starlight, now come back, showed a black gulf before his feet. He leaped, landed with a shaking impact on another rock surface, dashed forward without falling. He saw the top of a mast above an edge of darkness and almost bowled over the small figure that was staring raptly in the direction from which he had just fled. The Mouser seized him by the shoulder, dragged him to the edge, pulled him over. They clove the water together and swam out to the sloop anchored in the rock-sheltered lee. The Mouser started to heave at the anchor but Fafhrd slashed the line with a knife snatched from the Mouser's belt and jerked up the sail in swift, swishing rushes.

Slowly the sloop began to move. Gradually the ripples became wavelets, the wavelets became smacking waves. Then they slipped past a black, foam-edged sword of rock and were in the open sea. Still Fafhrd did not speak, but crowded on all canvas and did all else possible to coax speed from the storm-battered sloop. Resigned to mystification, the Mouser helped him.

They had not been long underway when the blow fell. The Mouser, looking sternward, gave a hoarse incredulous cry. The wave swiftly overtaking them was higher than the mast. And something was sucking the sloop back. The Mouser raised his arms shieldingly. Then the sloop began to climb; up, up, up until it reached the top, overbalanced, and plummeted down on the opposite side. The first wave was followed by a second and a third, and a fourth, each almost as high. A larger boat would surely have been swamped. Finally the waves gave way to a choppy, foaming, unpredictable chaos, in which every ounce of effort and a thousand quick decisions were needed to keep the sloop afloat.

When the pale foredawn came, they were back on the homeward course again, a small improvised sail taking the place of the one ripped in the aftermath of the storm, enough water bailed from the hold to make the sloop seaworthy. Fafhrd, dazedly watching for the sunrise, felt weak as a woman. He only half heard the Mouser tell, in snatches, of how he had lost the galley in the storm, but followed what he guessed to be its general course until the storm cleared, and had sighted the strange island and landed there, mistakenly believing it be the galley's home port.

The Mouser then brought thin, bitter wine and salt fish, but Fafhrd pushed them away and said, "One thing I must know. I never looked back. You were staring earnestly at something behind me. What was it?"

The Mouser shrugged his shoulders. "I don't know. The distance was too great and the light was queer. What I thought I saw was rather foolish. I'd have given a good deal to have been closer." He frowned, shrugged his shoulders again. "Well, what I thought I saw was this. A crowd of men wearing big black cloaks—they looked like Northerners—came rushing out of an opening of some sort. There was something odd about them: the light by which I saw them didn't seem to have any source. Then they waved the big black cloaks around as if they were fighting with them or doing some sort of dance. . . . I told you it was very foolish . . . and then they got down on their hands and knees and covered themselves up with the cloaks and crawled back into the place from which they had come. Now tell me I'm a liar."

Fafhrd shook his head. "Only those weren't cloaks," he said.

The Mouser began to sense that there was much more to it than he had even guessed. "What were they then?" he asked.

"I don't know," said Fafhrd.

"But then what was the place, I mean the island that almost sucked us down when it sank?"

"Simorgya," said Fafhrd and lifted his head and began to grin in a cruel, chilly, wild-eyed way that took the Mouser back. "Simorgya," repeated Fafhrd, and pulled himself to the side of the boat and glared down at the rushing water. "Simorgya. And now it's sunk again. And may it soak there forever and rot in its own corruption, till all's muck!" He trembled spasmodically with the passion of his curse, then sank back. Along the rim of the east a ruddy smudge began to show.

[*Unknown Worlds,* February 1942;
Night's Black Agents (Arkham House, 1947)]

DIARY IN THE SNOW

Jan. 6: Two hours since my arrival at Lone Top, and I'm still sitting in front of the fire, soaking in the heat. The taxi ride was hellishly cold and the breath-taking half-mile tramp through the drifts with John completed my transformation to an icicle. The driver from Terrestrial told me this was one of the loneliest spots in Montana, and it surely looked like it—miles and miles of tenantless, starlit snow with mysterious auroral splotches and ghostly beams flickering to the north—a beautiful, if frightening sight.

And I've even turned the cold to account! It suggested to me that I put my monsters on a drearily frigid planet, one that is circling a dead or dying sun. That will give them a motivation for wanting to invade and capture the Earth. Good!

Well, here I am—a jobless man with a book to write. My friends (such as they are, or were) never believed I'd take this step, and when they finally saw I was in earnest, they tried to convince me I was a fool. And toward the end I *was* afraid I'd lose my nerve, but then—it was as if forces beyond my knowledge or control were packing my bag, insulting my boss, and buying my ticket. A very pleasant illusion, after weeks of qualms and indecision!

How wonderful to be away from people and newspapers and advertisements and movies—all that damnable intellectual static! I confess I had a rather unpleasant shock when I first came in here and noticed the big radio standing right between the fireplace and window. How awful it would be to have that thing blatting at you in this cabin, with no place to escape except the tiny storeroom. It would be worse than the city! But so far John hasn't turned it on, and I have my fingers crossed.

John is a magnificent host—understanding as well as incomparably generous. After getting me coffee and a snack, and setting out the whiskey, he's retired to the other armchair and busied himself with some scribbling of his own.

Well, in a moment I'll talk as much as he wants to (*if* he wants to) though I'm still reverberating from my trip. I feel as if I'd been catapulted out of an intolerable clangor and discord into the heart of quietness. It gives me a crazy, lightheaded feeling, like a balloon that touches the earth only to bounce upward again.

Better stop here though. I'd hate to think of how quiet a quietness would have to be, in order to be as much quieter than this place, as this is quieter than the city!

A man ought to be able to listen to his thoughts out here—really *hear* things.

Just John, and me—and my monsters!

Jan. 7: Wonderful day. Crisp, but no wind, and a flood of yellow sunlight to put a warmth and dazzle into the snow banks. John showed me all around the place this morning. It's a snug little cabin he's got, and a good thing too!—because it's quite as lonely as it seemed last night. No houses in sight, and I'd judge there hasn't been anything down the road since my taxi—the marks where it turned around stand out sharply. John says a farmer drives by, though, every two days—he has an arrangement with him for getting milk and other necessities.

You can't see Terrestrial, there are hills in the way. John tells me that power and telephone wires have never gotten closer than six miles. The radio runs on storage batteries. When the drifts get bad he has to snowshoe all the way into Terrestrial.

I confess I feel a little awestruck at my own temerity—a confirmed desk-worker like myself plunging into a truly rugged environment like this. But John seems to think nothing of it. He says I'll have to learn to snowshoe. I had my first lesson this morning and cut a ludicrous figure. I'll be virtually a prisoner until I learn my way around. But any price is worth paying to get away from the thought-destroying din and soul-killing routine of the city!

And there's a good side to the enforced isolation—it will make me concentrate on my book.

Well, that does it. I've popped the word, and now I'll have to start writing the thing itself—and am I scared! It's been so long since I've finished anything of my own—even attempted it. So damned long. I'd begun to be afraid (begun, hell!) that I'd never do anything but take notes and make outlines—outlines that became more and more complicated and lifeless with the years. And yet there were those early fragments of writing from my school days that ought to have encouraged me. Even much later, when I'd developed some literary judgement, I used to think those fragments showed flashes of real promise—until I burned them. They should have given me courage—at any rate, something should have—but whatever promising ideas I'd have in the morning would be shredded to tatters by that horrible hackwriting job by the time night came.

And now that I have taken the plunge, it seems hilariously strange that I should have been driven to it by an idea for a fantasy story. The very sort of writing I've always jeered at—childish playing around with interplanetary space and alien monsters. The farthest thing you could imagine from my wearisome outlines, which eventually got so filled up with character analysis (or even—Heaven help me—psychoanalysis) and dismal authentic backgrounds and "my own experience" and just heaps of social and political "significance" that there wasn't room for anything else. Yes, it does seem ludicrously paradoxical that, instead of all those profound and "important" things, it should have been an idea about black-furred, long-tentacled monsters on another planet, peering unwinkingly at the earth and longing for its warmth and life, that so began to sing in my mind, night and day, that I finally got the strength to sweep aside all those miserable little fences against insecurity I'd been so painfully long in building—and take a chance!

John says it's natural and wholesome for a beginning writer to turn to fantasy. And he's certainly made a go of that type of writing himself. (But he's built up his ability as courageously and doggedly through the years as he has this cabin. In comparison, I have a long, long way to go.)

In any case, my book won't be a cheap romance of the fabulous, despite its "cosmic" background. And when you get down to that, what's wrong with a cosmic background? I've lived a long time now with my monsters and devoted a lot of serious thought to them. I'll make them real.

That night: I just had an exhilaratingly eerie experience. I'd stepped outside for a breather and a look at the snow and stars, when my attention was caught by a beam of violet light some distance away. Though not exactly bright, it had a jewelly gleam and seemed to go up into the sky as far as I could see, without losing any of its needlelike thinness—a very perplexing thing. It was moving around slowly as if it were questing for something. For a shivery moment I had the feeling it came from the stars and was looking for me.

I was about to call John when it winked out. I'm sorry he didn't see it. He tells me it must have been an auroral manifestation, but it certainly didn't look anywhere near that far away—I believe auroras are supposed to be high in the stratosphere, where the air is as rarified as in a fluorescent tube—and besides I always thought they were blotchy. However, I suppose he must be right—he tells me he's seen some very queer ones in past years, and of course my own experience of them is practically nil.

I asked him if there mightn't be some secret military research going on nearby—perhaps with atomic power or some new kind of searchlight or radar beam—but he scouted the idea.

Whatever it was, it stimulated my imagination. Not that I need it! I'm almost worried by the degree to which my mind has come alive during my few hours at Lone Top. I'm afraid my mind is becoming too keen, like a knife with such a paper-thin edge that it keeps curling over whenever you try to cut something. . . .

Jan. 9: At last, after several false starts, I've made a real beginning. I've pictured my monsters holding conclave at the bottom of a fantastically deep crack or canyon in their midnight planet. Except for a thin, jagged-edged ribbon of stars overhead, there is no light—their hoard of radiation is so depleted that ages ago they were forced to stop wasting any of it on the mere luxury of vision. But their strange eyes have become accommodated to starlight (though even they, wise as they are, do not know how to get any real warmth out of it) and they can perceive each other vaguely—great woolly, spidery shapes crouched on the rocks or draped along the ragged walls. It is unimaginably cold there—their insulating fur is bathed in a frigidity akin to that of interstellar space. They communicate by means of thought—infrequent, well-shaped thoughts, for even thinking uses up energy. They recall their glorious past—their spendthrift youth, their vigorous prime. They commemorate the agony of their eon-long battle against the cold. They reiterate their savage and unshakable determination to survive.

It's a good piece of writing. Even honest John says so, although twitting me sardonically for writing such a wild sort of tale after many years of politely scorning his fantastic stories.

But it was pretty bad for a while there, when I was making those false starts—I began to see myself crawling back in defeat to the grinning city. I can confess now that for years I've been afraid that I never had any real creative ability, that my promising early fragments were just a freak of childhood. Children show flashes of all sorts of odd abilities which they lose when they grow up—eidetic imagery, maybe even clairvoyance, things of that sort. What people praised in those first little stories of mine was a rich human sympathy, an unusually acute insight into adult human motives. And what I was afraid of was that all this had been *telepathy,* an unconscious picking up of snatches of thought and emotion from the adult minds around me—things that sounded very genuine and impressive when written down, especially by a child, but that actually required no more creative ability than taking dictation. I even developed an acute worry that some day I'd find myself doing automatic writing! Odd, what nonsensical fears an artist's mind will cook up when it's going through a dry period—John says it's true of the whole fraternity.

At any rate, the book I'm now writing disposes in a laughably complete fashion of that crazy theory. A story about fabulous monsters on a planet dozens of light-years away can't very well be telepathy!

I suppose it was the broadcast last night that started me thinking again about that silly old notion. The broadcast wasn't silly though—a singularly intelligent discussion of future scientific possibilities—atomic energy, brain waves, new methods of radio transmission, that sort of thing—and not popularized for an oafish audience, thank God. Must be a program of some local university—John says *now* will I stop disparaging all educational institutions not located in the east!

My first apprehensions about the radio turned out to be completely groundless—I ought to have known that John isn't the sort of person to go in for soap operas and jazz. He uses the instrument intelligently—just a brief daily news summary (*not* a long-winded "commentary"), classical music when available, and an occasionally high-grade lecture or round-table discussion. Last night's scientific broadcast was new to him though—he was out at the time and didn't recognize the station from my description.

I'm rather indebted to that program. I think it was while listening to it that the prologue of my story "jelled." Some chance word or thought provided a crystallization point for my ideas. My mind had become sufficiently fatigued—probably a reaction to my earlier over-keenness—for my churning ideas to settle into place. At any rate, I was suddenly so tired and groggy that I hardly remembered the finish of the program or John coming in or my piling off to bed. John said I looked out on my feet. He thought I'd taken a bit too much, but I referred him to the impartial judgement of the whiskey bottle, and its almost unchanged level refuted the base calumny!

In the morning I woke up fresh as a youngster and ripped off the prologue as if I'd been in the habit of turning out that much writing daily for the past ten years!

Had another snowshoe lesson today and didn't do much better—I grudge all time spent away from my book. John says I really ought to hurry up and learn, in case anything should happen to him while we were cut off from Terrestrial—small chance with reliable John! The radio reports a big blizzard farther east, but so far it hasn't touched us—the sun is bright, the sky dark blue. A local cold snap is predicted.

But what do I care how long I'm confined to the cabin. I have begun to create my monsters!

That night: I'm vindicated! John has just seen my violet beam, confirmed its non-auroral nature, and gone completely overboard as to its nearness—he claimed at first that it was actually hitting the cabin!

He was approaching from the south when he saw it—apparently striking the roof in a coruscation of ghostly violet sparks. He hurried up, calling to me excitedly. It was a moment before I heard him—I'd just caught the mumbly beginning of what seemed to be another of those interesting scientific broadcasts (must be a series) and was trying to tune in more clearly and having a hard time, the radio being mulish or my own manipulations inadequate.

By the time I got outside the beam had faded. We spent several chilly minutes straining our eyes in all directions, but saw nothing except the stars.

John admits now that the beam seeming to strike the roof must have been an optical illusion, but still stoutly insists that it was fairly near. I have become the champion of the auroral theory! For, thinking it over, I can see that the chances are it is some bizarre auroral phenomenon—Arctic and Antarctic explorers, for instance, have reported all sorts of peculiar polar lights. It is very easy to be deceived as to distance in this clear atmosphere, as John himself has said.

Or else—who knows?—it might be some unusual form of static electricity, something akin to St. Elmo's fire.

John has been trying to tune in on the program I started to catch, but no soap. There seems to be a lot of waily static in that sector of the dial. He informs me in his sardonic way that all sorts of unusual things have begun to happen since my arrival!

John has given up in disgust and is going to bed. I think I'll follow his example, though I may have another try at the radio first—my old dislike of the brute is beginning to fade, now that it's my only link with the rest of the world.

Next morning—the 10th: We've got the cold snap the radio predicted. I don't notice much difference, except it took longer to get the place warm and everything was a little tightened up. Later on I'm going to help John split firewood—I insisted on it. He enquired with mild maliciousness whether I'd succeeded where he failed at catching the tail-end of that scientific broadcast—said the last thing he heard going to sleep was moany static. I admitted that, as far as I knew, I hadn't—sleep must have struck the sledgehammer blow it favors in this rugged locality while I was still twisting the dial; my memories of getting to bed are rather blurry, though I vaguely recall John sleepily snarling at me, "For God's sake turn down the radio."

We did run across one more odd phenomenon, though—or something that could pass for an odd phenomenon with a little grooming. In the middle of breakfast I noticed John looking intently over my shoulder. I turned and after a moment saw that it was something in the frost on the window by the radio. On closer examination we were considerably puzzled.

There was a queer sinuous pattern in the frost. It was composed of several parallel rows of tiny, roughly triangular humps with faint, hairlike veins going out to either side, all perceptibly thicker than the rest of the frost. I've never seen frost deposited in a pattern like it. The nearest analogy that occurs to me—not a very accurate one—is a squid's tentacle. For some reason there comes to my mind that description in *King Lear* of a demon glimpsed peering down from a cliff. "Horns whelk'd and wav'd like the enridged sea." I got the impression the pattern had been formed by an object *even colder than the frost* resting lightly against the glass, though that of course is impossible.

I was surprised to hear John say he thought the pattern was in the glass itself, but by scraping off a portion of the frost he did reveal a very faint bluish or lavender pattern which was rather similar.

After discussing various possibilities, we've decided that the cold snap—one of the most sudden in years, John says—brought out a latent imperfection in the glass, touching off some change in molecular organization that absorbed enough heat to account for the difference in thickness of the frost. The same change producing the faint lavender tint—if it wasn't there before.

I feel extraordinarily happy and mentally alive today. All these "odd phenomena" I've been noting down don't really amount to a hoot, except to show that a sense of strangeness, a delightful feeling of adventurous expectancy, has come back into my life—something I thought the city had ground out of me forever, with its blinkered concentration on "practical" matters, its noisy and faddish narrow-mindedness.

Best of all, there is my book. I have another scene all shaped in my mind.

Before supper: I've struck a snag. I don't know how I'm going to get my monsters to Earth. I got through the new scene all right—it tells how the monsters have for ages been greedily watching the Earth and several other habitable planets that are nearby (in light-years). They have telescopes which do not depend on lenses, but amplify the starlight just as a radio amplifies radio waves or a public address system the human voice. Those telescopes are extraordinarily sensitive—there are no limits to what can be accom-

plished by selection and amplification—they can see houses and people—
they tune in on wave-lengths that are not distorted by our atmosphere—
they catch radio-type as well as visual-type waves, and hear our voices—they
make use of modes of radiation which our scientists have not yet discovered
and which travel at many times the speed of the slower modes, almost in-
stantaneously.

But all this intimate knowledge of our daily life, this interplanetary voy-
eurism, profits them not in the least, except to whet their appetites to a bitter frenzy. It does not bring them an iota of warmth; on the contrary, it is a
steady drain on their radiation bank. And yet they continue to spy minutely
on us . . . watching . . . waiting . . . for the right moment.

And that's where the rub comes. Just what is this right moment they are
waiting for? How the devil are they ever going to accomplish the trip? I suppose if I were a seasoned science-fiction writer this difficulty wouldn't even
faze me—I'd solve it in a wink by means of space-ships or the fourth dimension, or what not. But none of those ideas seem right to me. For instance, a
few healthy rocket blasts would use up what little energy they have left. I
want something that's really plausible.

Oh well, mustn't worry about that—I'll get an idea sooner or later. The
important thing is that the writing continues to hold up strongly. John
picked up the last few pages for a glance, sat down to read them closely,
gave me a sharp look when he'd finished, remarked, "I don't know what *I've*
been writing science-fiction for, the past fifteen years," and ducked out to
get an armful of wood. Quite a compliment.

Have I started on my real career at last? I hardly dare ask myself, after the
many disappointments and blind alleys of those piddling, purposeless city
years. And yet even during the blackest periods I used to feel that I was being
groomed for some important or at least significant purpose, that I was being
tested by moods and miseries, being held back until the right moment came.

An illusion?

Jan. 11: This is becoming very interesting. More odd patterns in the frost
and glass this morning—a new set. But at twenty below it's not to be wondered that inorganic materials get freakish. What an initial drop in temperature accomplished, a further sudden drop might very well repeat. John is
quite impressed by it though, and inclined to theorize about obscure points
in physics. Wish I could recall the details of last night's scientific broadcast—I
think something was said about low temperature phenomena that might have
a bearing on cases like this. But I was dopey as usual and must have dozed
through most of it—rather a shame, because the beginning was very intriguing—something about wireless transmission of power and the production of
physical effects at far distant points, the future possibilities of some sort of
scientific "teleportation." John refers sarcastically to my "private university"—
he went to bed early again and missed the program. But he says he half woke
at one time and heard me listening to "a lot of nightmarish static" and sleepily implored me either to tune it better or shut it off. Odd—it seemed clear as

a bell to me, at least the beginning did, and I don't remember him shouting at all. Probably he was having a nightmare. But I must be careful not to risk disturbing him again. It's funny to think of a confirmed radio-hater like myself in the role of an offensively noise-hungry "fan."

I wonder, though, if my presence is beginning to annoy John. He seemed jumpy and irritable all morning, and suddenly decided to get worried about my pre-bedtime dopeyness. I told him it was the natural result of the change in climate and my unaccustomed creative activity. I'm not used to physical exertion either, and my brief snowshoeing lessons and woodchopping chores, though they would seem trivial to a tougher man, are enough to really fag my muscles. Small wonder if an overpowering tiredness hits me at the end of the day.

But John said he had been feeling unusually sleepy and sluggish himself toward bedtime, and advanced the unpleasant hypothesis of carbon monoxide poisoning—something not to be taken lightly in a cabin sealed as tightly as this. He immediately subjected stove and fireplace to a minute inspection and carefully searched both chimneys for cracks or obstructions, inside and out, despite the truly fiendish cold—I went outside to try and help him, and got a dose of it—brr! The surrounding trackless snowfields looked bright and inviting, but to a man afoot—unless he were a seasoned winter veteran—lethal!

Everything proved to be in perfect order, so our fears were allayed. But John continued to rehearse scare stories of carbon monoxide poisoning, such as the tragic end of Andre's balloon expedition to the Arctic, and remained fidgety and restless—and all of a sudden he decided to snowshoe into Terrestrial for some spare radio parts and other unnecessary oddments. I asked him wasn't the bi-weekly trudge down to meet the farmer's car enough for him, and why in any case pick the coldest day of the year? But he merely snorted, "That all you know about our weather?" and set out. I'm a bit bothered, though he certainly must know how to take care of himself.

Maybe my presence does upset him. After all, he's lived alone here for years, except for infrequent trips—practically a hermit. Having someone living with him may very well disorder his routine of existence—and of creative work—completely. Added to that, I'm another writer—a dangerous combination. It's quite possible that, despite our friendship (friendship would have nothing to do with it), I get on his nerves. I must have a long talk with him when he returns and sound him out on this—indirectly, of course.

But now to my monsters. They have a scene that is crying out in my brain to be expressed.

Later: The snag in my writing is developing into a brick wall. I can't seem to figure out *any* plausible way of getting my monsters to Earth. There's a block in my mind whenever I try to think in that direction. I certainly hope it's not going to be the way it was with so many of my early stories—magnificently atmospheric prologues that bogged down completely as soon as I was forced to work out the mechanics of the plot; and the more impressive and evocative the beginning, the more crushing the fall—and the more likely it would be to hinge on some trifling detail that persisted in thwarting my inventiveness, such as how to get two characters introduced to each other or how does the hero make a living.

Well, I won't let it defeat me this time! I'll go right ahead with the later portion of the story, and then sooner or later I'll just have to think through the snag.

I thought I had the thing licked when I started this noon. I pictured the monsters with a secret outpost established on Earth. Using Earth's energy resources, they are eventually able to work out a means of transporting their entire race here—or else dragging off the Earth and Sun to their own dead solar system and sacred home planet across the trackless light-years of interstellar space, like Prometheus stealing fire from heaven, humanity being wiped out in the process.

But, as should have been obvious to me, that still leaves the problem of getting the outpost here.

The section about the outpost looks very good though. Of course the pioneer monsters will have to keep their presence hidden from humanity while they "try out" our planet, become acclimated to Earth, develop resistance to inimical bacteria strains, et cetera, and measure up man from close range, deciding on the best weapons to use against him when the time for extermination arrives.

For it won't be entirely a one-sided struggle. Man won't be completely powerless against these creatures. For instance, he could probably wipe out the outpost if he ever discovered its existence. But of course that won't happen.

I envisage a number of shivery scenes—people getting glimpses of the monsters in far, lonely places—seeing spidery, shadowy shapes in deep forests—coming on hurriedly deserted mountain lairs or encampments that disturbingly suggest neither human beings nor animals—strange black swimmers noted by boats off the usual steamship lanes—engineers and scientists bothered by inexplicable drains on power lines and peculiar thefts of equipment—a vague but mounting general dread—the "irrational" conviction that we are being listened to and spied on, "measured for our coffins"— eventually, as the creatures grow bolder, dark polypous forms momentarily seen scuttling across city roofs or clinging to high walls in the more poorly lighted sections, at night—black furry masks pressed for an instant against windowpanes—

Yes, it should work out very nicely.

I wish John would get back though. It's almost dark, and still no sign of him. I've popped out several times for a look-see, but there's nothing except his snowshoe tracks going over the hill. I confess I'm getting a bit edgy. I suppose I've frightened myself with my own story—it wouldn't be the first time that's happened to a writer. I find myself looking quickly at the window, or listening for strange sounds, and my imagination insists on playing around unpleasantly with the "odd phenomena" of the past few days—the violet auroral beam, the queer patterns in the frost, my silly notions about telepathic powers. My mental state is extraordinarily heightened and I have the illusion, both pleasurable and frightening, of standing at the doorway of an unknown alien realm and being able to rend the filmy curtain with a twitch of my finger if I choose.

But such nervousness is only natural, considering the isolation of the place and John's delay. I certainly hope he isn't going to snowshoe back in the dark—at a temperature like this any accident or misjudgement might have fatal consequences. And if he did get into trouble I wouldn't be any help to him.

As I get things ready for supper, I keep the radio going. It provides a not unpleasant companionship.

Jan. 12: We had quite a high old time last night. John popped in well past the supper hour—he'd gotten a ride with his farmer. He had a bottle of fantastically high-proof rum with him (he says when you have to pack your liquor, you want as much alcohol and as little water as possible) and after supper we settled down for a long palaver. Oddly I had trouble getting into the spirit of the evening. I was restless and wanted to be fiddling with my writing, or the radio, or something. But the liquor helped to lull such nervous impulses, and after a while we opened our minds to each other and talked about everything under the sun.

One thing I'm glad we settled: any ideas I had about my presence annoying John are pure moonshine. He's pleased to have a comrade out here, and the fact that he's doing me a big favor really makes him feel swell. (It's up to me not to disappoint his generosity.) And if any further proof were needed, he's started a new story this morning (said he's been mulling it in his mind the past couple of days—hence his restlessness) and is typing away at it like sixty!

I feel very normal and down-to-earth this morning. I realize now that during the past few days I have been extraordinarily keyed up, both mentally and imaginatively. It's rather a relief to get over a mental binge like that (with the aid of physical binge!) but also faintly depressing—a strange bloom rubbed off things. I find my mind turning to practical matters, such as where am I going to sell my stories and how am I going to earn a living writing when my small savings give out? John and I talked about it for quite a while.

Well, I suppose I should be getting to my writing, though for once I'd rather knock around in the snow with John. The weather's moderated.

Jan. 13—evening: Got to face it—my writing has bogged down completely. It's not just the snag—I can't write *anything* on the story. I've torn up so damn many half pages! Not a single word rings true, or even feels true while I'm writing it—it's all fakey. My monsters are miserable puppets or papier-mâché and moth-eaten black fur.

John says not to worry, but *he* can talk that way—*his* story is going great guns; he put in a herculean stint of typing today and just now rolled into bed after a couple of quick drinks.

I took his advice yesterday, spent most of the day outdoors, practicing snowshoeing, chopping wood, et cetera. But it didn't make me feel a bit keener this morning.

I don't think I should have congratulated myself on getting over my "mental binge." It was really my creative energy. Without it, I'm no good at all. It's as if I had been "listening" for my story and contact had been suddenly broken off. I remember having the same experience with some of my earlier writing. You ring and ring, but the other end of the line has gone dead.

I don't think the drinking helps either. We had another bottle session last night—good fun, but it dulls the mind, at least mine. And I don't believe John would have stopped at a couple even this evening, if I hadn't begged off.

I think John is worried about me in a friendly way—considers me a mild neurotic case and dutifully plies me with the more vigorous animal activities, such as snowshoeing and boozing. I catch a clinical look in his eyes, and then there's the way he boosts the "healthy, practical outlook" in our conversations, steers them away from morbid topics.

Of course I'm somewhat neurotic. Every creative artist is. And I did get a bit up in the air when we had our carbon monoxide scare—but so did he! Why the devil should he try to inhibit my imagination? He must know how important it is to me, how crucial, that I finish this story.

Mustn't force myself, though. That's the worst thing. I ought to turn in, but I don't feel a bit sleepy. John's snoring—damn him!

I think I'll fish around on the radio—keep it turned low. I'd like to catch another of those scientific programs—they stimulate my imagination. Wonder where they come from? John brought a couple of papers and I looked through the radio sections, but couldn't find the station.

Jan. 14: I'd give a good deal to know just what's happening here. More odd humpy patterns this morning—there's been another cold snap—and they weren't altogether in the frost. But first there was that crazy dual sleepwalking session. There may be something in John's monoxide theory—at any rate *some* theory is needed.

Late last night I awoke sitting up, still fully clothed, with John shaking me. There was a frozen, purposeful look on his face, but his eyes were closed. It was a few moments before I could make him stop pushing at me. At first he was confused, almost antagonistic, but after a while he woke up completely and told me that he had been having a fearful nightmare.

It began, he said, with an unpleasant moaning, wailing sound that had been torturing his ears for hours. Then he seemed to wake up and see the room, but it was changed—it was filled with violet sparks that showered and fell and rose again, ceaselessly. He felt an extreme chill, as of interstellar space. He was seized by the fear that something horrible was trying to get into the cabin. He felt that somehow *I* was letting it in, unknowingly, and that he must get to me and make me stop, but his limbs were held down as if by huge weights. He remembers making an agonizing, protracted effort.

For my part, I must have fallen asleep at the radio. It was turned on low, but not tuned to any station.

The sources of his nightmare are pretty obvious: the violet auroral beam, the "nightmarish" (prescient!) static of a few evenings ago, the monoxide fear, his partially concealed worry about me, and finally the rather heavy drinking we've both been doing. In fact, the whole business is nothing so terribly out of the way, except for the tracks—and how, or why, they should tie in with the sleepwalking session I haven't the ghost of an idea.

They were the same pattern as before, but much thicker—great ridgy welts of ice. And I had the odd illusion that they exuded a cold more intense than that of the rest of the frost. When we had scraped them away—a difficult job—we saw that the glass reproduced the pattern more distinctly and in a more pronounced hue. But strangest of all, we have traced what certainly seems to be a faint continuation on the inner windowsill, where the tracks take the form of a cracking and *disintegration* of the paint—it flakes off at a touch and the flakes, faintly lavender, crumble to powder. We also think we've found another continuation on the back of the chair by the window, though that is problematic.

What can have produced them is completely beyond us. Conceivably one of us might have "faked" them in some bizarre sleepwalking state, but how?—there's no object in the cabin that could produce that sinuous, chainy pattern with hairlike border. And even if there were, how could we possibly use it to produce a ridged pattern? Or is it possible that John is engineering an elaborate practical joke—no, it couldn't be anything like that!

We carefully inspected the other windows, including the one in the storeroom, but found no similar patterns.

John is planning to remove the pane eventually and submit it to a physicist for examination. He is very worked up about the thing. I can't quite make him out. He almost seems frightened. A few minutes ago he vaguely suggested something about our going into Terrestrial and rooming there for a few days.

But that would be ridiculous. I'm sure there's nothing inexplicable about this business. Even the matter of the tracks must have some very simple explanation that we would see at once if we were trained physicists.

I, for one, am going to forget all about it. My mind's come alive on the story again and I'm itching to write. Nothing must get in the way.

After supper: I feel strangely nervous, although my writing is going well again, thank God! I think I've licked the snag! I still don't see how I'm going to get my monsters to the Earth, but I have the inward conviction that the right method will suddenly pop into my mind when the time comes. Irrational, but the feeling is strong enough to satisfy me completely.

Meanwhile I'm writing the sections immediately before and after the first monster's arrival on Earth—creeping up on the event from both sides! The latter section is particularly effective. I show the monster floundering around in the snow (he naturally chooses to arrive in a cold region, since that would be the least unlike the climate of his own planet). I picture his temporary bewilderment at Earth's radiation storms, his awkward but swift movements, his hurried search for a suitable hiding place. An ignorant oaf glimpses him or his tracks, tells what he has seen, is laughed at for a superstitious fool. Perhaps, though, the monster is forced to kill someone. . . .

Odd that I should see all that so clearly and still be completely blind as to the section immediately preceding. But I'm convinced I'll know tomorrow!

John picked up the last pages, put them down after a moment. "Too damned realistic!" he observed.

I should be pleased, and yet now that I'm written out for the day I suddenly find myself apprehensive and—yes—frightened. My tired, overactive mind persists in playing around in a morbid way with the events of last night. I tell myself I'm just frightening myself with my story, "pretending" that it's true—as an author will—and carrying the pretense a little too far.

But I'm very much afraid that there's more to it than that—some actual thing or influence that we don't understand.

For instance, on rereading my previous entries in this diary, I find that I have omitted several important points—as if my unconscious mind were deliberately trying to suppress them.

For one thing, I failed to mention that the color in the glass and on the windowsill was identical with that of the violet beam.

Perhaps there is a natural connection—the beam a bizarre form of static electricity and the track its imprint, like lightning and the marks it produces.

This hint of a scientific explanation ought to relieve me, I suppose, but it doesn't.

Secondly, there's the feeling that John's nightmare was somehow partly real.

Thirdly, I said nothing about our instant fear, as soon as we first saw the patterns in the frost, that they had been produced by some, well, creature, though how a creature could be colder than its environment, I don't know. John said nothing, but I knew he had exactly the same idea as I: that a groping something had rested its chilled feeler against the windowpane.

The fear reached its highest pitch this morning. We still hadn't opened our minds to each other, but as soon as we had examined the tracks, we both started, as if by unspoken agreement, to wander around. It was like that scene reproduced so often in movies—two rivals are looking for the girl who is the object of their affections and who has coyly gone off somewhere. They begin to amble around silently, upstairs and down, indoors and out. Every once in a while they meet, start back a bit, nod, and pass each other by without a word.

That's how it was with John and me and our "creature." It wasn't at all amusing.

But we found nothing.

I can tell that John is as bothered by all this as I am. However, we don't talk about it—our ideas aren't of the sort that lend themselves to reasonable conversation.

He says one thing—that he wants to see me in bed first tonight. He's taking no chances of a repetition of the events that led up to the sleepwalking session. I'm certainly agreeable—I don't relish an experience like that any more than he does.

If only we weren't so damnably isolated! Of course, we could always get into Terrestrial at a pinch—unless a blizzard cut us off. The weatherman hints at such a possibility in the next few days.

John has kept the radio going all day, and I must confess I'm wholeheartedly grateful. Even the inanest program creates an illusion of social companionship and keeps the imagination from wandering too far.

I wish we were both in the city.

Jan. 15: This business has taken a disagreeable turn. We are planning to get out today.

There is a hostile, murderous being in the cabin, or somehow able to enter it at will without disturbing a locked door and tight-frozen windows. It is something unknown to science and alien to life as we know it. It comes from some realm of eternal cold.

I fully understand the extraordinary implications of those words. I would not put them down if I did not think they were true.

Or else we are up against an unknown natural force that behaves so like a hostile, murderous being that we dare not treat it otherwise.

We are waiting for the farmer's car, will ride back with him. We considered making the trip afoot, setting out at once, but John's injury and my inexperience decided us against it.

We have had another sleepwalking session, only this one did not end so innocuously.

It began, so far as we are able to reconstruct, with John's nightmare, which was an exact repetition of the one he had the night before, except that all the feelings, John says, were intensified.

Similarly, my first conscious sensations were of John shaking me and pushing at me. Only this time the room was in darkness, except for red glints from the fireplace.

Our struggle was much more violent. A chair was overturned. We slewed around, slammed against the wall, the radio slid to the floor with a crash.

Then John quieted. I hurried to light the lamp.

As I turned back, I heard him grunt with pain.

He was staring stupidly at his right wrist.

Encircling it like a double bracelet, deeply indenting it, were marks like those in the frost.

The indented flesh was purplish and caked with frozen blood.

The flesh to either side of the indentation was white, cold to my touch, and covered with fine hairlike marks of the same violet hue as in the beam and the glass.

It was a minute before the crystals of blood melted.

We disinfected and bandaged the wound. Swabbing with the disinfectant had no effect on the violet hairlines.

Then we searched the cabin without result, and while waiting for morning, decided on our present plans.

We have tried and tried to reconstruct what else happened. Presumably I got up in my sleep—or else John pulled me out of bed—but then . . .?

I wish I could get rid of the feeling that I am unconsciously in league with the being or force that injured John—trying to let it in.

Strangely, I am just as eager as yesterday to get at my writing. I have the feeling that once I got started, I would be past the snag in no time. Under the circumstances, the feeling disgusts me. Truly, creative ability fattens on horror in a most inhuman fashion.

The farmer's car should be here any minute. It looks dark outside. I wish we could get a weather broadcast, but the radio is out of commission.

Later: Can't possibly get away today. A tremendous blizzard literally burst on us a few minutes after I finished writing the last entry. John tells me he was almost certain it was coming, but hoped it would miss us at the last moment. No chance of the farmer now.

The fury of the storm would frighten me, were it not for the other thing. The beams creak. The wind screams and roars, sucking heat out of the place. A freakishly heavy gust just now came down the fireplace chimney, scattering embers. We are keeping a bigger fire in the stove, which draws better. Though barely sunset, we can see nothing outside, except the meager reflections of our lights on the blasts and eddies of snow.

John has been busy repairing the radio, despite his bad hand—we must find out how long the storm is expected to last. Although I know next to nothing of the mechanism, I have been helping him by holding things.

Now that we have no alternative but to stay here, we feel less panicky. Already the happenings of last night are beginning to seem incredible, remote. Of course, there must be some unknown force loose in this vicinity, but now that we are on guard, it is unlikely that it can harm us again. After all, it has only showed itself while we were both asleep, and we are planning to stay awake tonight—at least one of us. John wants to watch straight through. I protested because of his wounded hand, but he says it doesn't hurt much—just a dull throb. It isn't badly swollen. He says it still feels as though it were faintly anaesthetized by ice.

On the whole the storm and the sense of physical danger it brings have had a stimulating effect on me. I feel eager to be doing something. That inappropriate urge to be working at my story keeps plaguing me.

Evening: About to turn in for a while. All of a sudden feel completely washed up. But, thank Heaven, the radio is going at last. Some ultra-inane program, but it steadies me. Weather report that the blizzard may be over tomorrow. John is in good spirits and on the alert. The axe—best weapon we can muster—leans against his chair.

Next day—Must put down coherent record events just as happened. *May need it*—though even if accused, don't see how they can explain how I made the marks.

Must stay in cabin! Blizzard means *certain* death. *It* can be escaped from—possibly.

Mustn't panic again. Think I escaped serious frostbite. No question about sprained or badly strained ankle. No one could get to Terrestrial. Crazy for me to try. Merest luck I found the cabin. Must keep myself in hand. Must! Even if it is here watching me.

To begin, last night. First—confused dreams snow and black spidery monsters—reflection of my book. Second—sleepwalking—blackness and violet sparks—John—violent surging movements—falling through space—breath of searing cold—crash—sudden pain—flood of white sparks—blackout.

Third—this morning. Weak—terribly feverish—staring at wall—pattern in grain of wood—*familiar*—pattern jumped to nearer surface—John's head and back—no surprise or horror, at first—muttered, "John's sick too. Gone to sleep on the floor, like me."—*recognized pattern.*

Worked over him an hour—longer—hopeless—skull eaten in—hair dissolved—falls to powder at touch—violet lines—track twisted downward—shirt eaten through—spine laid bare—flesh near track snow white and icy to touch, much colder than cabin—trembling all the while, partly from cold—blizzard still raging—both fires out—got them going—searched cabin—John's body into storeroom—covered—coffee—crazy itch to write—tried to work on smashed radio—had to keep doing something—hands moving faster and faster—began to tremble—more and more—threw on clothes—strapped on snowshoes—out into the blizzard—full force of wind—knocked down twice—tried to go on by crouching—snowshoes tangled—down a third time—pain—struggled like something'd caught me—more pain—lay still—face lashed by ice—had to get back—crawled—crawled forever—no feeling—glimpsed open door of cabin, *behind* me—made it—

I must keep control of myself. I must keep my thoughts logical. Reconstruct!

John asleep. What made him sleep? Meanwhile, am I letting the thing in? How? He starts up suddenly. Struggles with the thing and me. Knocks me down. Is caught like Laocoon. Strikes with the axe. Misses. Hits the radio. No chance for a second blow. Squeezed, frozen, corroded to death.

Then? I was helpless. Why did it stop?

Is it sure of me and saving me for tonight? Or does it need me? At times I have the crazy feeling that the story I have been writing is true—that one of my monsters killed John—that I am trying to help them reach the Earth.

But that's mental weakness—an attempt to rationalize the incredible. This is not fantasy—it's *real.* I must fight any such trends toward insanity.

I must make plans. As long as the blizzard lasts, I'm trapped here. It will try to get me tonight. I must keep awake. When the blizzard lifts, I can try smoke signals. Or, if my ankle improves, attempt it to Terrestrial along the road. The farmer ought to be coming by, though John did say that when the roads are blocked—

John—

If only I weren't so completely alone. If only I had the radio.

Later: Got the radio going! A miracle of luck—I must have absorbed more knowledge than I realized, helping fix it yesterday. My fingers moved nimbly, as if they remembered more than my conscious mind, and pretty soon I had all the smashed parts replaced with spares.

It was good to hear those first voices.

The blizzard will end tonight, it is predicted.

I feel considerably reassured. I fully realize the dangers of the coming night, but I believe that with luck I'll be able to escape them.

My emotions are exhausted. I think I can face whatever comes, coolly and calmly.

I would be completely confident except for that persistent, unnerving feeling that a segment of my unconscious mind is under the control of something outside myself.

My chief fear is that I will yield to some sudden irrational impulse, such as the urge to write, which at times becomes incomprehensibly intense—I feel I *must* complete the "snag section" of my story.

Such impulses may be traps, to get me off guard.

I'll listen to the radio. Hope I find a good, steadying program.

That fantastic urge to finish my story!

(*The first lines of the next entry in Alderman's diary are wholly unintelligible—a frantic, automatic scribbling done in great haste. At several places the penpoint has penetrated the paper. Abruptly the message becomes coherent, although the writing speed seems, if anything, to increase. The transition is startling, as though a gibbering lunatic had suddenly put on the glib semblance of sanity. The change in person is also noteworthy, and obviously related to the last line of the preceding entry.*)

The spider-creature noted that contact had been reestablished and coolly asked for more power, although it meant draining the last reserves. It would not do to undershoot the mark this time—there was not enough left for another attempt.

They should succeed, however. The interfering biped had been eliminated, and the other biped was responding beautifully.

How long this moment had been anticipated! How many eons had been spent waiting for the emergence of sufficiently intelligent animals on that faraway planet and their development of adequate radiation excitors—maddeningly slow processes even with telepathic urging! How long, too, at the end, it had taken to select and mold one of the bipeds into a suitably sensitive subject! For a while it had seemed that he was going to escape them by hiding among the crude thought-storms of his duller fellows, but at last he had been tempted into the open. Conditions were right for the establishment of that delicate admixture of physical and mental radiations which opened the door between the stars and built the web across the cosmic chasms.

And now the spider-creature was halfway across that web. Five times already he had crossed it, only to be repulsed at the very end. He must not fail this time. The fate of the world hung on it.

The tractable biped's mind was becoming restive, though not as yet to an alarming degree. Because his conscious mind could not bear the reality of what he was doing, the biped was inscribing it as a fictional account—his customary rationalization.

And now the spider-creature was across the bridge. His transmuted flesh tingled as it began to reassemble, shuddered at the first radiation blasts of this raw, hot planet. It was like being reborn.

The biped's mind was in turmoil. Obviously the crasser, planet-tethered portion of it was straining to gain control and would soon overpower the more sensitive segment—but not soon enough. Dispassionately the spider-creature scanned it and noted: an almost unendurable horror, the intent to set fire to its habitation with an inflammable oil in an effort to injure the invader (that was good—it would destroy evidence), and the further intent to flee as soon as it regained control of its body (that must be prevented—the biped must be overtaken and eliminated; its story would not be believed, but alive it constituted a danger, nevertheless).

The spider-creature broke free, its crossing accomplished. As the mental portion of it underwent the final transformation, it felt its control of the biped's mind snap and it prepared for pursuit.

At that first moment of exultation, however, it felt a twinge of pity for the small, frantic, doomed animal that had helped alter so signally the destiny of its planet.

It could so easily have saved itself. It had only to have resisted one of the telepathic promptings. It had only to have maintained its previous detestation of the voice of the herd. It had only not to have undone the work of defensive sabotage its comrade, in dying, had achieved. It had only not to have repaired the radio.

Final Comment by Willard P. Cronin, M.D., Terrestrial, Montana: The fire at John Wendle's residence was noted at 3:00 A.M. on the morning of January 17th, shortly after the blizzard ended. I was a member of the party that immediately set out to render aid, and was among the first to sight the gutted cabin. In its ruin was discovered a single, badly-charred body, later identified as that of Wendle. There were indications that the fire had been started by the deliberate smashing of a kerosene lamp.

It should be obvious to any rational person that Thomas Alderman's "diary" is the work of an insane mind, and almost certainly fabricated in an effort to shift to other and fabulous shoulders the guilt for a murderous crime, which he also sought to conceal entirely—by arson.

Interrogation of Alderman's former city associates confirms the picture of a weak-minded and antisocial dreamer, a miserable failure in his vocation. Very possibly the motive for his crime was jealousy of a fellow hackwriter who, although his stories

were largely a puerile bilge of pseudoscience designed for immature minds, had at
least some small financial success. As for the similarly childish "story" that Alderman
claimed to be writing, there is no evidence that it even existed, though it is impossible,
of course, to disprove that it did indeed exist and was destroyed in the fire.

Most unfortunately, some of the more lurid details of the "diary" have been
noised around in Terrestrial, giving rise to scare stories among the more ignorant
and credulous inhabitants.

It is equally unfortunate that an uneducated and superstitious miner named
Evans, a member of the rescue party and of the group that followed Alderman's
footprints away from the charred cabin, should have strayed from that group and
shortly returned in panic with a wild account of having found a set of "big, sprawly,
ropey tracks" paralleling Alderman's trail. Doubly unfortunate that a sudden re-
sumption of the snowfall prevented his yarn from being disproved by such visual
evidence as even the most brutish minds must accept.

It is no use pointing out to such low-grade mentalities that no reputable citizen
of Terrestrial has seen anything in the least out of the ordinary in the snowfields,
that no unusual auroras whatever have been reported by meteorologists, and that
there were no radio broadcasts which could possibly have agreed, either in hour or
content, with those "scientific programs" of which Alderman made so much.

With the exasperating and ludicrous consistency characteristic of epidemics of
mass hallucination, stories of "strange tracks" in the snow and distant fleeting
glimpses of "a big black spidery thing" continue to trickle in.

One wishes, with an understandably angry fervor, that the whole episode could
have had the satisfying and all-decisive conclusion that the public trial of Thomas
Alderman would have provided.

That, however, was not to be. About two miles from the cabin, the group following Alderman's footprints came upon his body in the snow. The expression on his
frozen face was sufficient in itself to prove his insanity. One stiff hand, half buried in
the snow, clutched the notebook containing the "diary." On the back of the other,
which was clapped to his frosted eyes, was something that, although furnishing
more fuel for the delusions of morons like Evans, provides the educated and scientific
intellect with a clue as to the source of one of the more bizarre details in Alderman's
fabrication.

This thing on the back of his hand obviously must have been a crude bit of tat-
tooing, though so old and inexpertly done that the characteristic punctures and
discrete dye granules were not apparent.

A few wavy violet lines.

[*Night's Black Agents* (Arkham House, 1947)]

THE DREAMS OF ALBERT MORELAND

I think of the autumn of 1939, not as the beginning of the Second World War, but as the period in which Albert Moreland dreamed the dream. The two events—the war and the dream—are not, however, divorced in my mind. Indeed, I sometimes fear that there is a connection between them, but it is a connection which no sane person will consider seriously, if he is wise.

Albert Moreland was, and perhaps still is, a professional chessplayer. That fact has an important bearing on the dream, or dreams. He made most of his scant income at a games arcade in Lower Manhattan, taking on all comers—the enthusiast who gets a kick out of trying to beat an expert, the lonely man who turns to chess as to a drug, or the down-and-outer tempted into purchasing a half hour of intellectual dignity for a quarter.

After I got to know Moreland, I often wandered into the arcade and watched him playing as many as three or four games simultaneously, oblivious to the clicking and whirring of the pinball games and the intermittent reports from the shooting gallery. He got fifteen cents for every win; the house took the extra dime. When he lost, neither got anything.

Eventually I found out that he was a much better player than he needed to be for his arcade job. He had won casual games from internationally famous masters. A couple of Manhattan clubs had wanted to groom him for the big tournaments, but lack of ambition kept him drifting along in obscurity. I got the impression that he thought chess too trivial a business to warrant serious consideration, although he was perfectly willing to dribble his life away at the arcade, waiting for something really important to come along, if it ever did. Once in a while he eked out his income by playing on a club team, getting as much as five dollars.

I met him at the old brownstone house where we both had rooms on the same floor, and it was there that he first told me about the dream.

We had just finished a game of chess, and I was idly watching the battle-scarred pieces slide off the board and pile up in a fold of the blanket on his cot. Outside a fretful wind eddied the dry grit. There was a surge of traffic noises, and the buzz of a defective neon sign. I had just lost, but I was glad that Moreland never let me win, as he occasionally did with the players at the arcade, to encourage them. Indeed, I thought myself fortunate in being able to play with Moreland at all, not knowing then that I was probably the best friend he had.

I was saying something obvious about chess.

"You think it a complicated game?" he inquired, peering at me with quizzical intentness, his dark eyes like round windows pushed up under heavy eaves. "Well, perhaps it is. But I play a game a thousand times more complex every night in my dreams. And the queer thing is that the game goes on night after night. The same game. I never really sleep. Only dream about the game."

Then he told me, speaking with a mixture of facetious jest and uncomfortable seriousness that was to characterize many of our conversations.

The images of his dream, as he described them, were impressively simple, without any of the usual merging and incongruity. A board so vast he sometimes had to walk out on it to move his pieces. A great many more squares than in chess and arranged in patches of different colors, the power of the pieces varying according to the color of the square on which they stood. Above and to each side of the board only blackness, but a blackness that suggested starless infinity, as if, as he put it, the scene were laid on the very top of the universe.

When he was awake he could not quite remember all the rules of the game, although he recalled a great many isolated points, including the interesting fact that—quite unlike chess—his pieces and those of his adversary did not duplicate each other. Yet he was convinced that he not only understood the game perfectly while dreaming, but also was able to play it in the highly strategic manner of the master chessplayer. It was, he said, as though his night mind had many more dimensions of thought than his waking mind, and were able to grasp intuitively complex series of moves that would ordinarily have to be reasoned out step by step.

"A feeling of increased mental power is a very ordinary dream-delusion, isn't it?" he added, peering at me sharply. "And so I suppose you might say it's a very ordinary dream."

I did not know quite how to take that last remark, so I prodded him with a question.

"What do the pieces look like?"

It turned out that they were similar to those of chess in that they were considerably stylized and yet suggested the original forms—architectural, animal, ornamental—which had served as their inspiration. But there the similarity ended. The inspiring forms, so far as he could guess at them, were grotesque in the extreme. There were terraced towers subtly distorted out of the perpendicular, strangely asymmetric polygons that made him think of temples and tombs, vegetable-animal shapes which defied classification and whose formalized limbs and external organs suggested a variety of unknown functions. The more powerful pieces seemed to be modeled after life forms, for they carried stylized weapons and other implements, and wore things similar to crowns and tiaras—a little like the king, queen and bishop in chess—while the carving indicated voluminous robes and hoods. But they were in no other sense anthropomorphic. Moreland sought in vain for earthly analogies, mentioning Hindu idols, prehistoric reptiles, futurist sculpture, squids bearing daggers in their tentacles, and huge ants and mantes and other insects with fantastically adapted end-organs.

"I think you would have to search the whole universe—every planet and every dead sun—before you could find the original models," he said, frowning. "Remember, there is nothing cloudy or vague about the pieces themselves in my dream. They are as tangible as this rook." He picked up the piece, clenched his fist around it for a moment, and then held it out toward me on his open palm. "It is only in what they suggest that the vagueness lies."

It was strange, but his words seemed to open some dream-eye in my own mind, so that I could almost see the things he described. I asked him if he experienced fear during his dream.

He replied that the pieces one and all filled him with repugnance—those based on higher life forms usually to a greater degree than the architectural ones. He hated to have to touch or handle them. There was one piece in particular which had an intensely morbid fascination for his dream-self. He identified it as "the archer" because the stylized weapon it bore gave the impression of being able to hurt at a distance; but like the rest it was quite inhuman. He described it as representing a kind of intermediate, warped life form which had achieved more than human intellectual power without losing—but rather gaining—in brute cruelty and malignity. It was one of the opposing pieces for which there was no duplicate among his own. The mingled fear and loathing it inspired in him sometimes became so great that they interfered with his strategic grasp of the whole dream-game, and he was afraid his feeling toward it would sometime rise to such a pitch that he would be forced to capture it just to get it off the board, even though such a capture might compromise his whole position.

"God knows how my mind ever cooked up such a hideous entity," he finished, with a quick grin. "Five hundred years ago I'd have said the Devil put it there."

"Speaking of the Devil," I asked, immediately feeling my flippancy was silly, "whom do you play against in your dream?"

Again he frowned. "I don't know. The opposing pieces move by themselves. I will have made a move, and then, after waiting for what seems like an eon, all on edge as in chess, one of the opposing pieces will begin to shake a little and then to wobble back and forth. Gradually the movement increases in extent until the piece gets off balance and begins to rock and careen across the board, like a water tumbler on a pitching ship, until it reaches the proper square. Then, slowly as it began, the movement subsides. I don't know, but it always makes me think of some huge, invisible, senile creature—crafty, selfish, cruel. You've watched that trembly old man at the arcade? The one who always drags the pieces across the board without lifting them, his hand constantly shaking? It's a little like that."

I nodded. His description made it very vivid. For the first time I began to think of how unpleasant such a dream might be.

"And it goes on night after night?" I asked.

"Night after night!" he affirmed with sudden fierceness. "And always the same game. It has been more than a month now, and my forces are just beginning to grapple with the enemy. It's draining off my mental energy. I wish it would stop. I'm getting so that I hate to go to sleep." He paused and turned away. "It seems queer," he said after a moment in a softer voice, smiling apologetically, "it seems queer to get so worked up over a dream. But if you've had bad ones, you know how they can cloud your thoughts all day. And I haven't really managed to get over to you the sort of feeling that trips me while I'm dreaming, and while my brain is working at the game and plotting move-sequence after move-sequence and weighing a thousand complex possibilities. There's repugnance, yes, and fear. I've told you that. But the dominant feeling is one of responsibility. I must not lose the game. More than my own personal welfare depends upon it. There are some terrible stakes involved, though I am never quite sure what they are.

"When you were a little child, did you ever worry tremendously about something, with that complete lack of proportion characteristic of childhood? Did you ever feel that everything, literally everything, depended upon your performing some trivial action, some unimportant duty, in just the right way? Well, while I dream, I have the feeling that I'm playing for some stake as big as the fate of mankind. One wrong move may plunge the universe into unending night. Sometimes, in my dream, I feel sure of it."

His voice trailed off and he stared at the chessmen. I made some remarks and started to tell about an air-raid nightmare I had just had, but it didn't seem very important. And I gave him some vague advice about changing his sleeping habits, which did not seem very important either, although he accepted it with good grace. As I started back to my room he said, "Amusing to think, isn't it, that I'll be playing the game again as soon as my head hits the pillow?" He grinned and added lightly, "Perhaps it will be over sooner than I expect. Lately I've had the feeling that my adversary is about to unleash a surprise attack, although he pretends to be on the defensive."

He grinned again and shut the door.

As I waited for sleep, staring at the wavy churning darkness that is more in the eyes than outside them, I began to wonder whether Moreland did not stand in greater need of psychiatric treatment than most chessplayers. Certainly a person without family, friends, or proper occupation is liable to mental aberrations. Yet he seemed sane enough. Perhaps the dream was a compensation for his failure to use anything like the full potentialities of his highly talented mind, even at chess-playing. Certainly it was a satisfyingly grandiose vision, with its unearthly background and its implications of stupendous mental skill.

There floated into my mind the lines from the *Rubaiyat* about the cosmic chessplayer who, "Hither and thither moves and checks, and slays, And one by one back in the Closet lays."

Then I thought of the emotional atmosphere of his dreams, and the feelings of terror and boundless responsibility, of tremendous duties and cataclysmic consequences—feelings I recognized from my own dreams—and I compared them with the mad, dismal state of the world (for it was October, and sense of utter catastrophe had not yet been dulled) and I thought of the million drifting Morelands suddenly shocked into a realization of the desperate plight of things and of priceless chances lost forever in the past and of their own ill-defined but certain complicity in the disaster. I began to see Moreland's dream as the symbol of a last-ditch, too-late struggle against the implacable forces of fate and chance. And my night thoughts began to revolve around the fancy that some cosmic beings, neither gods nor men, had created human life long ago as a jest or experiment or artistic form, and had now decided to base the fate of their creation on the result of a game of skill played against one of their creatures.

Suddenly I realized that I was wide awake and that the darkness was no longer restful. I snapped on the light and impulsively decided to see if Moreland was still up.

The hall was as shadowy and funereal as that of most boarding houses late at night, and I tried to minimize the inevitable dry creakings. I waited for a few moments in front of Moreland's door, but heard nothing, so instead of knocking, I presumed upon our familiarity and edged open the door, quietly, in order not to disturb him if he were abed.

It was then that I heard his voice, and so certain was my impression that the sound came from a considerable distance that I immediately walked back to the stair-well and called, "Moreland, are you down there?"

Only then did I realize what he had said. Perhaps it was the peculiarity of the words that caused them first to register on my mind as merely a series of sounds.

The words were, "My spider-thing seizes your armor-bearer. I threaten."

It instantly occurred to me that the words were similar in general form to any one of a number of conventional expressions in chess, such as, "My rook captures your bishop. I give check." But there are no such pieces as "spider-things" or "armor-bearers" in chess or any other game I know of.

I automatically walked back toward his room, though I still doubted he was there. The voice had sounded much too far away—outside the building or at least in a remote section of it.

But he was lying on the cot, his upturned face revealed by the light of a distant electric advertisement, which blinked on and off at regular intervals. The traffic sounds, which had been almost inaudible in the hall, made the half-darkness restless and irritably alive. The defective neon sign still buzzed and droned insectlike as it had earlier in the evening.

I tiptoed over and looked down at him. His face, more pale than it should have been because of some quality of the intermittent light, was set in an expression of painfully intense concentration—forehead vertically furrowed, muscles around the eye contracted, lips pursed to a line. I wondered if I ought to awaken him. I was acutely aware of the impersonally murmuring city all around us—block on block of shuttling, routined, aloof existence—

and the contrast made his sleeping face seem all the more sensitive and vividly individual and unguarded, like some soft though purposefully tense organism which has lost its protective shell.

As I waited uncertainly, the tight lips opened a little without losing any of their tautness. He spoke, and for a second time the impression of distance was so compelling that I involuntarily looked over my shoulder and out the dustily glowing window. Then I began to tremble.

"My coiled-thing writhes to the thirteenth square of the green ruler's domain," was what he said, but I can only suggest the quality of the voice. Some inconceivable sort of distance had drained it of all richness and throatiness and overtones so that it was hollow and flat and faint and disturbingly mournful, as voices sometimes sound in open country, or from up on a high roof, or when there is a bad telephone connection. I felt I was the victim of some gruesome deception, and yet I knew that ventriloquism is a matter of motionless lips and clever suggestion rather than any really convincing change in the quality of the voice itself. Without volition there rose in my mind visions of infinite space, unending darkness. I felt as if I were being wrenched up and away from the world, so that Manhattan lay below me like a black asymmetric spearhead outlined by leaden waters, and then still farther outward at increasing speed until earth and sun and stars and galaxies were all lost and I was beyond the universe. To such a degree did the quality of Moreland's voice affect me.

I do not know how long I stood there waiting for him to speak again, with the noises of Manhattan flowing around yet not quite touching me, and the electric sign blinking on and off unalterably like the ticking of a clock. I could only think about the game that was being played, and wonder whether Moreland's adversary had yet made an answering move, and whether things were going for or against Moreland. There was no telling from his face; its intensity of concentration did not change. During those moments or minutes I stood there, I believed implicitly in the reality of the game. As if I myself were somehow dreaming, I could not question the rationality of my belief or break the spell which bound me.

When finally his lips parted a little and I experienced again that impression of impossible, eerie ventriloquism—the words this time being, "My horned-creature vaults over the twisted tower, challenging the archer"—my fear broke loose from whatever controlled it and I stumbled toward the door.

Then came what was, in an oblique way, the strangest part of the whole episode. In the time it took me to walk the length of the corridor back to my room, most of my fear and most of the feeling of complete alienage and other-worldliness which had dominated me while I was watching Moreland's face receded so swiftly that I even forgot, for the time being, how great they had been. I do not know why that happened. Perhaps it was because the unwholesome realm of Moreland's dream was so grotesquely dissimilar to anything in the real world. Whatever the cause, by the time I opened the door to my room I was thinking, "Such nightmares can't be wholesome. Perhaps he should see a psychiatrist. Yet it's only a dream," and so on. I felt tired and stupid. Very soon I was asleep.

But some wraith of the original emotions must have lingered, for I awoke next morning with the fear that something had happened to Moreland. Dressing hurriedly, I knocked at his door, but found the room empty, the bedclothes still rumpled. I inquired of the landlady, and she said he had gone out at eight-fifteen as usual. The bald statement did not quite satisfy my vague anxiety. But since my job-hunting that day happened to lie in the direction of the arcade, I had an excuse to wander in. Moreland was stolidly pushing pieces around with an abstracted, tousle-haired fellow of Slavic features, and casually conducting two rapid-fire checker games on the side. Reassured, I went on without bothering him.

That evening we had a long talk about dreams in general, and I found him surprisingly well-read on the subject and scientifically cautious in his attitudes. Rather to my chagrin, it was I who introduced such dubious topics as clairvoyance, mental telepathy, and the possibility of strange telescopings and other distortions of time and space during dream states. Some foolish reticence about admitting I had pushed my way into his room last night kept me from telling him what I had heard and seen, but he freely told me he had had another installment of the usual dream. He seemed to take a more philosophical attitude now that he had shared his experiences with someone. Together we speculated as to the possible daytime sources of his dream. It was after twelve when we said goodnight.

I went away with the feeling of having been let down—vaguely unsatisfied. I think the fear I had experienced the previous night and then almost forgotten must have been gnawing at me obscurely.

And the following evening it found an avenue of return. Thinking Moreland must be tired of talking about dreams, I coaxed him into a game of chess. But in the middle of the game he put back a piece he was about to move, and said, "You know, that damned dream of mine is getting very bothersome."

It turned out that his dream adversary had finally loosed the long-threatened attack, and that the dream itself had turned into a kind of nightmare. "It's very much like what happens to you in a game of chess," he explained. "You go along confident that you have a strong position and that the game is taking the right direction. Every move your opponent makes is one you have foreseen. You get to feeling almost omniscient. Suddenly he makes a totally unexpected attacking move. For a moment you think it must be a stupid blunder on his part. Then you look a little more closely and realize that you have totally overlooked something and that his attack is a sound one. Then you begin to sweat.

"Of course, I've always experienced fear and anxiety and a sense of overpowering responsibility during the dream. But my pieces were like a wall, protecting me. Now I can see only the cracks in that wall. At any one of a hundred weak points it might conceivably be broken. Whenever one of the opposing pieces begins to wobble and shake, I wonder whether, when its move is completed, there will flash into my mind the unalterable and unavoidable combination of moves leading to my defeat. Last night I thought I saw such a move, and the terror was so great that everything swirled and I seemed to drop through millions of miles of emptiness in an instant. Yet just in that instant of waking I realized I had miscalculated, and that my position, though perilous, was still secure. It was so vivid that I almost carried with me into my waking thoughts the reason why, but then some of the steps in the train of dream-reasoning dropped out, as if my waking mind were not big enough to hold them all."

He also told me that his fixation on "the archer" was becoming increasingly troublesome. It filled him with a special kind of terror, different in quality, but perhaps higher in pitch than that engendered in him by the dream as a whole: a crazy morbid terror, characterized by intense repugnance, nerve-twisting exasperation, and reckless suicidal impulses.

"I can't get rid of the feeling," he said, "that the beastly thing will in some unfair and underhanded manner be the means of my defeat."

He looked very tired to me, although his face was of the compact, tough-skinned sort that does not readily show fatigue, and I felt concern for his physical and nervous welfare. I suggested that he consult a doctor (I did not like to say psychiatrist) and pointed out that sleeping tablets might be of some help.

"But in a deeper sleep the dream might be even more vivid and real," he answered, grimacing sardonically. "No, I'd rather play out the game under the present conditions."

I was glad to find that he still viewed the dream as an interesting and temporary psychological phenomenon (what else he could have viewed it as, I did not stop to analyze). Even while admitting to me the exceptional intensity of his emotions, he maintained something of a jesting air. Once he compared his dream to a paranoid's delusions of persecution, and asked whether I didn't think it was good enough to get him admitted to an asylum.

"Then I could forget the arcade and devote all my time to dream-chess," he said, laughing sharply as soon as he saw I was beginning to wonder whether he had not meant the remark half-seriously.

But some part of my mind was not convinced by his protestations, and when later I tossed in the dark, my imagination perversely kept picturing the universe as a great arena in which each creature is doomed to engage in a losing game of skill against demoniac mentalities which, however long they may play cat and mouse, are always assured of final mastery—or almost assured, so that it would be a miracle if they were beaten. I found myself comparing them to certain chessplayers, who if they cannot beat an opponent by superior skill, will capitalize on unpleasant personal mannerisms in order to exasperate him and break down the lucidity of his thinking.

This mood colored my own nebulous dreams and persisted into the next day. As I walked the streets I felt myself inundated by an omnipresent anxiety, and I sensed taut, nervous misery in each passing face. For once I seemed able to look behind the mask which every person wears and which is so characteristically pronounced in a congested city, and see what lay behind—the egotistical sensitivity, the smouldering irritation, the thwarted longing, the defeat . . . and, above all, the anxiety, too ill-defined and lacking in definite object to be called fear, but nonetheless infecting every thought and action, and making trivial things terrible. And it seemed to me that social, economic, and physiological factors, even Death and the War, were insufficient to explain such anxiety, and that it was in reality an upwelling from something dubious and horrible in the very constitution of the universe.

That evening I found myself at the arcade. Here too I sensed a difference in things, for Moreland's abstraction was not the calculating boredom with which I was familiar, and his tiredness was shockingly apparent. One of his three opponents, after shifting around restlessly, called his attention to a move, and Moreland jerked his head as if he had been dozing. He immediately made an answering move, and quickly lost his queen and the game by a trap that was very obvious even to me. A little later he lost another game by an equally elementary oversight. The boss of the arcade, a big beefy man, ambled over and stood behind Moreland, his heavy-jowled face impassive, seeming to study the position of the pieces in the last game. Moreland lost that too.

"Who won?" asked the boss.

Moreland indicated his opponent. The boss grunted noncommittally and walked off.

No one else sat down to play. It was near closing time. I was not sure whether Moreland had noticed me, but after a while he stood up and nodded at me, and got his hat and coat. We walked the long stretch back to the rooming house. He hardly spoke a word, and my sensation of morbid insight into the world around persisted and kept me silent. He walked as usual with long, slightly stiff-kneed strides, hands in his pockets, hat pulled low, frowning at the pavement a dozen feet ahead.

When we reached the room he sat down without taking off his coat and said, "Of course, it was the dream made me lose those games. When I woke this morning it was terribly vivid, and I almost remembered the exact position and all the rules. I started to make a diagram. . . ."

He indicated a piece of wrapping paper on the table. Hasty crisscrossed lines, incomplete, represented what seemed to be the corner of an indefinitely larger pattern. There were about five hundred squares. On various squares were marks and names standing for pieces, and there were arrows radiating out from the pieces to show their power of movement.

"I got that far. Then I began to forget," he said tiredly, staring at the floor. "But I'm still very close to it. Like a mathematical puzzle you've not quite solved. Parts of the board kept flashing into my mind all day, so that I felt with a little more effort I would be able to grasp the whole. Yet I can't."

His voice changed. "I'm going to lose, you know. It's that piece I call 'the archer.' Last night I couldn't concentrate on the board; it kept drawing my eyes. The worst thing is that it's the spearhead of my adversary's attack. I ache to capture it. But I must not, for it's a kind of catspaw too, the bait of the strategic trap my adversary is laying. If I capture it, I will expose myself to defeat. So I must watch it coming closer and closer—it has an ugly, double-angled sort of hopping move—knowing that my only chance is to sit tight until my adversary overreaches himself and I can counterattack. But I won't be able to. Soon, perhaps tonight, my nerve will crack and I will capture it."

I was studying the diagram with great interest, and only half heard the rest—a description of the actual appearance of "the archer." I heard him say something about "a five-lobed head . . . the head almost hidden by a hood . . . appendages, each with four joints, appearing from under the robe . . . an eight-pronged weapon with wheels and levers about it, and little bag-shaped receptacles, as though for poison . . . posture suggesting it is lifting the weapon to aim it . . . all intricately carved in some lustrous red stone, speckled with violet . . . an expression of bestial, supernatural malevolence. . . ."

Just then all my attention focussed suddenly on the diagram, and I felt a tightening shiver of excitement, for I recognized two familiar names, which I had never heard Moreland mention while awake. "Spider-thing" and "green ruler."

Without pausing to think, I told him of how I had listened to his sleep-talking three nights before, and about the peculiar phrases he had spoken which tallied so well with the entries on the diagram. I poured out my account with melodramatic haste. My discovery of the entries on the diagram, nothing exceptionally amazing in itself, probably made such a great impression on me because I had hitherto strangely forgotten or repressed the intense fear I had experienced when I had watched Moreland sleeping.

Before I was finished, however, I noticed the growing anxiety of his expression, and abruptly realized that what I was saying might not have the best effect on him. So I minimized my recollection of the unwholesome quality of his voice—the overpowering impression of distance—and the fear it engendered in me.

Even so, it was obvious that he had received a severe shock. For a little while he seemed to be on the verge of some serious nervous derangement, walking up and down with fierce, jerky movements, throwing out crazy statements, coming back again and again to the diabolical convincingness of the dream—which my revelation seemed to have intensified for him—and finally breaking down into vague appeals for help.

Those appeals had an immediate effect on me, making me forget any wild thoughts of my own and putting everything on a personal level. All my instincts were now to aid Moreland, and I once again saw the whole matter as something for a psychiatrist to handle. Our roles had changed. I was no longer the half-awed listener, but the steadying friend to whom he turned for advice. That, more than anything, gave me a feeling of confidence and made my previous speculations seem childish and unhealthy. I felt contemptuous of myself for having encouraged his delusive trains of imagination, and I did as much as I could to make up for it.

After a while my repeated reassurances seemed to take effect. He grew calm and our talk became reasonable once more, though every now and then he would appeal to me about some particular point that worried him. I discovered for the first time the extent to which he had taken the dream seriously. During his lonely broodings, he told me, he had sometimes become convinced that his mind left his body while he slept and traveled immeasurable distances to some transcosmic realm where the game was played. He had the illusion, he said, of getting perilously close to the innermost secrets of the universe and finding they were rotten and evil and sardonic. At times he had been terribly afraid that the pathway between his mind and the realm of the game would "open up" to such a degree that he would be "sucked up bodily from the world," as he put it. His belief that loss of the game would doom the world itself had been much stronger than he had ever admitted to me previously. He had traced a frightening relationship between the progress of the game and of the War, and had begun to believe that the ultimate issue of the War—though not necessarily the victory of either side—hung on the outcome of the game.

At times it had got so bad, he revealed, that his only relief had been in the thought that, no matter what happened, he could never convince others of the reality of his dream. They would always be able to view it as a manifestation of insanity or overwrought imagination. No matter how vivid it became to him he would never have concrete, objective proof.

"It's this way," he said. "You saw me sleeping, didn't you? Right here on this cot. You heard me talk in my sleep, didn't you? About the game. Well, that absolutely proves to you that it's all just a dream, doesn't it? You couldn't rightly believe anything else, could you?"

I do not know why those last ambiguous questions of his should have had such a reassuring effect on me of all people, who had only three nights ago trembled at the indescribable quality of his voice as he talked from his dream. But they did. They seemed like the final seal on an agreement between us to the effect that the dream was only a dream and meant nothing. I began to feel rather buoyant and self-satisfied, like a doctor who has just pulled his patient through a dangerous crisis. I talked to Moreland in what I now realize was almost a pompously sympathetic way, without noticing how dispirited were his obedient nods of agreement. He said little after those last questions.

I even persuaded him to go out to a nearby lunchroom for a midnight snack, as if—God help me!—I were celebrating my victory over the dream. As we sat at the not-too-dirty counter, smoking our cigarettes and sipping burningly hot coffee, I noticed that he had begun to smile again, which added to my satisfaction. I was blind to the ultimate dejection and submissive hopelessness that lay behind those smiles. As I left him at the door of his room, he suddenly caught hold of my hand and said, "I want to tell you how grateful I am for the way you've worked to pull me out of this mess." I made a deprecating gesture. "No wait," he continued. "It does mean a lot. Well, anyway, thanks."

I went away with a contented, almost virtuous feeling. I had no apprehensions whatever. I only mused, in a heavily philosophic way, over the strange forms fear and anxiety can assume in our pitiably tangled civilization.

As soon as I was dressed next morning, I rapped briskly at his door and impulsively pushed in without waiting for an answer. For once sunlight was pouring through the dusty window.

Then I saw it, and everything else receded.

It was lying on the crumpled bedclothes, half hidden by a fold of blanket, a thing perhaps ten inches high, as solid as any statuette, and as undeniably real. But from the first glance I knew that its form bore no relation to any earthly creature. This fact would have been as apparent to someone who knew nothing of art as to an expert. I also knew that the red, violet-flecked substance from which it had been carved or cast had no classification among the earthly gems and minerals. Every detail was there. The five-lobed head, almost hidden by a hood. The appendages, each with four joints, appearing from under the robe. The eight-pronged weapon with wheels and levers about it, and the little bag-shaped receptacles, as though for poison. Posture suggesting it was lifting the weapon to aim it. An expression of bestial, supernatural malevolence.

Beyond doubting, it was the thing of which Moreland had dreamed. The thing which had horrified and fascinated him, as it now did me, which had rasped unendurably on his nerves, as it now began to rasp on mine. The thing which had been the spearhead and catspaw of his adversary's attack, and whose capture—and it now seemed evident that it had been captured—meant the probable loss of the game. The thing which had somehow been sucked back along an ever-opening path across unimaginable distances from a realm of madness ruling the universe.

Beyond doubting, it was "the archer."

Hardly knowing what moved me, save fear, or what my purpose was, I fled from the room. Then I realized that I must find Moreland. No one had seen him leaving the house. I searched for him all day. The arcade. Chess clubs. Libraries.

It was evening when I went back and forced myself to enter his room. The figure was no longer there. No one at the house professed to know anything about it when I questioned them, but some of the denials were too angry, and I know that "the archer," being obviously a thing of value and having no overly great terrors for those who do not know its history, has most probably found its way into the hands of some wealthy and eccentric collector. Other things have vanished by a similar route in the past.

Or it may be that Moreland returned secretly and took it away with him.

But I am certain that it was not made on earth.

And although there are reasons to fear the contrary, I feel that somewhere—in some cheap boarding house or lodging place, or in some madhouse—Albert Moreland, if the game is not already lost and the forfeiture begun, is still playing that unbelievable game for stakes it is unwholesome to contemplate.

[*Night's Black Agents* (Arkham House, 1947)]

THE DEAD MAN

Professor Max Redford opened the frosted glass door of the reception room and beckoned to me. I followed him eagerly. When the most newsworthy doctor at one of America's foremost medical schools phones a popular-science writer and asks him to drop over, but won't tell him why, there is cause for excitement. Especially when that doctor's researches, though always well-founded, have tended toward the sensational. I remembered the rabbits so allergic to light that an open shade raised blisters on their shaved skins, the hypnotized heart patient whose blood-pressure slowly changed, the mold that fed on blood clots in a living animal's brain. Fully half my best articles with a medical slant came from Max. We had been rather close friends for several years.

As we hurried along the hushed corridor, he suddenly asked me, "What is death?"

That wasn't the sort of question I was expecting. I gave him a quick look. His bullet-shaped head, with its shock of close-cropped grizzled hair, was hunched forward. The eyes behind the thick lenses were bright, almost mischievous. He was smiling.

I shrugged.

"I have something to show you," he said.

"What, Max?"

"You'll see."

"A story?"

He shook his head. "At present I don't want a word released to the public or the profession."

"But some day—?" I suggested.

"Maybe one of the biggest."

We entered his office. On the examination table lay a man, the lower half of his body covered by a white sheet. He seemed to be asleep.

Right there I got a shock. For although I hadn't the faintest idea who the man was, I did recognize him. I was certain that I had seen that handsome face once before—through the French windows of the living room of Max's home, some weeks ago. It had been pressed passionately to the face of Velda, Max's attractive young wife, and those arms had been cradling her back. Max and I had just arrived at his lonely suburban place after a long evening session at the laboratory, and he had been locking the car when I glanced through the window. When we had got inside, the man had been gone, and Max had greeted

Velda with his usual tenderness. I had been bothered by the incident, but of course there had been nothing I could do about it.

I turned from the examination table, trying to hide my surprise. Max sat down at his desk and began to rap on it with a pencil. Nervous excitement, I supposed.

From the man on the examination table, now behind me, came a dry, hacking cough.

"Take a look at him," said Max, "and tell me what disease he's suffering from."

"I'm no doctor," I protested.

"I know that, but there are some symptoms that should have an obvious meaning even to a layman."

"But I didn't even notice he was ill," I said.

Max goggled his eyes at me. "You didn't?"

Shrugging my shoulders, I turned—and wondered how in the world I could have missed it at the first glance. I supposed I had been so flustered at recognizing the man that I hadn't noticed anything about him—I had been seeing the memory image more than the actual person. For Max was right. Anyone could have hazarded a diagnosis of this case. The general pallor, the hectic spots of color over the cheek bones, the emaciated wrists, the prominent ribs, the deep depressions around the collar bones, and above all the continued racking cough that even as I watched brought a bit of blood specked mucous to the lips—all pointed at an advanced stage of chronic tuberculosis. I told Max so.

Max stared at me thoughtfully, rapping again on the table. I wondered if he sensed what I was trying to hide from him. Certainly I felt very uncomfortable. The presence of that man, presumably Velda's lover, in Max's office, unconscious and suffering from a deadly disease, and Max so sardonic-seeming and full of suppressed excitement, and then that queer question he had asked me about death—taken all together, they made a peculiarly nasty picture.

What Max said next didn't help either.

"You're quite sure it's tuberculosis?"

"Naturally I could be wrong," I admitted uneasily. "It might be some other disease with the same symptoms or—" I had been about to say, "or the effects of some poison," but I checked myself. "But the symptoms are there, unmistakably," I finished.

"You're positive?" He seemed to enjoy drawing it out.

"Of course!"

He smiled. "Take another look."

"I don't need to," I protested. For the first time in our relationship I was wondering if there wasn't something extremely unpleasant about Max.

"Take one, just the same."

Unwillingly I turned—and for several moments there was room in my mind for nothing but astonishment.

"What kind of trick is this?" I finally asked Max, shakily.

For the man on the examination table had changed. Unmistakably the same man, though for a moment I questioned even that, for now instead of the cadaverous spectre of tuberculosis, a totally different picture presented itself. The wrists, so thin a minute ago, were now swollen, the chest had become so unhealthily puffy that the ribs and collar bones were lost to view, the skin had a bluish tinge, and from between the sagging lips came a labored, wheezy breathing.

I still had a sense of horror, but now it was overlaid with an emotion that can be even stronger, an emotion that can outweigh all considerations of human personality and morals: the excitement of scientific discovery. Whoever this man was, whatever Max's motives might be, whatever unsuspected strain of evil there might exist deep in his nature, he had *hit* on something here, something revolutionary. I didn't know what it was, but my heart pounded and little chills of excitement chased over my skin.

Max refused to answer any of the questions I bombarded him with. All he would do was sit back and smile at me and say, "And now, after your second look, what do you think's wrong with him?"

He finally badgered me into making a statement.

"Well of course there's something fishy about it, but if you insist, here's my idea: Heart disease, perhaps caused by kidney trouble. In any case, something badly out of order with his pump—"

Max's smile was infuriatingly bland. Again he rapped with his pencil, like some supercilious teacher.

"You're sure of that?" he prodded.

"Just as sure as I was the first time that it was tuberculosis."

"Well, take another look . . . and meet John Fearing."

I turned, and almost before I realized it, my hand had been firmly clasped and was being vigorously shaken by that of one of the finest physical specimens I have ever seen. I remember thinking dazedly, "Yes, he's as incredibly handsome and beautifully built as he seemed to me when I glimpsed him kissing Velda. And along with it a strange sort of smoothness, like you felt in Rudolf Valentino. No wonder a woman might find him irresistible."

"I could have introduced you to John long ago," Max was saying. "He lives right near us, with his mother, and often drops over. But, well . . ." he chuckled, ". . . I've been a little jealous about John. I haven't introduced him to anyone connected with the profession. I've wanted to keep him to myself until we got a little further along with our experiments.

"And, John," Max went on, "this is Fred Alexander, the writer. He's one science popularizer who never strays a hairsbreadth into sensationalism and who takes infinite pains to make his reporting accurate. We can trust him not to breathe a word about out experiments until we tell him to. I've been thinking for some time now that we ought to let a third person in on our work, and I didn't want it to be a scientist or yet an ordinary layman. Fred here struck me as having just the right sort of general knowledge and sympathetic approach. So I rang him up—and I believe we've succeeded in giving him quite a surprise."

"You certainly have," I agreed fervently.

John Fearing dropped my hand and stepped back. I was still running my eyes over his marvellously proportioned, athletic body. I couldn't spot a trace of the symptoms of the two dreadful diseases that had seemed to be wracking it minutes ago, or of any other sort of ill health. As he stood there so coolly, with the sheet loosely caught around his waist and falling in easy folds, it seemed to me that he might well be the model for one of the great classical Greek statues. His eyes had something of the same tranquil, ox-like, "all-body" look.

Turning toward Max, I was conscious of a minor shock. I had never thought of Max as ugly. If I'd ever thought of him at all in regard to looks, it had been as a man rather youthful for his middle age, stalwart, and with pleasingly rugged features.

Now, compared to Fearing, Max seemed a humped and dark-browed dwarf.

But this feeling of mine was immediately swallowed up in my excited curiosity.

Fearing looked at Max. "What diseases did I do this time," he asked casually.

"Tuberculosis and nephritis," Max told him. They both acted pleased. In fact, mutual trust and affection showed so plainly in their manner toward each other that I was inclined to dismiss my suspicions of some sinister underlying hatred.

After all, I told myself, the embrace I had witnessed might have been merely momentary physical intoxication on the part of the two young and lovely people, if it had been even that much. Certainly what Max had said about his desire to keep Fearing a secret from his friends and colleagues might very well explain why Fearing had disappeared that night. On the other hand, if a deeper and less fleeting feeling did exist between Max's pretty wife and protégé, Max might very well be aware of it and inclined to condone it. I knew him to be a remarkably tolerant man in some respects. In any case, I had probably exaggerated the importance of the matter.

And I certainly didn't want any such speculations distracting my thoughts now, when I was bending all my mental efforts to comprehend the amazing experiment that had just been conducted before my eyes.

Suddenly I got a glimmer of part of it.

"Hypnotism?" I asked Max.

He nodded, beaming.

"And the pencil-rappings were 'cues'? I mean, signals for him to carry out instructions given to him in an earlier stage of the trance?"

"That's right."

"I seem to recall now," I said, "that the raps were different in each case. I suppose each combination of raps was hooked up with a special set of instructions you'd given him."

"Exactly," said Max. "John won't respond until he gets the right signal. It seems a rather complicated way of going about it, but it isn't really. You know how a sergeant will give his men a set of orders and then bark out 'March!'? Well, the raps are John's marching signals. It works out better than giving him the instructions at the same time he's supposed to be carrying them out. Besides," and he looked at me roguishly, "it's a lot more dramatic."

"I'll say it is!" I assured him. "Max, let's get to the important point. How in the world did John fake those symptoms?"

Max raised his hands. "I'll explain everything. I didn't call you in just to mystify you. Sit down."

I hurriedly complied. Fearing effortlessly lifted himself onto the edge of the examination table and sat there placidly attentive, forearms loosely dropped along his thighs.

"As you know," Max began, "it's a well-established fact that the human mind can create all sorts of tangible symptoms of disease, without the disease itself being present in any way. Statistics show that about half the people who consult doctors are suffering from such imaginary ailments."

"Yes," I protested, "but the symptoms are never so extreme, or created with such swiftness. Why, there was even blood in the mucous. And those swollen wrists—"

Again Max raised his hands. "The difference is only one of degree. Please hear me out.

"Now John here," he continued, "is a very well adjusted, healthy-minded person, but a few years ago he was anything but that." He looked at Fearing, who nodded his agreement. "No, our John was a regular bad boy of the hospitals. Rather, his subconscious mind was, for of course there is no question of faking in these matters, the individual sincerely believes that he is sick. At all events, our John seemed to go through an unbelievable series of dangerous illnesses that frightened his mother to distraction and baffled his doctors, until it was realized that the illnesses were of emotional origin. That discovery wasn't made for a long time because of the very reason you mentioned—the unusual severity of the symptoms.

"However in the end it was the extraordinary power of John's subconscious to fake symptoms that gave the show away. It began to fake the symptoms of too many diseases, the onsets and recoveries were too fast, it jumped around too much. And then it made the mistake of faking the symptoms of germ diseases, when laboratory tests showed that the germs in question weren't present.

"The truth having been recognized, John was put in the hands of a competent psychiatrist, who eventually succeeded in straightening out the personality difficulties that had caused him to seek refuge in sickness. They turned out to be quite simple ones—an overprotective and emotionally demanding mother and a jealous and unaffectionate father, whose death a few years back had burdened John with guilt feelings.

"It was at that time—just after the brilliant success of the psychiatrist's treatment—that I ran across the case. It happened through Velda. She became friends with the Fearings, mother and son, when they moved into our neighborhood, and she visited with them a lot."

As he said that, I couldn't resist shooting a quick glance at Fearing, but I couldn't see any signs of uneasiness or smugness. I felt rather abashed.

"One evening when John was over at our place, he mentioned his amazing history of imaginary illnesses, and pretty soon I wormed the whole story out of him. I was immediately struck with something about his case that the other doctors had missed. Or if they had noticed it, they hadn't seen the implications—or the possibilities.

"Here was a person whose body was fantastically obedient to the dictates of his subconscious mind. All people are to some degree psychosomatic, to give it its technical name—you know, *psyche* and *soma*, mind and body. But our John was psychosomatic to a vastly greater degree. One in a million. Perhaps unique.

"Very likely some rare hereditary strain was responsible for this. I don't believe John will be angry with me if I tell you that his mother used to be— she's really changed herself a great deal under the psychiatrist's guidance— but that she used to be an excessively hysterical and emotionally tempestuous person, with all sorts of imaginary ailments herself, though not as extreme as John's, of course. And his father was almost exactly the same type."

"That's quite fight, Dr. Redford," Fearing said earnestly.

Max nodded. "Apparently the combination of these two hereditary strains in John produced far more than a doubling of his parents' sensitivities.

"Just as the chameleon inherits a color-changing ability that other animals lack, so John has inherited a degree of psychosomatic control that is not apparent in other people—at least not without some kind of psychological training of which at present I have only a glimmering.

"All this was borne in on me as I absorbed John's story, hanging on every word. You know, I think both John and Velda were quite startled at the intensity of my interest." Max chuckled. "But they didn't realize that I was on to something. Here, right in my hands, was a person with, to put it popularly, only the most tenuous of boundaries between his mental and material atoms—for of course, as you know, both mind and matter are ultimately electrical in nature. Our John's subconscious mind had perfect control of his heart-beat and circulatory system. It could flood his tissues with fluids, producing instant swellings, or dehydrate them, giving the effect of emaciation. It could play on his internal organs and ductless glands as if they were musical instruments, creating any life-time it wanted. It could produce horrible discords, turn John into an idiot, say, or an invalid, as it tried to do, or perhaps an acromegalic monster, with gigantic hands and head, by stimulating bone-growth after maturity.

"Or his subconscious mind could keep all his organs in perfect tune, making him the magnificently healthy creature you see today."

I looked at John Fearing and realized that my earlier impression of the excellence of his physique had, if anything, fallen short of the mark. It wasn't just that he was a clear-eyed, unblemished, athletically-built young man. There was more to it than that—something intangible. It occurred to me that if any man could be said to radiate health, in the literal meaning of that ridiculous cliché, it was John Fearing. I knew it was just my imagination, but I seemed to see a pulsating, faintly golden aura about him.

And his mind appeared to be in as perfect balance as his body. He was wonderfully poised as he sat there with just the sheet pulled around him. Not the faintest suggestion of nerves. Completely alive, yet in a sense completely impassive.

It was only too easy to imagine such a man making love successfully, with complete naturalness and confidence, without any of the little haltings and clumsinesses, the jarrings of rhythm, the cowardices of body, the treacheries of mind that betray the average neurotic—which is to say, the average person. Suddenly it hit me, right between the eyes as they say, that Velda *must* love John, that no woman could avoid becoming infatuated with such a man. Not just a football star or a muscle maniac, but a creature infinitely subtler.

And yet, in spite of all this, I was conscious of something a shade repellant about Fearing. Perhaps it was that he seemed too well-balanced, too smooth-running, like a gleaming dynamo say, or a beautiful painting without that little touch of ugliness or dashing contrast which creates individuality. In most people, too, one senses the eternal conflict between the weak and indecisive tyrant Mind and the stubborn and rebellious slave Body, but in Fearing the conflict seemed completely absent, which struck me as unpleasant. There was a kind of deep-seated toughness about him, a suggestion of indestructibility. One might have said, "He'd make a nasty ghost."

Of course all this may just have been envy on my part for Fearing's poise and physique, or some sort of jealousy I felt on Max's account.

But whatever the sources of my feeling of revulsion, I now began to believe that Max shared it. Not that Max had slackened in his genial, affectionate, almost fatherly manner toward John, but that he was so effortful about it. Those elephantine "our Johns," for example. I didn't get the feeling that he was concealing a jealous hatred, however, but that he was earnestly fighting an irrational inward aversion.

As for Fearing, he seemed completely unaware of any hostile feeling on Max's part. His manner was completely open and amiable.

For that matter, I wondered if Max himself were aware of his own feeling. All these thoughts didn't take much time. I was intent on Max's story.

Max leaned across the desk. He was blinking, excitedly, which, with his glasses, gave an odd effect of flashing eyes.

"My imagination was stirred," he went on. "There was no end to the things that might be learned from such a super-psychosomatic individual. We could study disease symptoms under perfect conditions, by producing them in controlled amounts in a healthy individual. All sorts of physiological mysteries could be explored. We could trace out the exact patterns of all the nervous processes that are normally beyond the mind's reach Then if we could learn to impart John's ability to other people—but that's getting a bit ahead of my story.

"I talked to John. He saw my point, realized the service he might render mankind, and gladly agreed to undergo some experiments.

"But at the first attempt a snag appeared. John could not produce any symptoms by a conscious effort, no matter how hard he tried. As I said before, you can't consciously fake a psychosomatic illness, and that was what I was asking John to do. And since he'd undergone psychiatric treatment his subconscious mind was so well behaved that it wouldn't yield to any ordinary blandishments.

"At that point we almost gave up the project. But then I thought of a way we might be able to get around the snag: suggestions given directly to the subconscious mind through hypnotism.

"John proved a good hypnotic subject. We tried it—and it worked!"

Max's eyes looked bright as stars as he said that.

"That's about how matters stand today," he finished off, sinking back in his chair. "We've started a little special work on arterial tension, the lymphatic glands and their nerve supply, one or two other things. But mainly we've been perfecting our setup, getting used to the hypnotic relationship. The important work still lies ahead."

I exhaled appreciatively. Then an unpleasant thought struck me. I wasn't going to voice it, but Max asked, "What is it, Fred?" and I couldn't think of anything else to say, and after all it was a thought that would have occurred to anyone.

"Well, with all this creation of extreme symptoms," I began, "isn't there a certain amount of—"

Max supplied the word. "Danger?" He shook his head. "We are always very careful."

"And in any case," Fearing's bell-like voice broke in, "the possibilities being what they are, I would consider almost any risks worth running." He smiled cheerfully.

The double meaning I momentarily fancied in his words nettled me. I went on impulsively, "But surely some people would be apt to consider it extremely dangerous. Your mother, for instance, or Velda."

Max looked at me sharply.

"Neither my mother nor Mrs. Redford know anything of the extent of our experiments," Fearing assured me.

There was a pause. Unexpectedly, Max grinned at me, stretched, and said to Fearing, "How do you feel now?"

"Perfectly fit."

"Feel up to another little demonstration?"

"Certainly."

"That reminds me, Max," I said abruptly, "out in the corridor you mentioned something about—"

He shot me a warning glance.

"We'll go into that some other time," he said.

"What diseases are you going to have me do this time?" Fearing queried.

Max wagged his finger. "You know you're never told that. Can't have your conscious mind messing things up. We'll have some new signals, though. And, Fred, I hope you won't mind waiting outside while I put John under and give him his instructions—acquaint him with the new signals. I'm afraid we still haven't gotten far along enough to risk the possibly disturbing presence of a third person during the early stages of an experiment. One or two more sessions and it should be all right, though. Understand, Fred, this is just the first of a large number of experiments I want you to witness. I'm asking a great deal of you, you see. The only tangible compensation I can offer you is exclusive rights to break the story to the public when we feel the time is ripe."

"Believe me, I consider it a great honor," I assured him sincerely as I went out.

In the corridor I lit a cigarette, puffed it a moment, and then the tremendous implications of Max's experiments really hit me.

Suppose, as Max had hinted, that it proved possible to impart Fearing's ability to other people?

The benefits would be incalculable. People would be able to help their bodies in the fight against disease and degenerative processes. For instance, they could cut down the flow of blood from a wound, or even stop it completely. They could marshal all the body's resources to fight local infections and stop disease germs before they ever got started. Conceivably, they could heal sick organs, get them working in the right rhythm, unharden arteries, avert or stifle cancers.

It might be possible to prevent disease, even ageing, altogether.

We might look forward to a race of immortals, immune to time and decay.

A happy race, untroubled by those conflicts of body and mind, of instinct and conscience, that sap Mankind's best energies and are at the root of all discords and wars.

There was literally no limit to the possibilities.

I hardly felt I'd been in the corridor a minute, my mind was soaring so, when Max softly opened the door and beckoned to me.

Again Fearing lay stretched on the table. His eyes were closed, but he still looked every whit as vibrantly healthy as before. His chest rose and fell rhythmically with his breathing. I almost fancied I could see the blood coursing under the fair skin.

I was aware of a tremendous suppressed excitement in Max.

"We can talk, of course," he said. "Best keep it low, though."

"He's hypnotized?" I asked.

"Yes."

"And you've given him the instructions?"

"Yes. Watch."

"What are they this time, Max?"

Max's lips jerked oddly.

"Just watch."

He rapped with the pencil.

I watched. For five, ten seconds nothing seemed to happen.

Fearing's chest stopped moving.

His skin was growing pale.

There was a weak convulsive shudder. His eyelids fell open, showing only the whites. Then there was no further movement whatever.

"Approach him," Max ordered, his voice thick. "Take his pulse."

Almost shaking with excitement, I complied.

To my fumbling fingers, Fearing's wrist felt cold. I could not find a pulse.

"Fetch that mirror," Max's finger stabbed at a nearby shelf. "Hold it to his lips and nostrils."

The polished surface remained unclouded.

I backed away. Wonder gave place to fear. All my worst suspicions returned intensified. Once again I seemed to sense a strain of submerged evil in my friend.

"I told you I would show you something with a bearing on the question, 'What is death?'" Max was saying huskily. "Here you see death perfectly counterfeited—death-in-life. I would defy any doctor in the world to prove this man alive." There was a note of triumph in his voice.

My own was uneven with horror. "You instructed him to be dead?"

"Yes."

"And he didn't know it ahead of time?"

"Of course not."

For an interminable period—perhaps three or four seconds—I stared at the blanched form of Fearing. Then I turned to Max.

"I don't like this," I said. "Get him out of it."

There was something sneering about the smile he gave me.

"Watch!" He commanded fiercely, and rapped again.

It was only some change in the light, I told myself, that was giving Fearing's flesh a greenish tinge.

Then I saw the limp arms and legs stiffen and the face tighten into a sardonic mask.

"Touch him!"

Unwillingly, only to get the thing over with as swiftly as possible, I obeyed. Fearing's arm felt stiff as a board and, if anything, colder than before.

Rigor Mortis.

But that faint odor of putrescence—I knew that could only be my imagination.

"For God's sake, Max," I pleaded, "you've got to get him out of it." Then, throwing aside reserve, "I don't know what you're trying to do, but you can't. Velda—"

Max jerked as I spoke the name. Instantly the terrifying shell that had gathered around him seemed to drop away. It was as if that one word had roused him from a dream. "Of course," he said, in his natural voice. He smiled reassuringly and rapped.

Eagerly I watched Fearing.

Max rapped again: Three—one.

It takes time, I told myself. Now the muscles were beginning to relax, weren't they?

But Max was rapping again. The signal printed itself indelibly on my brain: three—one.

And yet again. Three—one. Three—one. THREE—ONE.

I looked at Max. In his tortured expression I read a ghastly certainty.

I wouldn't ever want to relive the next few hours. I imagine that in all history there was never a trick conceived for reviving the dying that Max didn't employ, along with all the modern methods—injections, even into the heart itself, electrical stimulation, use of a new lightweight plastic version of the iron lung, surgical entry into the chest and direct massage of the heart.

Whatever suspicions I had had of Max vanished utterly during those hours. The frantic genuineness and inspired ingenuity of his efforts to revive Fearing couldn't possibly have been faked. No more could his tragic, rigidly suppressed grief have been simulated. I saw Max's emotion stripped to the raw during those hours, and they were all good.

One of the first things he did was to call in several of the other faculty doctors. They helped him, though I could tell that from the first they looked upon the case as hopeless, and would have considered the whole business definitely irregular, if it hadn't been for their extreme loyalty to Max, far beyond any consideration of professional solidarity. Their attitude showed me, as nothing else ever had, Max's stature as a medical man.

Max was completely frank with them and everyone else. He made no effort whatsoever to suppress the slightest detail of the events leading up to the tragedy. He was bitter in his self-accusations, insisting that his judgment had been unforgivably at fault in the final experiment. He would have gone even further than that if it hadn't been for his colleagues. It was they who dissuaded him from resigning from the faculty and describing his experiments in such inaccurately harsh terms as to invite criminal prosecution.

And then there was Max's praiseworthy behavior toward Fearing's mother. While they were still working on Fearing, though without any real hope, she burst in. Whatever reforms the psychiatrist may have achieved in her personality were washed out now. I still can close my eyes and visualize that hateful, overdressed woman stamping around like an angry parrot, screaming the vilest accusations at Max at the top of her voice and talking about her son and herself in the most disgusting terms. But although he was near the breaking point, Max was never anything but compassionate toward her, accepting all the blame she heaped on his head.

A little later Velda joined Max. If I'd still had any of my early suspicions, her manner would have dissipated them. She was completely practical and self-possessed, betraying no personal concern whatsoever in Fearing's death. If anything, she was too cool and unmoved. But that may have been what Max needed at the time.

The next days were understandably difficult. While most of the newspapers were admirably reserved and judicious in reporting the case, one of the tabloids played up Max as "The Doctor Who Ordered a Man to Die," featuring an exclusive interview with Fearing's mother.

The chorus of wild bleats from various anti-science cults was of course to be expected. It led to a number of stories that crept into the fringe of print and would have been more unpleasant if they hadn't been so ridiculous. One man, evidently drawing on Poe's story, "The Facts in the Case of M. Valdemar," demanded that a "death watch" be maintained on Fearing and, on the morning of the funeral, hinted darkly that they were interring a man who was somehow still alive.

Even the medical profession was by no means wholly behind Max. A number of local doctors, unconnected with the medical school, were severe in their criticisms of him. Such sensational experiments reflected on the profession, were of doubtful value in any case, and so forth. Though none of these criticisms were released to the public.

The funeral was held on the third day. I attended it out of friendship for Max, who felt it his duty to be present. Fearing's mother was there, of course, dressed in a black outfit that somehow managed to look loud and common. Since the tabloid interview there had been a complete break between her and our group, so that her wailing tirades and nauseous sobbing endearments could only be directed at the empty air and the bronze-fitted casket.

Max looked old. Velda stood beside him, holding his arm. She was as impassive as on the day of Fearing's death.

There was only one odd thing about her behavior. She insisted that we remain at the cemetery until the casket had been placed in the tomb and the workman had fixed in place the marble slab that closed it. She watched the whole process with a dispassionate intentness.

I thought that perhaps she did it on Max's account, to impress on him that the whole affair was over and done with. Or she may conceivably have feared some unlikely final demonstration or foray on the part of the wilder anti-science groups and felt that the presence of a few intelligent witnesses was advisable to prevent some final garish news item from erupting into print.

And there may actually have been justification for such a fear. Despite the efforts of the cemetery authorities, a number of the morbidly curious managed to view the interment and as I accompanied Max and Velda the few blocks to their home, there were altogether too many people roaming the quiet, rather ill-kempt streets of the scantily populated suburb. Undoubtedly we were being followed and pointed at. When, with feelings of considerable relief, we finally got inside, there was a sharp, loud knock on the door we had just closed.

Someone had thrown a stone at the house.

For the next six months I saw nothing of Max. Actually this was as much due to my friendship for him as to the press of my work, which did keep me usually busy at the time. I felt that Max didn't want to be reminded in any way, even by the presence of a friend, of the tragic accident that had clouded his life.

I think, you see, that only I, and perhaps a few of Max's most imaginative colleagues, had any inkling of how hard Max had been hit by the experience and, especially, *why* it had hit him so hard. It wasn't so much that he had caused the death of a man through a perhaps injudicious experiment. That was the smaller part. It was that, in so doing, he had wrecked a line of research that promised tremendous benefits to mankind. Fearing, you see, was irreplaceable. As Max had said, he was probably unique. And their work had been barely begun. Max had obtained almost no results of a measured scientific nature and he hadn't as yet any ideas whatever of the crucial thing: how to impart Fearing's ability to other people, if that were possible. Max was a realist. To his clear, unsuperstitious mind, the death of one man was not nearly so important as the loss of possible benefits to millions. That he had played fast and loose with humanity's future—yes, he'd have put it that way—was, I knew, what hurt him most. It would be a long time before he regained his old enthusiasm.

One morning I ran across a news item stating that Fearing's mother had sold her house and gone for a European tour.

Of Velda I had no information.

Naturally I recalled the affair from time to time, turning it over in my mind. I reviewed the suspicions I'd had at the time, seeking some clue that might have escaped me, but always coming to the conclusion that the suspicions were more than wiped out by Max's tragic sincerity and Velda's composure after the event.

I tried to visualize the weird and miraculous transformations I had witnessed in Max's office. Somehow, try as I might, they began to seem more and more unreal. I had been excited that morning, I told myself, and my mind had exaggerated what I had seen. This unwillingness to trust my own memory filled me at times with a strange poignant grief, perhaps similar to what Max must have felt at the breakdown of his research, as if some marvelous imaginative vision had faded from the world.

And occasionally I pictured Fearing as I'd seen him that morning, so radiantly healthy, his mind and body so unshakably knit. It was very hard to think of a man like that being dead.

Then, after six months, I received a brief message from Max. If I were free, would I visit him at his home that evening? Nothing more.

I felt a thrill of elation. Perhaps the period of thralldom to the past was over and the brilliant old mind was getting to work again. I had to break an engagement, but of course I went.

It had just stopped raining when I swung down from the interurban. Remnants of daylight showed a panorama of dripping trees, weed-bordered sidewalks, and gloom-invested houses. Max had happened to build in one of those subdivisions that doesn't quite make the grade, while the unpredictable pulse of suburban life begins to beat more strongly farther out.

I passed the cemetery in which Fearing had been interred. The branches of unpruned trees brushed the wall, making sections of the sidewalk a leafy tunnel. I was glad I had a flashlight in my pocket for the walk back. It occurred to me that it was unfortunate Max had this unnecessary reminder almost on his doorstep.

I walked rapidly past houses that were more and more frequently separated by empty lots, and along a sidewalk that became progressively more cracked and weed-grown. There popped into my mind a conversation I had had with Max a couple of years ago. I had asked him if Velda didn't find it lonely out here, and he had laughingly assured me that both he and Velda had a passion for being alone and liked to be as far away as possible from spying neighbors.

I wondered if one of the houses I had passed had been that belonging to the Fearings.

Eventually I arrived at Max's place, a compact two-story dwelling. There were only a few more houses beyond it on the street. Beyond those, I knew, the weeds reigned supreme, the once hopeful sidewalks were completely silted and grown over, and the lamp-poles rusted lightlessly. Unsuccessful subdivisions are dismal spots.

In my nostrils, all the way had been the smell of wet cold earth and stone.

The living room lights were on, but I saw no one through the French window where I had once glimpsed Velda and Fearing. The hall was dark. I rapped at the door. It opened instantly. I faced Velda.

I haven't described Velda. She was one of those very beautiful, dignified, almost forbidding, yet quite sexy girls that a successful, cultured man is apt to marry if he waits until he's middle-aged. Tall. Slim. Small head. Blonde hair drawn tightly across it. Blue eyes. Compact, distinguished features. Sloping shoulders, and then a body that a cynic would call the main attraction. And perhaps with partial inaccuracy, because an alert, well-informed, quite courageous mind went with it. Exquisite manners, but not much apparent warmth.

That was Velda as I remembered her.

The Velda I faced now was different. She was wearing a gray silk dressing gown. In the dim light from the street lamp behind me, the tight-drawn hair looked, not gray, but brittle. The tall beautiful body somehow seemed sterile, weedlike. She crouched like an old woman. The distinguished features in the face she lifted toward mine were pinched. The blue eyes, white circled, were much too staring.

She touched a finger to her thinned lips, and with the other hand timidly took hold of the lapel of my coat, as if to draw me away to some place where we could talk secretly.

Max stepped out of the darkness behind her and put his hands on her shoulders. She didn't stiffen. In fact, she hardly reacted except to softly drop her hand from my coat. She may have winked at me, as if to say, "Later, perhaps," but I can't be sure.

"You'd better be getting upstairs, dear," he said gently. "It's time you took a little rest."

At the foot of the stairs he switched on the light. We watched her as she went up, slowly, holding on to the rail.

When she was out of sight Max shook his head and said, rather lightly, "Too bad about Velda. I'm afraid that in a little while—However, I didn't ask you out here to talk about that."

I was shocked at his seeming callousness. A moment later, however, he said something which gave me a hint of the philosophy that underlay it.

"We're so mysteriously fragile, Fred. Some slight change in a gland's function, some faint shadow falling on a knot of nerve tissue, and—pouf. And there's nothing we can do about it, because we don't know, Fred, we simply don't know. If we could trace the thoughts in their courses, if we could set their healing magic radiating through the brain—but that's not to be for awhile yet. Meanwhile, there's nothing we can do about it, except to face it cheerfully. Though it is hard when the person whose mind goes develops a murderous hatred of you at the same time. However, as I said, I don't want to talk about that, and you'll please me if you don't either."

We were still standing at the bottom of the stairs. Abruptly be changed his manner, clapped me on the shoulder, steered me into the living room, insisted that I have a drink, and busied himself starting a fire in the open grate, all the while chatting loudly about recent doings at the medical school and pressing me for details of my latest articles.

Then, giving me no time whatever to think, he settled himself in the opposite chair, the fire blazing between us, and launched into a description of a new research project he was getting started on. It concerned the enzymes and the mechanisms of temperature-control of insects, and seemed to have far-reaching implications in fields as diverse as insecticide manufacture and the glandular physiology of human beings.

There were times when he got so caught up in his subject that it almost seemed to me it was the old Max before me, as if all the events of the past year had been a bad dream.

Once he broke off momentarily, to lay his hand on a bulky typescript on the table beside him.

"This is what I've been keeping myself busy with these last few months, Fred," he said quickly. "A complete account of my experiments with Fearing, along with the underlying theories, as well as I can present them, and all pertinent material from other fields. I can't touch the thing again, of course, but I hope someone else will, and I want him to have the benefit of my mistakes. I'm rather doubtful if any of the journals will accept it, but if they don't I'll publish it at my own expense."

It really gave me a pang to think of how much he must have suffered pounding out that typescript, meticulously, of course, knowing that it wasn't his job any more or ever could be, knowing that it was the account of a failure and a personal tragedy, knowing that it wouldn't be at all well received by his profession, but feeling duty-bound to pass on information that might some day kindle another mind and prove of scientific value to mankind.

And then the tragedy of Velda, which I hadn't yet been able to properly assimilate, with its faint, last-twist-of-the-screw suggestion that if Max had continued his research with Fearing he might conceivably have learned enough to be able to avert the cloud shadowing her mind.

Yes, I thought then, and I still think, that Max's behavior that night, especially his enthusiasm about his new research project, into which he'd obviously thrown himself wholeheartedly, was an inspiring and at the same time heart-rending example of the sort of unsentimental courage you find in the best scientists.

Yet at the same time I had the feeling that his new project wasn't the real reason for his summoning me. He had something very different on his mind, I felt, and as an unhappy person will, was talking himself out on other subjects as a preliminary to getting around to it. After a while he did.

The fire had died down somewhat. We had temporarily exhausted the topic of his new project. I was conscious of having smoked too many cigarettes. I asked Max some inconsequential question about a new advance in aviation medicine.

He frowned at the crawling flames, as if he were carefully weighing his answer. Then abruptly he said, without looking toward me, "Fred, there's something I want to tell you, something I felt I must tell you, but something I haven't been able to bring myself to tell you until now. I hated John Fearing, because I knew he was having a love affair with my wife."

I looked down at my hands. After a moment I heard Max's voice again. It wasn't loud, but it was rough with emotion.

"Oh come on, Fred, don't pretend you didn't know. You saw them through the window that night. You'll be surprised to know, Fred, how hard it was for me not to avoid you, or pick some quarrel with you, after that happened. Just the thought that you knew. . . ."

"That's all I did see or know," I assured him. "Just that one glimpse." I turned and looked at him. His eyes were bright with tears.

"And yet you know, Fred," he went on, "that's the real reason I picked you to sit in on our experiments. I felt that knowing what you did, you would be better able than anyone else to check on my relationship with John."

There was one thing I had to say. "You are quite certain, Max, that your suspicions of Velda and Fearing were justified?"

One look at his face told me I needn't press that line of questioning any further. Max sat for a while with his head bowed. It was very quiet. The wind had died which earlier had splattered a few drops from nearby branches against the windowpanes.

Finally he said, "You know, Fred, it's very difficult to recapture lost emotions, either jealousy or scientific zeal. And yet those were the two main ones in this drama. For of course it wasn't until I had begun my experiments with Fearing that I found out about him and Velda." He paused, then went on with difficulty. "I'm afraid I'm not a very broadminded man, Fred, when it comes to sex and possession. I think that if John had been some ordinary person, or if I had found out earlier, I would have behaved differently. Rather brutally, perhaps. I don't know. But the fact that our experiments had begun, and that they promised so much, changed everything.

"You know, I really try to be a scientist, Fred," he went on, with the ghost, or cadaver rather, of a rueful smile. "And as a scientist, or just as a rational man, I had to admit that the possible benefits of our experiments infinitely outweighed any hurt to my vanity or manhood. It may sound grotesque, but as a scientist I even had to consider whether this love affair wasn't necessary to keep my subject cooperative and in a proper state of mind, and whether I shouldn't go out of my way to further it. As it was, I didn't have to vary my routine in order to give them plenty of opportunities, though I think that if that had been necessary, I might even have done it."

He clenched his fist. "You see, so very much depended on those experiments of ours. Though it's awfully hard for me to remember that now. The feeling's all gone . . . the tremendous vision . . . this typescript here is just dead stuff . . . an obligation. . . .

"I feel differently about a lot of things now. About Velda and John, too. Velda wasn't exactly the girl I thought I was marrying. I've realized lately that she had a tremendous need to be adored, a kind of cold lust for beauty and ecstasy, like some pagan priestess. And I cooped her up here—the old story—and tried to feed her on my enthusiasms. Not exactly the right diet. And yet, you know, Fred, my life's work was inspired by Velda to an extent that you might find hard to believe. Even before I'd met Velda. The expectancy of her.

"And John? I don't think anyone will ever know the truth about John. I was only beginning to understand him, and there were sides to his nature I couldn't touch. A remarkable creature. In one sense, a true superman. In another, a mindless animal. Astonishing weaknesses, or blind spots. The influence of his mother. And then the way his instincts and conscience went hand in hand. I feel that John may have been completely sincere both about his desire for Velda and his desire to help me aid mankind. It may never have occurred to him that the two desires didn't exactly go together. It's quite possible he felt that he was being very nice to both of us.

"Yes, and if John and Velda's affair were something that could happen now, I think I would feel very differently about it.

"But then—? God, Fred, it's so hard to think truthfully about *them!* Then there existed in me, side by side, every moment of the day and night, the highest pinnacles of scientific excitement and the deepest pits of jealous rage. The one strictly subordinated!" A note of passionate anger came into his voice. "For don't think I was weak, Fred. Don't think I ever deviated so much as a hairsbreadth from the course that was scientifically and humanistically right. I kept my hatred for John in absolute check. And when I say that, I mean that. I'm no ignoramus, Fred. I know that when one tries to suppress feelings, they have a way of bursting out through unsuspected channels, due to the trickery of the subconscious mind. Well, I was on the watch for that. I provided every conceivable safeguard. I was fantastically cautious about each experiment. I know it may not have looked that way to you, but even that last one—heavens, we had often done experiments twice as dangerous, or as seemingly dangerous, testing every step of the way. Why, Soviet scientists have had people technically dead for over five minutes. With John it couldn't have been one!

"And yet. . . .

"That's what tormented me so, don't you see, Fred, when I couldn't revive him. The thought that my unconscious mind had somehow tricked me and opened a channel for my all-too-conscious hatred, found a chink in the wall that I'd neglected to stop up, a doorway unguarded for a second. As he lay there dead before my eyes, I was tortured by the conviction that there was some little thing that would revive him at once if only I could remember what it was.

"Some little mistake or omission I'd made, which only had to be thought of to be corrected, but which my subconscious mind wouldn't let me remember. I felt that if only I could have relaxed my mind completely—but of course that was the one thing I couldn't do.

"I tried every way I knew to revive John, I reviewed every step I'd taken without finding a flaw, and yet that feeling of guilt persisted.

"Everything seemed to intensify it. Velda's frozen, suicidal calm, worse than the bitterest and most tempestuous accusations. The most childish things—even that silly occultist with his talk of a deathwatch on John.

"How John must hate me, I'd tell myself irrationally. Commanded to be dead, tricked into dying, not given the faintest hint of what was intended.

"And Velda. Never a reproachful word to me. Just freezing up, more and more, until her mind began to wither.

"And John. That miraculous body rotting in the tomb. Those magnificently knit muscles and nerves, failing apart cell by cell."

Max slumped in his chair exhausted. The last flame in the grate flickered out and the embers began to smoke. The silence was deadly.

And then I began to talk. Quietly. Nothing brilliant. I merely reviewed what I knew and what Max had told me. Pointed out how, being the scientist he was, he couldn't have done anything but what he did. Reminded him of how he'd checked and double-checked his every action. Showed him that he hadn't the shred of a reason for feeling guilty any longer.

And finally my talk began to take effect, though, as Max said, "I don't think it's anything you've said. I've been all over that. It's that at last I've unburdened myself to someone. But I do feet better."

And I'm sure he did. For the first time I truly sensed the old Max in him. Battered and exhausted of course, and deeply seared by a new wisdom, but something of the old Max, nevertheless.

"You know," he said, sinking back in his chair, "I think I can really relax now for the first time in six months."

Immediately the silence settled down again. I remember thinking, queerly, that it was dreadful that a place could be so silent.

The fire had stopped smoking. Its odor had been replaced by that seeping in from the outside—the smell of cold wet earth and stone.

My taut muscles jerked spasmodically at the sudden grating of Max's chair against the floor. His face was ghastly. His lips formed words, but only choking sounds came out. Then he managed to get control of his voice.

"The cue! The cue for him to come alive again! I forgot I changed the signals. I thought it was still—"

He tore a pencil from his pocket and rapped on the arm of the chair: three—one.

"But it should have been—" And he rapped: three—two.

It is hard for me to describe the feeling that went through me as he rapped that second signal.

The intense quiet had something to do with it. I remember wishing that some other sound would break in—the patter of raindrops, the creaking of a beam, the hollow surge of the interurban.

Just five little raps, unevenly spaced, but embued with a quality, force, and rhythm that was Max's and nobody else's in the world—as individual as his fingerprint, as inimitable as his signature.

Just five little raps—you'd think they'd be lost in the walls, gone in a second. But they say that no sound, however faint, ever dies. It becomes weaker and weaker as it dissipates, the agitations of the molecules less and less, but still it goes on to the end of the world and back, to the end of eternity.

I pictured that sound struggling through the walls, bursting into the night air with an eager upward sweep, like a black insect, darting through the wet tangled leaves, soaring crazily into the moist tattered clouds, perhaps dipping inquisitively to circle one of the rusted lamp-poles, before it streaked purposefully off along the dank street, up, up, over the trees, over the wall, and then swooped down toward wet cold earth and stone.

And I thought of Fearing, not yet quite rotted in his tomb.

Max and I looked at each other.

There came a piercing, blood-chilling scream from over our heads.

A moment of paralyzed silence. Then the wild clatter of footsteps down the stairs in the hall. As we sprang up together, the outside door slammed.

We didn't exchange a word. I stopped in the hall to snatch up my flashlight.

When we got outside we couldn't see Velda. But we didn't ask each other any questions as to which direction she'd taken.

We started to run. I caught sight of Velda almost a block ahead.

I'm not in too bad physical condition. I slowly drew ahead of Max as we ran. But I couldn't lessen the distance between myself and Velda. I could see her quite plainly as she passed through the pools of light cast by the street lamps. With the gray silk dressing gown flying out behind her, she sometimes looked like a skimming bat.

I kept repeating to myself, "But she couldn't have heard what we were saying. She couldn't have heard those raps."

Or could she?

I reached the cemetery. I shone my flashlight down the dark, leafy tunnel. There was no one in sight, but almost halfway down the block I noticed branches shaking where they dipped to the wall.

I ran to that point. The wall wasn't very high. I could lay my hand on its top. But I felt broken glass. I stripped off my coat, laid it over the top, and pulled myself up.

My flashlight showed a rag of gray silk snagged on a wicked barb of glass near my coat.

Max came up gasping. I helped him up the wall. We both dropped down inside. The grass was very wet. My flashlight wandered over wet, pale stones. I tried to remember where Fearing's tomb was. I couldn't.

We started to hunt. Max began to call, "Velda! Velda!"

I suddenly thought I remembered the lay-out of the place. I pushed on hurriedly. Max lagged behind, calling.

There was a muffled crash. It sounded some distance away. I couldn't tell the direction. I looked around uncertainly.

I saw that Max had turned back and was running. He vanished around a tomb.

I hurried after him as fast as I could, but I must have taken the wrong turning. I lost him.

I raced futilely up and down two aisles of tombstone and tomb. I kept flashing my light around, now near, now far. It showed pale stone, dark trees, wet grass, gravel path.

I heard a horrible, deep, gasping scream—Max's.

I ran wildly. I tripped over a headstone and sprawled flat on my face.

I heard another scream—Velda's. It went on and on.

I raced down another aisle.

I thought I would go on for ever, and forever hearing that scream, which hardly seemed to pause for inhalation.

Then I came around a tangled clump of trees and I saw them.

My flashlight wavered back and forth across the scene twice before I dropped it.

They were there, all three of them.

I know that the police have a very reasonable explanation for what I saw, and I know that explanation must be right, if there is any truth in what we have been taught to believe about mind and body and death. Of course there are always those who will not quite believe, who will advance other theories. Like Max, with his experiments.

The only thing the police can't decide for certain is whether Velda managed to break into the tomb and open the casket unaided—they did find a rusty old screwdriver nearby—or whether tomb and casket hadn't been broken into at an earlier date by some sort of cultists or, more likely, pranksters inspired by cultists. They have managed to explain away almost completely, all evidence that tomb and casket were burst from the inside.

Velda can't tell them. Her mind is beyond reach.

The police have no doubts whatsoever about Velda's ability to strangle Max to death. After all, it took three strong men to get her out of the cemetery. And it is from my own testimony that the police picked up Max's statement that Velda hated him murderously.

The odd position of Fearing's remains they attribute to some insane whim on Velda's part.

And of course, as I say, the police must be right. The only thing against their theory is the raps. And of course I can't make them understand just how tremendously significant those raps of Max, that diabolic three—two, seemed to me at the time.

I can only tell what I saw, in the flashlight's wavering gleam.

The marble slab closing Fearing's tomb had fallen forward. The tomb was open.

Velda was backed against a tombstone opposite it. Her gray silk dressing gown was wet and torn to ribbons. Blood dribbled from a gash above her knee. Her blond hair streamed down tangledly. Her features were contorted. She was staring down at the space between herself and Fearing's tomb. She was still screaming.

There before her, in the wet grass, Max lay on his back. His head was twisted backward.

And across the lower part of Max's body, the half-fleshed fingers stretching toward his throat, the graveclothes clinging in tatters to the blackened, shrunken body, was all that was left of Fearing.

[*Weird Tales,* November 1950]

A Bit of the Dark World

I

"There was a crack in his head and a little bit of the Dark World came through and pressed him to death."

—Rudyard Kipling in *The Phantom 'Rickshaw*

The antique-seeming dip-nosed black Volks touring car with its driver and two other passengers besides myself was buzzing up a saddle ridge of the Santa Monica Mountains, swinging close past the squat brush-choked peaks with their strange upjutting worn rocky pinnacles that looked like primeval monoliths or robed and hooded stone monsters.

We were moving with top down and slowly enough to glimpse sharply the occasional little pale lizard skitter or grasshopper whir up out of our way over the grey crushed stone. Once a shaggy grey cat—which Viki, clutching my arm in mock alarm, insisted was a wildcat—trotted across the narrow road ahead and disappeared in the dry aromatic underbrush. The whole area was a perfect fire hazard and none of us needed to be reminded of the no-cigarette rule.

It was a brilliantly clear day with compact clouds that emphasized the dizzying inverted depth of the blue sky. Between clouds, the sun was dazzlingly bright. More than once, as we headed straight toward the low-trending distant incandescent orb along a switchback stretch, I was stung by its beams and suffered the penalty of black patches swimming in my vision for a minute or so. Next time we'd all remember sunglasses.

We had met only two cars and glimpsed only half a dozen houses and cabins since leaving the Pacific Coast Highway—a remarkable loneliness considering that Los Angeles was a scant hour's drive behind us. It was a loneliness that had drawn Viki and myself apart with its silent intimations of mysteries and revelations, but not yet driven us together again by reason of its menace.

Franz Kinzman, sitting in front to the left, and his neighbor who had volunteered to do this stretch of the driving (a Mr. Morton or Morgan or Mortenson, I wasn't sure) seemed less affected by the landscape, as one would expect seeing they were both rather more familiar with it than Viki or I. Though it was hard to gauge reactions merely from the attitude of the back of Franz's close-cropped grey head or Mr. M.'s faded brown duck hat pulled low to shade his eyes.

We had just passed that point of the Little Sycamore Canyon road where all the Santa Barbara Islands—Anacapa, Santa Cruz, Santa Rosa, even distant San Miguel—are visible like an argosy of blue-grey, faintly granular clouds floating on the surface of the pale blue Pacific, when I suddenly remarked, for no profound major reason that I was aware of at the time, "I don't suppose it's any longer possible today to write a truly gripping story of supernatural horror—or for that matter to undergo a deeply disturbing experience of supernatural terror."

Oh, there were enough minor reasons for the topic of my remark. Viki and I had worked in a couple of cheap "monster" movies, Franz Kinzman was a distinguished science-fantasy writer as well as a research psychologist, and the three of us had often gabbed about the weird in life and art. Also, there had been the faintest hint of mystery in Franz's invitation to Viki and myself to spend with him the weekend of his return to Rim House after a month in LA. Finally, the abrupt transition from a teeming city to a forbidding expanse of nature always has an eerie sting—as Franz immediately brought up without turning his head.

"I'll tell you the first condition for such an experience," he said as the Volks entered a cool band of shadow. "You've got to get away from the Hive."

"The Hive?" Viki questioned, understanding very well what he meant, I was sure, but wanting to hear him talk and have him turn his head.

Franz obliged. He has a singularly handsome, thoughtful, *noble* face, hardly of our times, though looking all of his fifty years and with eyes dark-circled ever since the death of his wife and two sons in a jet crash a year ago.

"I mean the City," he said as we buzzed into the sun again. "The human stamping ground, where we've policemen to guard us and psychiatrists to monitor our minds and neighbors to jabber at us and where our ears are so full of the clack of the mass media that it's practically impossible to think or sense or feel anything deeply, anything that's beyond humanity. Today the City, in its figurative sense, covers the whole world and the seas and by anticipation the spaceways. I think what you mean, Glenn, is that it's hard to get out of the City even in the wilderness."

Mr. M. honked twice at a blind hairpin turn and put in the next remark. "I don't know about that," he said, hunching determinedly over the wheel, "but I should think you could find all the horror and terror you wanted, Mr. Seabury, without going away from home, though it'd make pretty grim films. I mean the Nazi death camps, brain-washing, Black-Dahlia sex murders, race riots, stuff like that, not to mention Hiroshima."

"Right," I countered, "but I'm talking about supernatural horror, which is almost the antithesis of even the worst human violence and cruelty. Hauntings, the suspension of scientific law, the intrusion of the utterly alien, the sense of something listening at the rim of the cosmos or scratching faintly at the other side of the sky."

As I said that, Franz looked around at me sharply with what seemed an expression of sudden excitement and apprehension, but at that moment the sun blinded me again and Viki said, "Doesn't science fiction give you that, Glenn? I mean, horrors from other planets, the extraterrestrial monster?"

"No," I told her, blinking at a fuzzy black globe that crawled across the mountains, "because the monster from Mars or wherever has (at least as visualized by the author) so many extra feet, so many tentacles, so many purple eyes—as real as the cop on the beat. Or if he's a gas, he's a describable gas. The exact sort of goon that men will be meeting when the spaceships start travelling the starways. I'm thinking of something . . . well . . . ghostly, utterly weird."

"And it's that thing, Glenn—that ghostly, utterly weird thing—that you believe can't be written about effectively any more, or experienced?" Franz asked me with an odd note of suppressed eagerness, eyeing me keenly although the Volks was travelling a jouncy section. "Why?"

"You started to sketch the reasons yourself a moment ago," I said. My newest black globe was slipping sideways now, pulsing, starting to fade. "We've become too smart and shrewd and sophisticated to be scared by fantasies. Most especially we've got an army of experts to explain away the supernatural sort of thing the instant it starts to happen. The physicist boys have put matter and energy through the finest sieves—there's no room left in it for mysterious rays and influences, except for the ones they've described and cataloged. The astronomers are keeping tabs on the rim of the cosmos with their giant telescopes. The earth's been pretty thoroughly explored, enough to show there aren't any lost worlds in darkest Africa or Mountains of Madness near the South Pole."

"What about religion?" Viki suggested.

"Most religions," I replied, "steer away from the supernatural today—at least the religions that would attract an intellectual person. They concentrate on brotherhood, social service, moral leadership—or dictatorship!—and fine-drawn reconciliations of theology to the facts of science. They're not really interested in miracles or devils."

"Well, the occult then," Viki persisted. "Psionics."

"Nothing much there either," I asserted. "If you *do* decide to go in for telepathy, ESP, hauntings—the supernatural sort of thing—you find that territory has all been staked out by Doctor Rhine, riffling his eternal Zenter cards, and a bunch of other parapsychologists who tell you they've got the whole benign spirit world firmly in hand and who are as busy classifying and file-carding as the physicists.

"But worst of all," I went on, as Mr. M. slowed the Volks for a potholed uphill stretch, "we've got seventy-seven breeds of certified psychiatrists and psychologists (excuse me, Franz!) all set to explain the least eerie feeling or sense of wonder we get in terms of the workings of our unconscious minds, our everyday human relationships, and our past emotional experiences."

Viki chuckled throatily and put in, "Supernatural dread almost always turns out to be nothing but childhood misconceptions and fears about sex. Mom's the witch with her breasts of mystery and her underground baby-factory, while the dark hot bristly demon dissolves to Dear Old Dad." At that moment the Volks, avoiding another dark spill of gravel, again aimed almost straight at the sun. I dodged it in part but Viki got it full in the eyes, as I could tell from the odd way she was blinking sideways at the turreted hills a moment later.

"Exactly," I told her. "The point is, Franz, that these experts *are* experts, all joking aside, and they've divvied up the outer and inner worlds between them, and if we just start to notice something strange we turn to them at once (either actually or in our imaginations) and they have rational down-to-earth, explanations all ready. And because each of the experts knows a *lot* more about his special field than we do, we have to accept their explanations—or else go off our own merry way, knowing in our heart of hearts that we're behaving like stubborn romantic adolescents or out-and-out crackpots.

"The result is," I finished, as the Volks got past the potholes, "that there's no room left in the world for the weird—though plenty for crude, contemptuous, wisecracking, fun-poking imitations of it, as shown by the floods of corny 'monster' films and the stacks of monster and madness magazines with their fractionally-educated hip cackling and beatnik jeers."

"Laughing in the dark," Franz said lightly, looking back where the thin dust the Volks raised was falling over the cliff toward the thorny dark ravines far below.

"Meaning?" Viki asked.

"People still are afraid," he stated simply, "and of the same things. They've just got more defenses against their fears. They've learned to talk louder and faster and smarter and funnier—*and* with more parroted expert-given authority—to shut their fears out. Why, I could tell you—" He checked himself. He really did seem intensely excited beneath the calm philosopher's mask. "I can make it clear," he said, "by an analogy."

"Do," Viki urged.

Half turned in his seat, Franz looked straight back at the two of us. A quarter of a mile ahead or so the road, climbing a little again, plunged into a stretch of heavy cloud-shadow, I noted with relief—I now had no less than three dark fuzzy globes crawling along the horizon and I yearned to be out of the sun. From the way Viki was squinting I could tell she was in the same fix. Mr. M. with his pulled-down hat and Franz, faced around, seemed less affected.

Franz said, "Imagine that mankind is just one man—and his family—living in a house in a clearing in the midst of a dark, dangerous forest, largely unknown, largely unexplored. While he works and while he rests, while he makes love to his wife or plays with his children, he's always keeping an eye on that forest.

"After a while he becomes prosperous enough to hire guards to watch the forest for him, men trained in scouting and woodcraft—your experts, Glenn. The man comes to depend on them for his safety, he defers to their judgment, he is perfectly willing to admit that each of them knows a little more about one small nearby sector of the forest than he does.

"But what if those guards should all come to him one day and say, 'Look, Master, there really is no forest out there at all, only some farmlands we're cultivating that stretch to the ends of the universe. In fact there never was a forest out there at all, Master—you imagined all those black trees and choked aisles because you were scared of the witchdoctor!'

"Would the man believe them? Would he have the faintest justification for believing them? Or would he simply decide that his hired guards, vain of their little skills and scoutings, had developed delusions of omniscience?"

The cloud-shadow was very close now, just at the top of the slight climb we'd almost finished. Franz Kinzman leaned closer to us against the back of the front seat and there was a hush in his voice as he said, "The dark dangerous forest is still there, my friends. Beyond the space of the astronauts and the astronomers, beyond the dark, tangled regions of Freudian and Jungian psychiatry, beyond the dubious psi-realms of Dr. Rhine, beyond the areas policed by the commissars and priests and motivations-research men, far far beyond the mad, beat, half-hysterical laughter . . . the utterly unknown still *is* and the eerie and ghostly lurk, as much wrapped in mystery as ever."

With an exhilarating chilling and glooming, the Volks rolled into the sharply-edged cloud-shadow. Switching around in his seat Franz began eagerly, instantly, rapidly to search the landscape ahead, which seemed suddenly to expand, gain depth, and spring into sharper existence with the screening off of the blinding sun.

Almost at once his gaze fixed on a smoothly ridged grey stone pinnacle that had just come into view on the opposite rim of the canyon valley beside us. He slapped Mr. M. on the shoulder and pointed with his other hand at a small parking area, surfaced like the road, on the hillside bulge we were crossing.

Then, as Mr. M. swung the car to a grating stop in the indicated area just on the brink of the drop, Franz raised himself in his seat and looking over the windshield, pointed commandingly at the grey pinnacle while lifting his other hand a little, fingers tautly spread, in a gesture enjoining silence.

I looked at the pinnacle. At first I saw nothing but the half-dozen rounded merging turrets of grey rock springing out of the brush-covered hilltop. Then it seemed that the last of my annoying after-images of the sun—dark, pulsing, fringe-edged—had found lodgement there.

I blinked and swung my eyes a little to make it go away or at least move off—after all it was nothing but a fading disturbance in my retina that, purely by chance, momentarily coincided with the pinnacle.

It would not move away. It clung to the pinnacle, a dark translucent pulsing shape, as if held there by some incredible magnetic attraction.

I shivered, I felt all my muscles faintly chill and tighten at this unnatural linkage between the space inside my head and the space outside it, at this weird tie between the sort of figures that one sees in the real world and the kind that swim before the eyes when one closes them in the dark.

I blinked my eyes harder, swung my head from side to side.

It was no use. The shaggy dark shape with the strange lines going out from it clung to the pinnacle like some giant clawed and crouching beast.

And instead of fading it now began to darken further, even to blacken, the faint lines got a black glitter, the whole thing began horridly to take on a definite appearance and expression, much as the figures we see swimming in the dark become faces or masks or muzzles or forms in response to our veering imagination—though now I felt no ability whatever to change the trend of the shaping of the thing on the pinnacle.

Viki's fingers dug into my arm with painful force. Without realizing it, we'd both stood up in the back of the car and were leaning forward, close to Franz. My own hands gripped the back of the front seat. Only Mr. M. hadn't raised up, though he was staring at the pinnacle too.

Viki began, in a slow rasping strained voice, "Why, it looks like—"

With a sharp jerk of his spread-fingered hand Franz commanded her to be silent. Then without taking his eyes away from the crag he dipped in the side pocket of his coat and was next reaching things back toward us.

I saw, without looking at them directly, that they were blank white cards and stub pencils. Viki and I took them—so did Mr. M.

Franz whispered hoarsely, "Don't say what you see. Write it down. Just your impressions. Now, quickly. The thing won't last long—I think."

For the next few seconds the four of us looked and scribbled and shivered—at least I know *I* was shuddering at one point, though not for an instant taking my eyes away.

Then, for me, the pinnacle was suddenly bare. I knew that it must have become so for the others too at almost the same instant, from the way their shoulders slumped and the strained sigh Viki gave.

We didn't say a word, just breathed hard for a moment or so, then passed the cards around and read them. Most of the writing or printing had the big sloppiness of something scribbled without looking at the paper, but beyond that there was a visible tremor or shakiness, especially in Viki's notes and my own.

Viki Quinn's:
    Black tiger, burning bright. Blinding fur—or vines. Stickiness.
Franz Kinzman's:
    Black Empress. Glittering cloak of threads. Visual glue.
Mine (Glenn Seabury's):
    Giant Spider. Black lighthouse. The web. The pull on the eyes.
Mr. M., whose writing was firmest:

I don't see anything. Except three people looking at a bare grey rock as if it were the door to Hell.

And it was Mr. M. who first looked up. We met his gaze. His lips sketched a tentative grin that seemed both sour and uneasy.

He said after a bit, "Well, you certainly had your young friends pretty well hypnotized, Mr. Kinzman."

Franz asked calmly, "Is that your explanation, Ed—hypnotic suggestion—for what happened, for what we thought happened?"

The other shrugged. "What else?" he asked more cheerfully. "Do you have another explanation, Franz?—something that would account for it not working on me?"

Franz hesitated. I hung on his answer, wild to know if he'd known it was coming, as he'd seemed to, and how he'd known, and whether he'd had any comparable previous experiences. The hypnotism notion, though clever, was pure nonsense.

Finally Franz shook his head and said firmly, "No."

Mr. M. shrugged and started the Volks.

None of us wanted to talk. The experience was still with us, pinning us down inside, and then the testimony of the cards was so complete in its way, the parallelisms so exact, the conviction of a shared experience so sure, that there was no great immediate urge to compare notes.

Viki did say to me, in the offhand way of a person checking a point of which he's almost certain, "'Black Lighthouse'—that means the light was black? Rays of darkness?"

"Of course," I told her and then asked in the same way, "Your 'vines', Viki, your 'threads', Franz—did they suggest those fine wire figures of curved planes and space you see in mathematical museums? Something linking a center to infinity?"

They both nodded. I said, "Like my web," and that was all the talk for a bit.

I took out a cigarette, remembered, and shoved it back in my top pocket.

Viki said, "Our descriptions . . . vaguely like descriptions of tarot cards . . . none of them actual tarots, though . . ." Her remarks trailed off unanswered.

Mr. M. stopped at the top of a narrow drive that led down sharply to a house of which the only visible part was the flat roof, topped by pale jagged gravel. He jumped out.

"Thanks for the lift, Franz," he said. "Remember to call on me—the phone's working again—if you people should need a lift in my car . . . or anything." He looked quickly toward the two of us in the back seat and grinned nervously. "Good-bye, Miss Quinn, Mr. Seabury. Don't—" he broke off, said simply, "So long," and walked rapidly down the drive.

Of course we guessed he'd been going to say, "Don't see any more black tigers with eight legs and lady's faces," or something like that.

Franz slid across into the driver's seat. As soon as the Volks got moving I knew one reason the steady competent Mr. M. might have wanted to drive the mountainous stretch. Franz didn't exactly try to make the old Volks behave like a sports car, but his handling of it was in that direction—skittish, a bit dashing.

He mused aloud, "One thing keeps nagging me: Why didn't Ed Mortenson see it?—if 'see' is the right word."

So at last I was sure of Mr. M.'s name. It seemed a triumph. Viki said, "I can think of one possible reason, Mr. Kinzman. He isn't going where we're going."

II

"Imagine one of the awful bird-catching spiders of South America translated into human form, and endowed with intelligence just less than human, and you will have some faint conception of the terror inspired by this appalling effigy."

—M. R. James in *Canon Alberic's Scrapbook*

Rim House was about two miles beyond Mr. Mortenson's place and likewise on the downhill (down-cliff, rather!) side of the road. It was reached by a decidedly one-lane drive. On the outside of the drive, edged by white-painted stones, was a near-vertical drop of over one hundred feet. On the inside was a forty-five degree brush-dotted rocky slope between the drive and the road, which was climbing sharply along this stretch.

After about one hundred yards the drive widened to become the short, narrow, jutting plateau or terrace on which stood Rim House, occupying about half the available space. Franz, who had taken the first part of the drive with confident briskness, slowed the Volks to a crawl as soon as the house came in view, so we could scan the outside layout while still somewhat above it.

The house was built to the very edge of the drop, which here plunged down further and even more sharply than it had along the drive. On the uphill side of the house, coming down to within two feet of it, was a dizzily expansive slope of raw earth with hardly a thing growing on it, as smoothly geometrical as a little section of the side of a vast brown cone. Along the very top of it a row of short white posts, so distant I couldn't see the cable joining them, marked the road we had left. The slope looked forty-five degrees to me—these things always look impossibly steep—but Franz said it was only thirty—a completely stabilized landslide. It had been burned over a year ago in a brush fire that had almost got the house and still more recently there had been some minor slides started by repairs to the road above, accounting for the slope's unvegetated appearance.

The house was long, one-storey, its walls finished in grey asbestos shingles. The nearly flat roof, finished in grey asbestos sheets, sloped gently from the cliff side in. Midway the length of the house was a bend, allowing the house to conform to the curving top of the cliff and dividing it into two equal sections or angles, to call them that. An unroofed porch, lightly railed (Franz called it "the deck") ran along the nearer angle of the house fronting north and thrusting several feet out over the drop, which at this point was three hundred feet.

On the side of the house toward the drive was a flagstone yard big enough to turn a car in and with a lightly roofed carport up against the house on the side away from the drop. As we drove down on to the yard there was a slight *clank* as we crossed a heavy metal plate bridging a small neat ditch that ran along the foot of the raw earth slope, carrying off the water that would come down it—and also the water that would drain from the roof—during Southern California's infrequent but sometimes severe winter rains.

Franz backed the car around before we got out. It required four movements—swing to the corner of the house where the deck started, back with a sharp turn until the rear wheels were almost in the ditch, forward with a reverse turn until the front wheels were at the cliff edge by the metal bridgelet, then back into the carport until the rear of the car was almost up against a door that Franz told us led to the kitchen.

The three of us got out and Franz led us to the center of the flagged yard for another look around before we went inside. I noticed that some of the grey flags were actually solid rock showing through the light soil cover, indicating that the plateau was not an earth terrace cut by men but a rocky flat-surfaced knob thrusting out of the hillside. It gave me a feeling of security which I especially welcomed because there were other impressions—sensations rather—that were distinctly disturbing to me.

They were minor sensations, all of them, barely on the threshold of awareness. Ordinarily I don't think I'd have noticed them—I don't consider myself a sensitive person—but undoubtedly the strange experience of the thing on the pinnacle had keyed me up. To begin with there was the hint of the nasty smell of burnt linen and with it an odd bitter brassy taste; I don't think I imagined these things, because I noticed Franz wrinkling his nostrils and working his tongue against his teeth. Then there was the feeling of being faintly brushed by threads, cobwebs, or the finest vines, although we were right out in the open and the nearest thing overhead was a cloud a half-mile up. And just as I felt that—the faintest feeling, mind you—I noticed Viki lightly and questingly run her hand across the top of her hair and down the back of her neck in the common gesture of "feeling for a spider."

All this time we were talking off and on—for one thing Franz was telling us about buying Rim House on quite inexpensive terms five years back from the heir of a wealthy surfing and sports-car enthusiast who had run himself off a turn in Decker Canyon.

Finally there were the sounds that were, I thought, breathing on the verge of audibility in the remarkably complete silence that flowed around us when the Volks' motor was cut off. I know that everyone who goes from the city to the country is troubled by sounds, but these were on the unusual side. There was an occasional whistling—too high-pitched for the ear's normal range—and a soft rumbling too low for it. But along with these perhaps fancied vibrations, three times I thought I heard the hissing rattle of fine gravel spilling down. Each time I looked quickly toward the slope, but never could catch the faintest sign of earth on the move, although there was admittedly a lot of slope to be scanned.

The third time I looked up the slope, some clouds had moved aside so that the upper rim of the sun peered back down at me. "Like a golden rifleman drawing a bead" was the grotesque figure of speech that sprang to my mind. I looked hurriedly away. I wanted no more black spots before my eyes for the present. Just then Franz led us up on the deck and into Rim House by the front door.

I was afraid that all the unpleasant sensations would intensify as we got inside—especially somehow the burnt-linen smell and the invisible cobwebs—so I was greatly cheered when instead they all vanished instantly, as though faced-down by the strong sense of Franz's genial, sympathetic, wide-ranging, highly-civilized personality that the living-room exuded.

It was a long room, narrow at first where it had to give space to the kitchen and utility room and a small bathroom at this end of the house, then broadening out to the full width of the building. There was no empty wall-space, it was completely lined with shelves—half of books, half of statuary, archaeological oddments, scientific instruments, tape recorder, hi-fi set and the like. Near the inner wall, beyond the narrow section, were a big desk, some filing cabinets, and a stand with the phone.

There were no windows looking out on the deck. But just beyond the desk, where the bend in the house came, was a big view window looking out across the canyon at the craggy hills that completely cut off any sight of the Pacific. Facing the view window and close to it was a long couch backed by a long table.

At the end of the living-room a narrow hall led down the middle of the second angle of the house to a door that in turn let out into a most private grassy space that could be used for sunbathing and was just big enough for a badminton court—if anyone felt nervy enough to leap about swatting at the bird on the edge of that great drop.

On the side of the hall toward the slope was a big bedroom—Franz's— and a large bathroom opening into the hall at the end of the house. On the other side were two only slightly smaller bedrooms, each with a view window that could be completely masked by heavy dark drapes. These rooms had been his boys', he remarked casually, but I noted with relief that there were no mementoes or signs whatever left of youthful occupancy: my closet, in fact, had some women's clothes hanging in the back of it. These two bedrooms, which he assigned to Viki and myself, had a connecting door which could be bolted from both sides, but now stood unbolted but shut—a typical indication, albeit a minor one, of Franz's civilized tactfulness: he did not know, or at least did not presume to guess, the exact relationship between Viki and myself, and so left us to make our own arrangements as we saw fit—without any spoken suggestion that we should do so.

Also, each door to the hall had a serviceable bolt—Franz clearly believed in privacy for guests—and in each room was a little bowl of silver coins, no collector's items, just current American coinage. Viki asked about that and Franz explained deprecatingly, smiling at his own romanticism, that he'd copied the old Spanish California custom of the host providing guests with convenience money in that fashion.

Having been introduced to the house, we unloaded the Volks of our trifling luggage and the provisions Franz had picked up in LA. He sighed faintly at the light film of dust that had accumulated everywhere during his month's absence and Viki insisted that we pitch in with him and do a bit of house-cleaning. Franz agreed without too much demurring. I think all of us were eager to work off the edge of this afternoon's experience and get feeling back in the real world again before we talked about it—I know I was.

Franz proved an easy man to help house-clean—thoughtful for his home but not at all fussy or finicky about it. And while wielding broom or mop Viki looked good in her sweater, toreador pants, and highbound sandals—she wears the modern young-female's uniform with style rather than the customary effect of dreary intellectuality mated to a solemnly biologic femaleness.

When we'd done, we sat down in the kitchen with mugs of black coffee—somehow none of us wanted a drink—and listened to Franz's stew simmer.

"You'll want to know," he said without preface, "if I've had any previous eerie experiences up here, if I knew something was apt to happen when I invited you up for the weekend, whether the phenomena—pretentious term, isn't it?—seem to be connected with anything in the past of the region or the house or my own past—or with current activities here, including the scientific-military installations of the missile people—and finally whether I have any overall theory to account for them—such as Ed's suggestion about hypnotism."

Viki nodded. He'd adequately stated what was in our minds.

"About that last, Franz," I said abruptly. "When Mr. Mortenson first made that suggestion, I thought it was completely impossible, but now I'm not quite so sure. I don't mean you'd deliberately hypnotize us, but aren't there kinds of self-hypnosis that can be communicated to others? At any rate, the conditions were favorable for suggestion operating—we'd just been talking about the supernatural, there was the sun and its after-images acting as an attention-capturer, then the sudden transition to shadow, and finally you pointing decisively at that pinnacle as if we all had to see something there."

"I don't believe that for one minute, Glenn," Viki said with conviction.

"Neither do I, really," I told her. "After all, the cards indicate we had remarkably similar visions—our descriptions were just different enough to make them convincing—and I don't see where that material could have been suggested to us during the trip out or at any earlier time when we were together. Still, the idea of some obscure sort of suggestion has crossed my mind. A blend of highway-hypnosis and sun-hypnosis, maybe? Franz, what were your earlier experiences? I take it there were some?"

He nodded but then looked at us both thoughtfully and said, "I don't think I should tell you about them in any detail, though. Not because I'm afraid of your being skeptical or anything like that, but simply because if I do, and then similar things happen to you, you'll be more likely to feel—and rightly—that the power of suggestion may have been at work.

"Still, I ought to answer your questions," he continued. "So here goes, briefly and in a general way. Yes, I had experiences while I was up here alone month before last—some of them like this afternoon's, some of them different. They didn't seem to link up with any particular folklore or occult theory or anything else, yet they frightened me so that I went down to LA and had my eyes checked by a very good oculist and had a psychiatrist and a couple of psychologists I trust give me a thorough checkup. They pronounced me fit and unwarped—likewise my eyes. After a month I had myself convinced that everything I'd seen or sensed had been hallucinatory, that I'd simply had a case of nerves, a fit of the horrors, from too much loneliness. I invited you two along partly to avoid restarting the cycle."

"You couldn't have been completely convinced, though," Viki pointed out. "You had those cards and pencils all ready in your pocket."

Franz grinned at the neatly-scored point. "Right," he said. "I was still keeping in mind the off-trail chance and preparing for it. And then when I got in the hills the set of my ideas changed. What had seemed completely inconceivable in LA became once more a borderline possibility. Queer. Come on, let's take a turn on the deck—it'll be cool by now."

We took our mugs along. It was moderately cool, all right, most of the canyon-valley had been in the shadow for at least two hours and a faint breeze flowed upward around our ankles. Once I'd got used to being on the edge of the terrific drop I found it exhilarating. Viki must have too, for she leaned over with deliberately showy daring to peer.

The floor of the canyon was choked with dark trees and undergrowth. This thinned out going up the opposite face until just across from us there was a magnificent upthrusted and folded stratum of pale tan rock that the canyon wall cut in cross-section and showed us like a geology book. Above this fold was more undergrowth, then a series of tan and grey rocks with dark gullies and caves between them, leading by steps to a high grey summit-crag.

The slope behind the house completely cut off the sun from us, of course, but its yellow rays were still striking the tops of the wall across from us, travelling up them as the sun sank. The clouds had blown away east, where a couple were still visible, and none had come from the west to replace them.

In spite of being in a much cheerier "normal mood," I'd braced myself just a bit for the eerie little sensations as we'd come onto the deck, but they weren't there. Which somehow wasn't quite as reassuring as it ought to have been. I made myself admire the variegated rocky wall opposite.

"God, what a view to wake up to every morning!" Viki said enthusiastically. "You can feel the shape of the air and the height of the sky."

"Yes, it's quite a prospect," Franz agreed.

Then they came, the little ones, faint-footed as before, feather-treading the sensory thresholds—the burnt-linen odor, the bitter brassy tang, the brushing of skyey cobwebs, the vibrations not quite sound, the hissing rattling spill of ghost gravel . . . the minor sensations, as I'd named them to myself . . .

I knew Viki and Franz were getting them too, simply because they said no more and I could sense them both holding very still . . . and then one of the last rays of the sun must have struck a mirror-surface in the summit-crag, perhaps an outcropping of quartz, for it struck back at me like a golden rapier, making me blink, and then for an instant the beam was glitteringly black and I thought I saw (though nothing like so clearly as I'd seen the black all-knowing spider-centipede on the pinnacle) a black shape—black with the queer churning blackness you see only at night with your eyes closed. The shape coiled rapidly down the crag, into the cavern gullies and around the rocks and sank finally and utterly into the undergrowth above the fold and disappeared.

Along the way Viki had grabbed my arm at the elbow and Franz had whipped round to look at us and then looked back.

It was strange. I felt frightened and at the same time eager, on the edge of marvels and mysteries about to be laid bare. And there had been something quite controlled about the behavior of all of us through it. One fantastically trivial point—none of us had spilled any coffee.

We studied the canyon wall above the fold for about two minutes.

Then Franz said, almost gaily, "Time for dinner. Talk afterwards."

I felt deeply grateful for the instant steadying, shielding, anti-hysterical and, yes, comforting effect of the house as we went back in. I knew it was an ally.

III

"When the hard-boiled rationalist came to consult me for the first time, he was in such a state of panic that not only he himself but I also felt the wind coming over the side of the lunatic asylum!"

—Carl Gustav Jung in *Psyche and Symbol*

We accompanied Franz's stew with chunks of dark pumpernickel and pale brick cheese and followed it with fruit and coffee, then took more coffee to the long couch facing the big view window in the living-room. There was a spectral yellow glow in the sky but it faded while we were settling ourselves. Soon the first star to the north glittered faintly—Dubhe perhaps.

"Why is black a frightening color?" Viki put before us.

"Night," Franz said. "Though you'll get an argument as to whether it's a color or absence of color or simply basic sensory field. But is it intrinsically frightening?"

Viki nodded with pursed lips.

I said, "Somehow the phrase 'the black spaces between the stars' has always been an ultimate to me in terror. I can look at the stars without thinking of it, but the phrase gets me."

Viki said, "My ultimate horror is the idea of inky black cracks appearing in things, first in the sidewalk and the sides of houses, then in the furniture and floors and cars and things, finally in the pages of books and people's faces and the blue sky. The cracks are *inky* black—nothing ever shows."

"As if the universe were a gigantic jigsaw puzzle," I suggested.

"A little like that. Or a Byzantine mosaic. Glittering gold and glittering *black*."

Franz said, "Your picture, Viki, suggests that sense of breaking-up we feel in the modern world. Families, nations, classes, other loyalty groups falling apart. Things changing before you get to know them. Death on the installment plan—or decay by jumps. Instantaneous birth. Something out of nothing. Reality replacing science-fiction so fast that you can't tell which is which. Constant sense of *déjà-vu*—'I was here before—but when, how?' Even the possibility that there's no real continuity between events, just inexplicable gaps. And of course every gap—every crack—means a new perching place for horror."

"It also suggests the fragmentation of knowledge, as somebody called it," I said. "A world too big and complex to grasp in more than patches. Too much for one man. Takes teams of experts—and teams of teams. Each expert has his field, his patch, his piece of the jigsaw puzzle, but between any two pieces is a no-man's land."

"Right, Glenn," Franz said sharply, "and today I think the three of us have plunged into one of the biggest of those no-man's-lands." He hesitated then and said with an odd diffidence, almost embarrassment, "You know, we're going to have to start talking sometime about what we saw—we can't let ourselves be gagged by this fear that anything we say will alter the picture of what the others saw and warp their testimony. Well, about the blackness of this thing or figure or manifestation I saw (I called it 'Black Empress', but Sphinx might have been a better word—there was the suggestion of a long tigerish or serpentine body in the midst of the black fringy sunburst)—but about its blackness, now, that blackness was more than anything else like the glimmering dark the eyes see in the absence of light."

"Right," I said.

"Oh, yes," Viki chimed.

"There was a sense," Franz went on, "that the thing was in my eyes, in my head, but also out there on the horizon, on the pinnacle I mean. That it was somehow both subjective—in my consciousness—and objective—in the material world—or . . ." (He hesitated and lowered his voice.) ". . . or existing in some sort of space more fundamental, more primal and less organized than either of those.

"Why shouldn't there be other kinds of space than those we know?" he went on a shade defensively. "Other chambers in the great universal cave? Men have tried to imagine four, five and more spatial dimensions. What's the space inside the atom or the nucleus *feel* like, or the space between the galaxies or beyond any galaxy? Oh, I know the questions I'm asking would be nonsense to most scientists—they're questions that don't make sense operationally or referentially, they'd say—but those same men can't give us the ghost of an answer to even the question of where and how the space of consciousness exists, how a jelly of nerve cells can support the huge flaming worlds of inner reality—they fob us off with the excuse (legitimate in its way) that science is about things that can be measured and pointed at, and who can measure or point at his thoughts? But consciousness *is*—it's the basis we all exist in and start from, it's the basis science starts from, whether or not science can get at it—so it's allowable for me to wonder whether there may not be a primal space that's a bridge between consciousness and matter . . . and whether the thing we saw may not exist in such a space."

"Maybe there *are* experts for this sort of thing and were missing them," Viki said seriously. "Not scientists, but mystics and occultists, some of them at any rate—the genuine few among the crowd of fakers. You've got some of their books in your library. I recognized the titles."

Franz shrugged. "I've never found anything in occult literature that seemed to have a bearing. You know, the occult—very much like stories of supernatural horror—is a sort of game. Most religions too. Believe in the game and accept its rules—or the premises of the story—and you can have the thrills or whatever it is you're after. Accept the spirit world and you can see ghosts and talk to the dear departed. Accept Heaven and you can have the hope of eternal life and the reassurance of an all-powerful god working on your side. Accept Hell and you can have devils and demons, if that's what you want. Accept—if only for story purposes—witchcraft, druidism, shamanism, magic or some modern variant and you can have werewolves, vampires, elementals. Or believe in the influence and power of a grave, an ancient house or monument, a dead religion, or an old stone with an inscription on it—and you can have inner things of the same general sort. But I'm thinking of the kind of horror—and wonder too, perhaps—that lies beyond any game, that's bigger than any game, that's fettered by no rules, conforms to no man-made theology, bows to no charms or protective rituals, that strides the world unseen and strikes without warning where it will, much the same as (though it's of a different order of existence than all of these) lightning or the plague or the enemy atom bomb. The sort of horror that the whole fabric of civilization was designed to protect us from and make us forget. The horror about which all man's learning tells us nothing."

I stood up and moved close to the window. There seemed to be quite a few stars now. I tried to make out the big fold of rock in the hillside opposite, but the reflections on the glass got in the way.

"Maybe so," Viki said, "but there are a couple of those books I'd like to look at again. I think they're behind your desk."

"What titles?" Franz asked. "I'll help you find them."

"Meanwhile I'll take a turn on the deck," I said as casually as I could, moving toward the other end of the room. They didn't call after me, but I had the feeling they watched me the whole way.

As soon as I'd pushed through the door—which took a definite effort of will—and shoved it to without quite shutting it behind me—which took another—I became aware of two things: that it was much darker than I'd anticipated—the big view window angled away from the deck and there was no other obvious light source except the stars—; two, that I found the darkness reassuring.

The reason for the latter seemed clear enough: the horror I'd glimpsed was associated with the sun, with blinding sunlight. Now I was safe from that—though if someone unseen should have struck a match in front of my face, the effect on me would have been extreme.

I moved forward by short steps, feeling in front of me with my hands at the level of the rail.

I knew why I'd come out here, I thought. I wanted to test my courage against the thing, whatever it was, illusory or real or something else, inside or outside our minds, or somehow as Franz had suggested, able to move in both regions. But beyond that, I realized now, there was the beginning of a fascination.

My hands touched the rail. I studied the black wall opposite, deliberately looking a little away and then back, as one does to make a faint star or a dim object come clear in the dark. After a bit I could make out a big pale fold and some of the rocks above it, but a couple of minutes' watching convinced me that it was possible endlessly to see dark shapes crossing it.

I looked up at the heavens. There was no Milky Way yet, but there would be soon, the stars were flashing on so brightly and thickly at this smog-free distance from LA. I saw the Pole Star straight above the dark star-silhouetted summit-crag of the hillside across from me, and the Great Bear and Cassiopeia swinging from it. I felt the bigness of the atmosphere, I got a hint of the stupendous distance between me and the stars, and then as if my vision could go out in all directions at will, piercing solidity as readily as the dark—I got a lasting, growing, wholly absorbing sense of the universe around me.

Lying behind me, a gently swelling, perfectly rounded section of the earth about a hundred miles high masked off the sun. Africa lay under my right foot through the earth's core, Australia under my left, and it was strange to think of the compressed incandescent stuff that lay between us under earth's cool mantle—blindingly glowing plastic metal or ore in a space where there were no eyes to see and no millionth of a free inch in which all that dazzling locked-up light could travel. I sensed the tortured ice of the frigid poles, the squeezed water in the deep seas, the fingers of mounting lava, the raw earth crawling and quivering with an infinitude of questing rootlets and burrowing worms.

Then for moments I felt I looked out glimmeringly through two billion pairs of human eyes, my consciousness running like fuse-fire from mind to mind. For moments more I dimly shared the feelings, the blind pressures and pulls of a billion trillion motes of microscopic life in the air, in the earth, in the bloodstream of man.

Then my consciousness seemed to move swiftly outward from earth in all directions, like an expanding globe of sentient gas. I passed the dusty dry mote that was Mars, I glimpsed milkily-banded Saturn with its great thin wheels of jumbled jagged ice. I passed frigid Pluto with its bitter nitrogen snows. I thought of how people are like plants—lonely little forts of mind with immense black distances barring them off from each other.

Then the speed of expansion of my consciousness became infinite and my mind was spread thin in the stars of the Milky Way and in the other gauzy star islands beyond it—above, below, to all sides, among the nadir stars as well as those of the zenith—and on the trillion trillion planets of those stars I sensed the infinite variety of self-conscious life—naked, clothed, furred, armor-shelled, and with cells floating free—clawed, handed, tentacled, pincered, ciliated, fingered by winds or magnetism—loving, hating, striving, despairing, imagining.

For a while it seemed to me that all these beings were joined in a dance that was fiercely joyous, poignantly sensuous, tenderly responsive.

Then the mood darkened and the beings fell apart into a trillion trillion trillion lonely motes locked off forever from each other, sensing only bleak meaninglessness in the cosmos around them, their eyes fixed forward only on universal death.

Simultaneously each dimensionless star seemed to become for me the vast sun it was, beating incandescently on the platform where my body stood and on the house behind it and the beings in it and on my body too, ageing them with the glare of a billion desert moons, crumbling them all to dust in one coruscatingly blinding instant.

Hands gently grasped my shoulders and at the same time Franz's voice said, "Steady, Glenn." I held still, though for a moment every nerve cell in me seemed on the verge of triggering, then I let out an uneven breath edged with laughter and turned and said in a voice that sounded to me quite dull, almost drugged, "I got lost in my imagination. For a minute there I seemed to be seeing everything. Where's Viki?"

"Inside leafing through *The Symbolism of the Tarot* and a couple of other books on the arcana of the fortune-telling cards, and grumbling that they don't have indexes. But what's this 'seeing everything', Glenn?"

Haltingly I tried to tell him about my "vision," not conveying a hundredth of it, I felt. By the time I finished I could see the blur of his face against the black wall of the house barely well enough to tell that he nodded.

"The universe fondling and devouring her children," his brooding comment came out of the dark. "I imagine you've run across in your reading, Glenn, the superficially sterile theory that the whole universe is in some sense alive or at least aware. There are lots of terms for it in the jargon of metaphysics: cosmotheism, theopantism, panpsychism, panpneumatism—but simply pantheism is the commonest. The idea that the universe is God, though for me God isn't the right term, it's been used to mean too many things. If you insist on a religious approach, perhaps what comes closest is the Greek idea of the Great God Pan, the mysterious nature deity, half animal, that frightened man and woman to panic in lonely places. Incidentally, panpneumatism is the most interesting to me of the obscurer concepts: old Karl von Hartmann's notion that the unconscious mind is the basic reality—it comes close to what we were saying inside about the possibility of a more fundamental space linking the inner and outer world and perhaps providing a bridge from anywhere to anywhere."

As he paused I heard a faint spill of gravel, then a second, though I got none of the other minor sensations.

"But whatever we call it," Franz went on, "there's something there, I feel—something less than God but more than the collective mind of man—a force, a power, an influence, a mood of things, a something more than subatomic particles, that is aware and that has grown with the universe and that helps to shape it." He had moved forward now so that I saw his head silhouetted against the thick stars and for a moment there was the grotesque illusion that it was the stars rather than his mouth that were speaking. "I think there are such influences, Glenn. Atomic particles alone can't sustain the flaming inner worlds of consciousness, there must be a pull from the future as well as a push from the past to keep us moving through time, there must be a ceiling of mind over life as well as a floor of matter beneath it."

Again, as his voice faded out, I heard the feathery hisses of gravel running—two close together, then two more. I thought uneasily of the slope behind the house.

"And if there are those influences," Franz continued, "I believe that man has grown enough in awareness today to be able to contact them without ritual or formula of belief, if they should chance to move or look his way. I think of them as sleepy tigers, Glenn, that mostly purr and dream and look at us through slitted eyes, but occasionally—perhaps when a man gets a hint of them—open their eyes to the full and stalk in his direction. When a man becomes ripe for them, when he's pondered the possibility of them, and then when he's closed his ears to the protective, mechanically-augmented chatter of humanity, they make themselves known to him."

The spills of gravel, still faint as illusions, were coming now in a rapid rhythm like—it occurred to me at that instant—padding footsteps, each footstep dislodging a little earth. I sensed a faint brief glow overhead.

"For they're the same thing, Glenn, as the horror and wonder I talked about inside, the horror and wonder that lives beyond any game, that strides the world unseen and strikes without warning where it will."

At that instant the silence was ripped by a shrill scream of terror from the flagged yard between the house and the drive. For an instant my muscles were chilled and constricted and there was a gagging pressure in my chest. Then I lunged toward that end of the deck.

Franz darted into the house.

I plunged off the end of the deck, almost fell, twisted to my feet—and stopped, suddenly at a loss for my next move.

Here I couldn't see a thing in the blackness. In stumbling I'd lost my sense of direction—for the moment I didn't know which ways were the slope, the house, and the cliff edge.

I heard Viki—I thought it had to be Viki—gasping and sobbing strainingly, but the direction of *that* wouldn't come clear, except it seemed more ahead of me than behind me.

Then I saw, stretching up before me, a half-dozen or so thin close-placed stalks of what I can only describe as a more gleaming blackness—it differed from the background as dead black velvet does from dead black felt. They were barely distinguishable yet very real. I followed them up with my eyes as they mounted against the starfields, almost invisible, like black wires, to where they ended—high up—in a bulb of darkness, defined only by the patch of stars it obscured, as tiny as the moon.

The black bulb swayed and there was a corresponding rapid joggling in the crowded black stalks—though if they were free to move at the base I ought to call them legs.

A door opened twenty feet from me and a beam of white light struck across the yard, showing a streak of flagstones and the beginning of the drive.

Franz had come out of the kitchen door with a powerful flashlight. My surroundings jumped sideways into place.

The beam swept back along the slope, showing nothing else, then forward toward the cliff edge. When it got to the spot where I'd seen the ribbony black legs, it stopped.

There were no stalks, legs or bands of any sort to be seen, but Viki was swaying and struggling there, her dark hair streaming across her face and half obscuring her agonized expression, her elbows tight to her sides, her hands near her shoulders and clawed outward—exactly as though she were gripping and struggling against the vertical bars of a tight cage.

The next instant the tension went out of her, as though whatever she'd been struggling against had vanished. She swayed and began to move in blind tottering steps toward the cliff edge.

That snapped my freeze and I ran toward her, grabbing her wrist as she stepped on the verge, and half-dragged, half-whirled her away from it. She didn't resist. Her movement toward the cliff had been accidental, not suicidal.

She looked at me, one side of her blanched face twitching, and said, "Glenn." My heart was thudding.

Franz yelled at us from the kitchen door, "Come on in!"

IV

"But the third Sister, who is also the youngest—! Hush! whisper whilst we talk of *her!* Her kingdom is not large, or else no flesh should live; but within that kingdom all power is hers. Her head, turreted like that of Cybele, rises almost beyond the reach of sight. She droops not; and her eyes, rising so high, *might* be hidden by distance. But, being what they are, they cannot be hidden ... This youngest sister moves with incalculable motions, bounding with a tiger's leaps. She carries no key; for, though coming rarely amongst men, she storms all doors at which she is permitted to enter at all. And her name is *Mater Tenebrarum,* Our Lady of Darkness."

—Thomas de Quincey in *Suspira de Profundis*

As soon as we got Viki inside she recovered rapidly from her shock and at once insisted on telling us her story. Her manner was startlingly assured, interested, almost gay, as if some protective door in her mind were already closed against the absolute reality of what had happened.

At one point she even said, "It all still could have been a series of chance little sounds and sights, you know, combined with suggestion working powerfully—like the night I saw a burglar standing against the wall beyond the foot of my bed, saw him so clearly in the dark that I could have described him down to the cut of his moustache and the droop of his left eyelid ... until the dawn coming on turned him into my roommate's black overcoat with a tan scarf thrown around the hanger and hook."

While she'd been reading, she said, she'd become aware of the ghost-spills of gravel, some of them seeming to rattle faintly against the back wall of the house, and she'd gone out at once through the kitchen to investigate.

Groping her way, moving a few steps beyond the Volks toward the center of the yard, she had looked toward the slope and at once seen moving across it an incredibly tall wispy shape that she described as "a giant harvestman, tall as ten trees. You know harvestmen, some people call them daddy longlegs, those utterly harmless pitifully fragile spiders that are nothing but a tiny brown inanimate-looking ball with eight bendy legs that are like lengths of stiffened brown thread."

She'd seen it quite clearly in spite of the darkness, because it was "black with a black shimmer." Once it had vanished completely when a car had turned the bend in the road above and its headlights had feebly swept the air high above the slope (that would have been the faint brief overhead glow

I'd sensed)—but when the headlights swung away the giant black glimmering harvestman had come back at once.

She hadn't been frightened (wonderstruck and terribly curious, rather) until the thing had come treading rapidly toward her, its shimmering black legs drawing closer and closer together until before she realized it they were a tight cage around her.

Then, as she discovered they weren't quite as thin and insubstantial as she'd imagined, and as she felt their feathery, almost bristly touch against her back and face and sides, she'd suddenly snapped and given that one terrific scream and started to struggle hysterically. "Spiders drive me wild," she finished lightly, "and there was the feeling I'd be sucked up the cage to the black brain in the stars—I thought of it as a black brain then, no reason why."

Franz didn't say anything for a bit. Then he began, in a rather heavy, halting way, "You know, I don't think I showed much foresight or consideration when I invited you two up here. Quite the opposite, in fact, even if I didn't then believe that . . . Anyway, I don't feel right about it. Look here, you could take the Volks right now . . . or I could drive . . . and—"

"I think I know what you're getting at, Mr. Kinzman, and why," Viki said with a little laugh, standing up, "but I for one have had quite enough excitement for one night. I have no desire to top it off with watching for ghosts in the headlights for the next two hours." She yawned. "I want to hit that luxurious hay you've provided for me, right this minute. Night-night, Franz, Glenn." With no more word she walked down the hall and went into her bedroom, the far one, and closed the door.

Franz said, in a low voice, "I think you know I meant that very seriously, Glenn. It still might be the best thing."

I said, "Viki's got some kind of inner protection built up now. To get her to leave Rim House, we'd have to break it down. That would be rough."

Franz said, "Better rough, maybe, than what else might happen here tonight."

I said, "So far Rim House has been a protection for us. It's shut things out."

He said, "It didn't shut out the footsteps Viki heard."

I said, remembering my vision of the cosmos, "But Franz, if we're up against the sort of influence we think we are, then it seems to me pretty ridiculous to imagine a few miles of distance or a few bright lights making any more difference to its power than the walls of a house."

He shrugged. "We don't know," he said. "Did you see it, Glenn? Holding the light I didn't see anything."

"Just like Viki described it," I assured him and went on to tell my own little tale. "If that was all suggestion," I said, "it was a pretty fancy variety." I squeezed my eyes and yawned; I was suddenly feeling very dull—reaction, I suppose. I finished, "While it was happening, and later while we were listening to Viki, there certainly were times when all I wanted was to be back in the old familiar world and the old familiar hydrogen bomb hanging over my head and all the rest of that stuff."

"But at the same time weren't you fascinated?" Franz demanded. "Didn't it make you crazy to know more?—the thought that you were seeing something utterly strange and that here was a chance really to understand the universe—at least to meet its unknown lords?"

"I don't know," I told him wearily. "I suppose so, in a way."

"What did the thing really seem like, Glenn?" Franz asked. "What kind of being?—if that's the right word."

"I'm not sure it is," I said. I found it difficult to summon the energy to answer his questions. "Not an animal. Not even an intelligence as we understand it. More like the things we saw on the pinnacle and the crag." I tried to marshal my fatigue-drugged thoughts. "Halfway between reality and a symbol," I said. "If that means anything."

"But weren't you fascinated?" Franz repeated.

"I don't know," I said, pushing to my feet with an effort. "Look, Franz, I'm too beat to be able to do any more thinking now. It's just too hard to talk about these things. G'night."

"Goodnight, Glenn," he said as I walked to my bedroom. Nothing more.

Midway getting undressed, it occurred to me that my dazed sleepiness might be my mind's defense against having to cope with the unknown, but even that thought wasn't enough to rouse me.

I pulled on my pajamas and put out the light. Just then the door to Viki's bedroom opened and she stood there, wearing a light robe.

I had thought of looking in on her, but had decided that if she were sleeping it was the best thing for her and any attempt to check on her might break her inner protections.

But now I could tell from her expression, by the light from her room, that they were shattered.

At the same moment my own inner protection—the false sleepiness—was gone.

Viki closed the door behind her and we moved together and put our arms around each other and stood there. After a while we lay down side by side on the bed under the view window that showed the stars.

Viki and I are lovers, but there wasn't an atom of passion in our embraces now. We were simply two, not so much frightened as completely overawed, people, seeking comfort and reassurance in each other's presence.

Not that we could hope to get any security, any protection from each other—the thing looming above us was too powerful for that—but only a sense of not being alone, of sharing whatever might happen.

There wasn't the faintest impulse to seek temporary escape in lovemaking, as we might have done to shut out a more physical threat, the thing was too weird for that. For once Viki's body was beautiful to me in a completely cold abstract way that had no more to do with desire than the colors in an insect's wing-case or the curve of a tree or the glitter of a snowfield. Yet within this strange form, I knew, was a friend.

We didn't speak a word to each other. There were no easy words for most of our thoughts, sometimes no words at all. Besides, we shrank from making the slightest sound, as two mice would while a cat sniffs past the clump of grass in which they are hiding.

For the sense of a presence looming around and over Rim House was overpoweringly strong. Dipping *into* Rim House now too, for all the minor sensations came drifting down on us like near-impalpable snow-flakes—the dark burnt taste and smell, the fluttering cobwebs, the bat-sounds and the wave-sounds and once again the feathery spills of gravel.

And above and behind them the sense of a black uprearing presence linked to the whole cosmos by the finest black filaments that in no way impeded it . . .

I didn't think of Franz, I hardly thought of the things that had happened today, though now and then I would worry at the edge of a memory . . .

We simply lay there and held still and looked at the stars. Minute after minute. Hour after hour.

At times we must have slept, I know I did, though blacked-out would be a better expression for it, for there was no rest and waking was a nightmarish business of slowly becoming aware of dark aches and chills.

After a long while I noticed that I could see the clock in the far corner of the room—because its dial was luminescent, I thought. The hands pointed to three o'clock. I gently turned Viki's face toward it and she nodded that she could see it too.

The stars were what was keeping us sane, I told myself, in a world that might dissolve to dust at the faintest breath from the nearer presence.

It was just after I noticed the clock that the stars began to change color, all of them. First they had a violet tinge, which gradually shifted to blue, then green.

In an unimportant corner of my mind I wondered what sort of fine mist or dust drifting through the air could work that change.

The stars turned to dim yellow, to orange, to dark furnace-red, and then—like the last sparks crawling on a sooty chimney wall above a dead fire—winked out.

I thought crazily of the stars all springing away from earth, moving with such impossible swiftness that their light had shifted beneath the red into invisible ranges.

We should have been in utter darkness then, but instead we began to see each other and the things around us outlined by the faintest glimmer. I thought it was the first hint of morning and I suppose Viki did too. We looked together at the clock. It was barely four-thirty. We watched the minute hand edge. Then we looked back at the window. It wasn't ghostly pale, as it would have been with dawn, but—and I could tell that Viki saw this too by the way she gripped my hand—it was a pitch-black square, framed by the white glimmer.

I could think of no explanation for the glimmer. It was a little like a whiter, paler version of the luminescence of the clock dial. But even more it was like the pictures one imagines in one's eyes in absolute darkness, when one wills the churning white sparks of the retinal field to coalesce into recognizable ghostly forms—it was as if that retinal dark had spilled out of our eyes into the room around us and we were seeing each other and our surroundings not by light but by the power of imagination—which each second increased the sense of miracle that the shimmering scene did not dissolve to churning chaos.

We watched the hand of the clock edge toward five. The thought that it must be getting light outside and that something barred us from seeing that light, finally stirred me to move and speak, though the sense of an inhuman inanimate presence was as strong as ever.

"We've got to try and get out of here," I whispered.

Moving across the bedroom like a shimmering ghost, Viki opened the connecting door. The light had been on in her room, I remembered.

There wasn't the faintest glimmer came through the door. Her bedroom was dead black.

I'd fix that, I thought. I switched on the lamp by the bed.

My room became solid black. I couldn't even see the face of the clock. *Light is darkness now,* I thought. *White is black.*

I switched off the light and the glimmer came back. I went to Viki where she was standing by the door and whispered to her to switch off the light in her room. Then I got dressed, mostly feeling around for my clothes, not trusting the ghostly light that was so much like a scene inside my head trembling on the verge of dissolution.

Viki came back. She was even carrying her little overnight bag. I inwardly approved the poise that action indicated, but I made no effort to take any of my own things. "My room was very cold," Viki said.

We stepped into the hall. I heard a familiar sound: the whir of a telephone dial. I saw a tall silver figure standing in the living-room. It was a moment before I realized it was Franz, seen by the glimmer. I heard him say, "Hello, operator. Operator!" We walked to him.

He looked at us, holding the receiver to his ear. Then he put it down again and said, "Glenn. Viki. I've been trying to phone Ed Mortenson, see if the stars changed there, or anything else. But it doesn't work for me. You try your luck at getting the operator, Glenn."

He dialled once, then handed me the receiver. I heard no ringing, no buzz, but a sound like wind wailing softly. "Hello, operator," I said. There was no response or change, just that wind sound. "Wait," Franz said softly.

It must have been at least five seconds when my own voice came back to me out of the phone, very faintly, half drowned in the lonely wind, like an echo from the end of the universe. "Hello, operator."

My hand shook as I put down the phone. "The radio?" I asked.

"The wind sound," he told me, "all over the dial."

"Just the same we've got to try to get out," I said.

"I suppose we should," he said with a faint ambiguous sigh. "I'm ready. Come on."

As I stepped onto the deck after Franz and Viki, I felt the intensified sense of a presence. The minor sensations were with us again, but far stronger now: the burnt taste made me gag almost, I wanted to claw at the cobwebs, the impalpable wind moaned and whistled loudly, the ghost-gravel hissed and splashed like the rapids of a river. All in near absolute darkness.

I wanted to run but Franz stepped forward to the barely glimmering rail. I held on to myself.

The faintest glimmer showed a few lines of the rock wall opposite. But from the sky above it was beating a dead inkier blackness—*blacker than black,* I thought—that was eating up the glimmer everywhere, dimming it moment by moment. And with the inkier blackness came a chill that struck into me like needles.

"Look," Franz said. "It's the sunrise."

"Franz, we've got to get moving," I said.

"In a moment," he answered softly, reaching back his hand. "You go ahead. Start the car. Pull out to the center of the yard. I'll join you there."

Viki took the keys from him. She's driven a Volks. There was still enough glimmer to see by, though I trusted it less than ever. Viki started the car, then forgot and switched on the headlights. They obscured yard and drive with a fan of blackness. She switched them off and pulled to the center of the yard.

I looked back. Although the air was black with the icy sunlight I could still see Franz clearly by the ghost light. He was standing where we'd left him, only leaning forward now, as though eagerly peering.

"Franz!" I called loudly against the weirdly wailing wind and the mounting gravel-roar. "Franz!"

There reared out of the canyon, facing Franz, towering above him, bending toward him a little, a filament-trailing form of shimmering velvet black—not the ghost light, but shimmering darkness itself—that looked like a gigantic hooded cobra, or a hooded madonna, or a vast centipede, or a giant figure of the cat-headed goddess Bast, or all or none of these.

I saw the silver of Franz's body begin to crumble and churn. In the same moment the dark form dipped down and enfolded him like the silk-gloved fingers of a colossal black hand or the petals of a vast black flower closing.

Feeling like someone who throws the first shovel of earth on the coffin of a friend, I croaked to Viki to go.

There was hardly any glimmer left—not enough to see the drive, I thought, as the Volks started up it.

Viki drove fast.

The sound of the spilling gravel grew louder and louder, drowning out the intangible wind, drowning out our motor. It rose to a thunder. Under the moving wheels, being transmitted up through them, I could feel the solid earth shaking.

A bright pit opened ahead of us on the canyon side. For a moment it was as if we were driving through veils of thick smoke, then suddenly Viki was braking, we were turning into the road and early daylight was almost blinding us.

But Viki didn't stop. She completed a near-full turn, so we were headed up the Little Sycamore Canyon road.

There was no trace of darkness at all, anywhere. The thunder that had shaken the ground was dying away.

She drove close to the edge where the road turned away at the head of the slope and she stopped the car there.

Around us were the turreted hills. The sun hadn't yet climbed above them but the sky was bright.

We looked down the slope. It was hollowed by the earth it had lost. No dust clouds obscured it anywhere, though there was dust rising now from the bottom of the canyon-valley.

The shrunken slope swept down straight from us to the cliff edge without a break, without a hummock, without one object thrusting up through. *Everything* had been carried away by the slide.

That was the end of Rim House and Franz Kinzman.

[*Fantastic*, February 1962; *Night's Black Agents*, rev. ed.
(Berkley Medallion, 1978)]

TO ARKHAM AND THE STARS

Early on the evening of September 14th last I stepped down onto the venerable brick platform of the Arkham station of the Boston and Maine Railroad. I could have flown in, arriving at the fine new Arkham Airport north of town, where I am told a suburb of quite tasteful Modern Colonial homes now covers most of Meadow Hill, but I found the older conveyance convenient and congenial.

Since I was carrying only a small valise and a flat square cardboard box of trifling weight, I elected to walk the three blocks to the Arkham House. Midway across the old Garrison Street Bridge, which repaired and resurfaced only ten years ago spans the rushing Miskatonic there, I paused to survey the city from that modest eminence, setting down my valise and resting my hand on the old iron railing while an occasional dinner-time car rumbled past close beside me.

To my right, just this side of the West Street Bridge where the Miskatonic begins its northward swing, there crouched in the rapid current the ill-regarded little island of gray standing stones, where as I had read in *The Arkham Advertiser* I have sent me, a group of bearded bongo-drumming delinquents had recently been arrested while celebrating a black mass in honor of Castro—or so one of them had wildly and outrageously asserted. (For a brief moment my thoughts turned queerly to Old Castro of the Cthulhu Cult.) Beyond the island and across the turn of the river loomed Hangman's Hill, now quite built-up, from behind which the sun was sending a spectral yellow afterglow. By this pale gloom-shot golden light I saw that Arkham is still a city of trees, with many a fine oak and maple, although the elms are all gone, victims of the Dutch disease, and that there are still many gambrel roofs to be seen among the newer tops. To my left I studied the new freeway where it cuts across the foot of French Hill above Powder Mill Street, providing rapid access to the missile-component, machine-tool, and chemical plants southeast of the city. My gaze dropping down and swinging south searched for a moment for the old Witch-House before I remembered it had been razed as long ago as 1931 and the then moldering tenements of the Polish Quarter have largely been replaced by a modest housing development in Colonial urban style, while the newest "foreigners" to crowd the city are the Puerto Ricans and the Negroes.

Taking up my valise, I descended the bridge and continued across River Street, past the rosily mellowed red-brick slant-roofed stout old warehouses which have happily escaped demolition. At the Arkham I confirmed my reservation and checked my valise with the pleasant elderly desk clerk, but, since I had dined early in Boston, I pressed on at once south on Garrison across Church to the University, continuing to carry my cardboard box.

The first academic edifices to interrupt my gaze were the new Administration Building and beyond it the Pickman Nuclear Laboratory, where Miskatonic has expanded east across Garrison, though of course without disturbing the Burying Ground at Lich and Parsonage. Both additions to the University struck me as magnificent structures, wholly compatible with the old quadrangle, and I gave silent thanks to the architect who had been so mindful of tradition.

It was full twilight now and several windows glowed in the nearer edifice, where faculty members must be carrying on the increasing paper work of the University. But before proceeding toward the room, behind one of the windows, which was my immediate destination, I took thoughtful note of the orderly student anti-segregation demonstration that was being carried on at the edge of campus in sympathy with similar demonstrations in southern cities. I observed that one of the placards read "Mazurewicz and Desrochers for Selectmen," showing me that the students must be taking a close interest in the government of the University city and making me wonder if those candidates were sons of the barely literate individuals innocently mixed up in the Witch-House case. *Tempora mutantur!*

Inside the pleasant corridors of the Administration Building I quickly found the sanctum of the Chairman of the Department of Literature. The slender silver-haired Professor Albert Wilmarth, hardly looking his more than seventy years, greeted me warmly though with that mocking sardonic note which has caused some to call him "unpleasantly" rather than simply "very" erudite. Before winding up his work, he courteously explained its nature.

"I have been getting off a refutation of some whippersnapper's claim that the late Young Gentleman of Providence who recorded so well so many of the weirder doings around Arkham was a 'horrifying figure' whose 'closest relation is with Peter Kürten, the Dülsseldorf murderer, who admitted that his days in solitary confinement were spent conjuring up sexual-sadistic fantasies.' Great God, doesn't the sapless youngster know that all normal men have sexual-sadistic fantasies? Even supposing that the literary fantasies of the late Young Gentleman had a deliberate sexual element and *were* indeed fantasies!" Turning from me with a somewhat sinister chuckle, he said to his attractive secretary, "Now remember, Miss Tilton, that goes to Colin Wilson, not Edmund—I took care of Edmund very thoroughly in an earlier letter! Carbon copies to Avram Davidson and Damon Knight. And while you're at it, see that they go out from the Hangman's Hill sub-station—I'd like them to carry that postmark!"

Getting his hat and a light topcoat and hesitating a moment at a mirror to assure himself that his high collar was spotless, the venerable yet sprightly Wilmarth led me out of the Administration Building back across Garrison to the old quadrangle, ignoring the traffic which dodged around us.

On the way he replied in answer to a remark of mine, "Yes, the architecture is damned good. Both it and the Pickman Lab—and the new Polish Quarter apartment development, too—were designed by Daniel Upton, who as you probably know has had a distinguished career ever since he was given a clean bill of mental health and discharged with a verdict of 'justified homicide' after he shot Asenath or rather old Ephraim Waite in the body of his friend Edward Derby. For a time that verdict got us almost as much criticism as the Lizzie Borden acquittal got Fall River, but it was well worth it!

"Young Danforth's another who's returned to us from the asylum—and permanently too, now that Morgan's research in mescaline and LSD has turned up those clever anti-hallucinogens," my conductor continued as we passed between the museum and the library where a successor of the great watchdog that had destroyed Wilbur Whateley clinked his chain as he paced in the shadows. "Young Danforth—Gad, he's nearly as old as I!—you know, the brilliant graduate assistant who survived with old Dyer the worst with which the Antarctic could face them back in '30 and '31. Danforth's gone into psychology, like Peaslee's Wingate and old Peaslee himself—it's a therapeutic vocation. Just now he's deep in a paper on Asenath Waite, showing she's quite as much an Anima-figure—that is, devouring witch-mother and glamorous fatal witch-girl—as Carl Jung maintained Haggard's Ayesha and William Sloane's Selena were."*

"But surely there's a difference there," I objected somewhat hesitatingly. "Sloane's and Haggard's women were fictional. You can't be implying, can you, that Asenath was a figment of the imagination of the Young Gentleman who wrote 'The Thing on the Doorstep'?—or rather fictionalized Upton's rough account. Besides, it wasn't really Asenath but Ephraim, as you pointed out yourself a moment ago."

"Of course, of course," Wilmarth quickly replied with another of those sinister and—yes, I must confess it—unpleasant chuckles. He added blandly, "But old Ephraim lends just the proper fierce male component to the Anima-figure—and after you've spent an adult lifetime at Miskatonic, you discover you've developed a rather different understanding from the herd's of the distinction between the imaginary and the real. Come along now."

We had entered the faculty lounge in the interim and he led me across its oak-paneled precincts to a large bay window where eight leather-upholstered easy chairs were set in a circle along with smoking stands and a table with cups, glasses, brandy decanter, and a blue-warmed urn of coffee. I looked around with a deep shiver of awe and feeling of personal unworthiness at the five elderly scholars and scientists, professors emeritus all, already seated at this figurative modern Round Table of high-minded battlers against worse than ogres and dragons—cosmic evil in all its mon-

---

*As in "The Meaning of Individuation," from *The Integration of the Personality,* Carl G. Jung, M.D., Farrar & Rinehart, 1939.

strous manifestations. There was Upham of Mathematics, in whose class poor Walter Gilman had expounded his astounding theories of hyperspace; Francis Morgan of Medicine and Comparative Anatomy, now the sole living survivor of the brave trio who had slain the Dunwich Horror on that dank September morning back in '28; Nathaniel Peaslee of Economics and Psychology, who had endured the dreadful underground journey Down Under in '35; his son Wingate of Psychology, who had been with him on that Australian expedition; and William Dyer of Geology who had been there too and four years before that undergone the horrendous adventure at the Mountains of Madness.

Save for Peaslee *père,* Dyer was the oldest present—well through his ninth decade—but it was he who, assuming a sort of informal chairmanship, now said to me sharply but warmly, "Sit down, sit down, youngster! I don't blame you for your hesitation. We call this Emeritus Alcove. Heaven pity the mere assistant professor who takes a chair without invitation! See here, what will you drink? Coffee, you say?—well, that's a prudent decision, but sometimes we need the other when our talk gets a little too far *outside,* if you take my meaning. But we're always glad to see intelligent friendly visitors from the ordinary 'outside'—Ha-ha!"

"If only to straighten out their misconceptions about Miskatonic," Wingate Peaslee put in a bit sourly. "They're forever enquiring if we offer courses in Comparative Witchcraft and so on. For your information, I'd sooner teach a course in Comparative Mass-Murder with *Mein Kampf* as the text than help anyone meddle with that stuff!"

"Particularly if one considers the sort of students we get today," Upham chimed, a bit wistfully.

"Of course, of course, Wingate," Wilmarth said soothingly to young Peaslee. "And we all know that the course in medieval metaphysics Asenath Waite took here was a completely innocent academic offering, free of arcane matters." This time he withheld his chuckle, but I sensed it was there.

Francis Morgan said, "I too have my problems discouraging sensationalism. For instance, I had to disappoint M.I.T. when they asked me for a sketch of the physiology and anatomy of the Ancient Ones, to be used in the course they give in the designing of structures and machines for 'imaginary'—Gad!—extra-terrestrial beings. Engineers are a callous breed—and in any case the Ancient Ones are not merely extra-terrestrial, but extra-cosmic. I've also had to limit access to the skeleton of Brown Jenkin, though that has given rise to a rumor that it is a file-and-brown-ochre fake like the Piltdown skull."

"Don't fret, Francis," Dyer told him. "I've had to turn down many similar requests *re* the antarctic Old Ones." He looked at me with his wonderfully bright wise old eyes, wrinkle-bedded. "You know, Miskatonic joined in the Antarctic activities of the Geophysical Year chiefly to keep exploration away from the Mountains of Madness, though the remaining Old Ones seem to be doing a pretty good job of that on their own account—hypnotic broadcasts of some type, I fancy. But that is quite all right because (This is strictly confidential!) the antarctic Old Ones appear to be *on our side,* even if their Shoggoths aren't. They're good fellows, as I've always maintained. Scientists to the last! Men!"

"Yes," Morgan agreed, "those barrel-bodied star-headed monstrosities better deserve the name than some of the specimens of genus homo scattered about the globe these days."

"Or some of our student body," Upham put in dolefully.

Dyer said, "And Wilmarth has been put to it to head off inquiries about the Plutonians in the Vermont hills and keep their existence secret with their help. How about that, Albert—are the crab-like space-flyers cooperating?"

"Oh yes, in their fashion," my conductor confirmed shortly with another of his unpleasant chuckles, this time fully uttered.

"More coffee?" Dyer asked me thoughtfully, and I passed him my cup and saucer which I had set rather awkwardly on my cardboard box atop my lap, simply because I didn't want to forget the box.

Old Nathaniel Peaslee lifted his brandy glass to his wrinkle-netted lips with tremulous but efficient fingers and spoke for the first time since my arrival. "We all have our secrets . . . and we work to see them kept," he whispered with a little whistle in his voice—imperfect dentures, perhaps. "Let the young spacemen at Woomera . . . fire their rockets over our old diggins, I say . . . and blow the sand more thickly there. It is better so."

Looking at Dyer, I ventured to ask, "I suppose you get inquiries from the Federal Government and the military forces, too. They might be more difficult to handle, I'd think."

"I'm glad you brought that up," he informed me eagerly. "I wanted to tell you about—"

But at that moment Ellery of Physics came striding briskly across the lounge, working his lips a little and with an angry frown creasing his forehead. This, I reminded myself, was the man who had analyzed an arm of a statuette figuring in the Witch-House case and discovered in it platinum, iron, tellurium, along with three unclassifiable heavy elements. He dropped into the empty chair and said, "Give me that decanter, Nate."

"A rough day at the Lab?" Upham inquired.

Ellery mollified his feelings with a generous sip of the ardent fluid and then nodded his head emphatically. "Cal Tech wanted *another* sample of the metal figurine Gilman brought back from dreamland. They're still botching their efforts to identify the trans-uranic metals in it. I had to give 'em a flat 'No!'—I told 'em we were working on the same project ourselves and closer to success. Thing'd be gone in a week if they had their way—sampled down to nothing! Californians! On the good side of the record, Libby wants to carbon-date some of the material from our museum—the Witch-House bones in particular—and I've told him 'Go ahead'."

Dyer said to him, "As chief of the Nuclear Lab, Ellery, perhaps you'll give our young visitor a sketch of what we might call Miskatonic's atomic history."

Ellery grunted but threw me a smile of sorts. "I don't see why not," he said, "though it's chiefly a history of two decades of warfare with official-dom. I should emphasize at the beginning, young man, that we're dashed lucky the Nuclear Laboratory is entirely financed by the Nathaniel Derby Pickman Foundation—"

"With some help from the Alumni Fund," Upham put in.

"Yes," Dyer told me. "We are very proud that Miskatonic has not ac-cepted one penny of Federal Assistance, or State for that matter. We are still in every sense of the words an independent private institution."

"—otherwise I don't know how we'd have held off the busybodies," El-lery swept on. "It began back in the earliest days when the Manhattan Proj-ect was still the Metallurgical Laboratory of the University of Chicago. Some big-wig had been reading the stories of the Young Gentleman of Providence and he sent a party to fetch the remains of the meteorite that fell here in '82 with its unknown radioactives. They were quite crestfallen when they dis-covered that the impact-site lay under the deepest part of the reservoir! They sent down two divers but both were lost and that was the end of that."

"Oh well, they probably didn't miss much," Upham said. "Wasn't the me-teorite supposed to have evanesced totally? Besides we've all been drinking the Arkham water from the Blasted Health Reservoir half our lifetimes."

"Yes, we have," Wilmarth put in and this time I found myself hating him for the unpleasant knowingness of his chuckle.

"Well, it apparently has not affected our longevity . . . as yet," old Peas-lee put in with a whistling little laugh.

"Since that date," Ellery continued, "there hasn't a month passed with-out Washington requesting or demanding specimens from our museum—mostly the art objects with unknown metals or radio-active elements in them, of course—and records from our science department and secret interviews with our scholars and so on. They even wanted the *Necro-nomicon!*—got the idea they'd discover in it terror-weapons worse than the H-bomb and the intercontinental ballistic missile."

"Which they would have," Wilmarth put in *sotto voce.*

"But they've never laid a finger on it!" Dyer asserted with a fierceness that almost startled me. "Nor on the Widener copy either!—*I saw to that.*" The grim tone of his voice made me forebear to ask him how. He continued solemnly, "Although it grieves me to say it, there are those in high places at Washington and in the Pentagon who are no more to be trusted with that accursed book than Wilbur Whateley. Even though the Russians are after it too, it *must* remain our sole responsibility. Merciful Creator, yes!"

"I'd rather have seen Wilbur get it," Wingate Peaslee put in gruffly.

"You wouldn't say that, Win," Francis Morgan interposed judiciously, "if you'd seen Wilbur after the library dog tore him—or of course his brother on Sentinel Hill. Gad!" He shook his head and sighed a bit tiredly. One or two of the others echoed him. With a faint preliminary grinding of its mechanism, a grandfather clock across the lounge slowly struck twelve.

"Gentlemen," I said, setting my coffee cup aside and standing up with my cardboard box, "you have entertained me in unparalleled fashion, but now it is—"

"—midnight and we all dissipate into violet and green vapors?" Wilmarth chuckled.

"No," I told him. "I was going to say that now it is September 15th and that I have in mind a short expedition, only so far as the Burying Ground behind the new Administration Building. I have here a wreath and I propose to lay it on the grave of Dr. Henry Armitage."

"The anniversary of his laying of the Dunwich Horror in 1928," Wilmarth exclaimed contritely. "A thoughtful remembrance. I'll go with you. You'll come too, Francis, of course? You had a hand in that deed."

Morgan slowly shook his head. "No, if you don't mind," he said. "My contribution was less than nothing. *I* thought a big-game rifle would be sufficient to knock over the beast. Gad!"

The others courteously begged off on one pretext or another and so it was only Wilmarth and I who wandered down Lich Street, now become a college walk for that block, between Administration and Pickman Lab, as a gibbous moon rose over French Hill, past whose base the lights of a few cars still whirled ghostlily along the new freeway.

I could have wished for a few more companions or a less sinister one than Wilmarth had struck me this morning. I couldn't help remembering how he had once been deceived by a monster masking as the scholarly Vermont recluse Henry Akeley, and how ironic and terrible it would be, if through him the same trick should be worked on another.

Nevertheless, I took advantage of the opportunity to ask him boldly, "Professor Wilmarth, your brush with the Plutonian beings occurred September 12th, 1928, almost exactly at the same time as the Dunwich affair. In fact, the very night you fled Akeley's farmhouse, Wilbur's brother was loose and ravening. Has there ever been any hint of an explanation of that monstrous coincidence?"

Wilmarth waited some seconds before replying and this time—Thank God!—there was no chuckle. In fact, his voice was quiet and without trace of levity as he at last replied, "Yes, of course there has been. I think I can risk telling you that I have kept in rather closer touch with the Plutonians or Yuggothians than perhaps even old Dyer guesses. I've had to! Besides, like Danforth's and Dyer's antarctic Old Ones, the Plutonians are not such utterly evil beings when one really gets to know them. Though they will always inspire my extremest awe!

"Well, from the hints they've given me, it appears that the Plutonians had got wind of Wilbur Whateley's intention of letting in the Ancient Ones and were preparing to block them by winning more human confederates, especially here at Miskatonic, and so on. Some of us realized it, but we were brushing the fringes of an intercosmic war."

This revelation left me speechless and it was not until the protesting black-painted iron gate had been pushed open and we stood among the age-darkened moonlit headstones that our conversation was resumed. As I reverently lifted Armitage's wreath from its container, Wilmarth gripped me by the elbow, and speaking almost into my ear, said with a quiet intensity, "There is another piece of information the Plutonians have supplied me which I believe I should share with you. You may not be willing to credit it at first—I wasn't!—but now I've come to believe it. You know the Plutonians' trick of extracting the living brains of beings unable to fly through space, preserving those brains immortally in metal cannisters, and carrying them about with them throughout the cosmos to see, via the proper instruments, and hear and comment on its secrets? Well—I'm afraid this will give you a nasty shock, but tell yourself there's a good side to it, for there is—on the night of March 14th, 1937, when the Young Gentleman lay dying in the Rhode Island Hospital, a secret entry was made into the Jane Brown wing, and to use his words—or rather, mine—his brain was removed 'by fissions so adroit that it would be crude to call the operation surgery,' so that he is now flying some course between Hydra and Polaris, safe in the arms of a night gaunt, reveling forever in the wonders of the universe he deeply loved." And with a gesture dignified yet grand, Wilmarth lifted his arm toward the North Star where it faintly shone in the gray sky high above Meadow Hill and the Miskatonic.

I shivered with mixed emotions. Suddenly the sky was full. I knew now the deeper reason I had all evening wanted to shudder at my conductor, yet was deeply happy that it was a reason by which I could respect him the more.

Arm in arm, we moved toward the simple grave of Dr. Armitage.

[*The Dark Brotherhood and Other Pieces,* by H. P. Lovecraft and
Divers Hands (Arkham House, 1966)]

THE TERROR FROM THE DEPTHS

Remember thee!
Ay, thou poor ghost, while memory holds a seat
In this distracted globe.

—Hamlet

The following manuscript was found in a curiously embossed copper and German silver casket of highly individual modern workmanship which was purchased at an auction of unclaimed property that had been held in police custody for the prescribed number of years in Los Angeles County, California. In the casket with the manuscript were two slim volumes of verse: *Azathoth and Other Horrors* by Edward Pickman Derby, Onyx Sphinx Press, Arkham, Massachusetts, and *The Tunneler Below* by Georg Reuter Fischer, Ptolemy Press, Hollywood, California. The manuscript was penned by the second of these poets, except for the two letters and the telegram interleafed into it. The casket and its contents had passed into police custody on March 16, 1937, upon the discovery of Fischer's mutilated body by his collapsed brick dwelling in Vultures Roost under circumstances of considerable horror.

Today one will search street maps of the Hollywood Hills area in vain for the unincorporated community of Vultures Roost. Shortly after the events narrated in these pages its name (already long criticized) was changed upon the urging of prudent real-estate dealers to Paradise Crest, which was in turn absorbed by the City of Los Angeles—an event not without parallel in that general neighborhood, as when after certain scandals best forgotten, the name of Runnymede was changed to Tarzana after the chief literary creation of its most illustrious and blameless inhabitant.

The magneto-optical method of detection referred to herein, "which has already discovered two new elements," is neither fraud nor fancy, but a technique highly regarded in the 1930s (though since discredited), as may be confirmed by consulting any table of elements from that period or the entries "alabamine" and "virginium" in *Webster's New International Dictionary*, second edition, unabridged. (They are not, of course, in today's tables.) While the "unknown master builder Simon Rodia" with whom Fischer's father conferred is the widely revered folk architect (now deceased) who created the matchlessly beautiful Watts Towers.

It is only with considerable effort that I can restrain myself from plunging into the very midst of a description of those unequivocably monstrous hints that have determined me to take—within the next eighteen hours and no later—a desperate and initially destructive step. There is much to write and only too little time in which to write it.

I myself need no written argument to bolster my beliefs. It is all more real to me than everyday experience. I have only to close my eyes to see Albert Wilmarth's horror-whitened long-jawed face and migraine-tormented brow. There may be something of clairvoyance in this, for I imagine his expression has not changed greatly since I last saw him. And I need not make the slightest effort to hear those hideously luring voices, like the susurrus of infernal bees and glorious wasps, which impinge upon an inner ear which I now can never and would never close. Indeed, as I listen to them, I wonder if there is anything to be gained from penning this necessarily outré document. It will be found—if it is found—in a locality where serious people do not attach any importance to strange revelations and where charlatanry is only too common. Perhaps that is well and perhaps I should make doubly sure by tearing up this sheet, for there is in my mind no doubt of the results that would follow a systematic, scientific effort to investigate those forces which have ambushed and shall soon claim (and perhaps welcome?) me.

I shall write, however, if only to satisfy a peculiar personal whim. Ever since I can remember I have been drawn to literary creation, but until this very day certain elusive circumstances and crepuscular forces have prevented my satisfactorily completing anything more than a number of poems, mostly short, and tiny prose sketches. It would interest me to discover if my new knowledge has freed me to some extent from those inhibitions. Time enough when I have completed this statement to consider the advisability of its destruction (before I perpetrate the greater and crucial destruction). Truth to tell, I am not especially moved by what may or may not happen to my fellow men; there have been *profound* influences (yes, from the depths indeed!) exerted upon my emotional growth and upon the ultimate direction of my loyalties—as will become clear to the reader in due course.

I might begin this narrative with a bald recital of the implications of the recorded findings of Professors Atwood and Pabodie's portable magneto-optic geo-scanner, or with Albert Wilmarth's horrendous revelations of the mind-shattering, planet-wide researches made during the past decade by a secret coterie of faculty members of far-off Miskatonic University in witch-haunted, shadow-beset Arkham and a few lonely colleagues in Boston and Providence, Rhode Island, or with the shivery clues that with nefarious innocence have found their way even into the poetry I have written during the past few years. If I did that, you would be immediately convinced that I was psychotic. The *reasons* that led me, step by step, to my present awesome convictions, would appear as progressive *symptoms,* and the monstrous horror behind it all would seem a shuddersome paranoid fantasy. Indeed, that will probably be your final judgement in any case, but I will nevertheless tell you what happened just as it happened to me. Then you will have the same opportunity as I had to discern, if you can, just where reality left off and imagination took up and where imagination stopped and psychosis supervened.

Perhaps within the next seventeen hours something will happen or be revealed that will in part substantiate what I shall write. I do not think so, for there is yet untold cunning in the decadent cosmic order which has entrapped me. Perhaps they will not let me finish this narrative; perhaps they will anticipate my own resolve. I am almost sure they have only held off thus far because they are sure I will do their work for them. No matter.

The sun is just now rising, red and raw, over the treacherous and crumbling hills of Griffith Park (Wilderness were a better designation). The sea fog still wraps the sprawling suburbs below, its last vestiges are sliding out of high, dry Laurel Canyon, but far off to the south I can begin to discern the black congeries of scaffold oil wells near Culver City, like stiff-legged robots massing for the attack. And if I were at the bedroom window that opens to the northwest, I would see night's shadows still lingering in the precipitous wilds of Hollywoodland above the faint, twisting, weed-encroached, serpent-haunted trails I have limped along daily for most of my natural life, tracing and retracing them ever more compulsively.

I can turn off the electric light now; my study is already pierced by shafts of low, red sunlight. I am at my table, ready to write the day through. Everything around me has the appearance of eminent normality and security. There are no signs remaining of Albert Wilmarth's frantic midnight departure with the magneto-optic apparatus he brought from the East, yet as if by clairvoyance I can see his long-jawed horror-sucked face as he clings automatically to the steering wheel of his little Austin scuttling across the desert like a frightened beetle, the geo-scanner lying on the seat beside him. This day's sun has reached him before me as he flees back toward his deeply beloved, impossibly distant New England. That sun's smoky red blaze must be in his fear-wide eyes, for I know that no power can turn him back toward the land that slips uncouth into the titan Pacific. I bear him no resentment—I have no reason to. His nerves were shattered by the terrors he bravely insisted on helping to investigate for ten long years against his steadier comrades' advice. And at the very end, I am certain, he saw horrors beyond imagining. Yet he waited to ask me to go with him and only I know how much that must have cost him. He gave me my opportunity to escape; if I had wanted to, I could have made the attempt.

But I believe my fate was decided many years ago.

My name is Georg Reuter Fischer. I was born in 1912 of Swiss parents in the city of Louisville, Kentucky, with an inwardly twisted right foot which might have been corrected by a brace, except that my father did not believe in interfering with the workings of Nature, his deity. He was a mason and stonecutter of great physical strength, vast energy, remarkable intuitive gifts (a dowser for water, oil, and metals), great natural artistry, unschooled but profoundly self-educated. A little after the Civil War, when he was a young boy, he had immigrated to this country with his father, also a mason, and upon the death of the latter, inherited a small but profitable business. Late in life he married my mother, Marie Reuter, daughter of a farmer for whom he had dowsed not only a well but a deposit of granite worth quarrying. I was the child of their age and their only child, coddled by my mother and the object of my father's more thoughtful devotion. I have few memories of our life in Louisville, but those few are eminently wholesome ones: visions of an ordered, cheerful household, of many cousins and friends, of visitings and laughter, and two great Christmas celebrations; also memories of fascinatedly watching my father at his stonecutting, bringing a profusion of flowers and leaves to life from death-pale granite.

And I will say here, because it is important to my story, that I afterward learned that our Fischer and Reuter relatives considered me exceptionally intelligent for my tender age. My father and mother always believed this, but one must allow for parental bias.

In 1917 my father profitably sold his business and brought his tiny family west, to build with his own hands a last home in this land of sunlight, crumbling sandstones, and sea-spawned hills, Southern California. This was in part because doctors had advised it as essential for the sake of my mother's failing health, slow victim of the dread tubercular scourge, but my father had always had a strong yearning for clear skies, year-round heat, and the primeval sea, a deep conviction that his destiny somehow lay west and was involved with Earth's hugest ocean: from which perhaps the moon was torn.

My father's deep-seated longing for this outwardly wholesome and bright, inwardly sinister and eaten-away landscape, where Nature herself presents the naïve face of youth masking the corruptions of age, has given me much food for thought, though it is in no way a remarkable longing. Many people migrate here, healthy as well as sick, drawn by the sun, the promise of perpetual summer, the broad if arid fields. The only unusual circumstance worthy of note is that there is a larger sprinkling than might be expected of persons of professed mystical and utopian bent. The Brothers of the Rose, the Theosophists, the Foursquare Gospelers, the Christian Scientists, Unity, the Brotherhood of the Grail, the spiritualists, the astrologers—all are here and many more besides. Believers in the need of return to primitive states and primitive wisdoms, practitioners of pseudo-disciplines dictated by pseudo-sciences—yes, even a few overly sociable hermits—one finds them everywhere; the majority awaken only my pity and distaste, so lacking in logic and avid for publicity are they. At no time—and let me emphasize this—have I been at all interested in their doings and in their ignorantly parroted principles, except possibly from the viewpoint of comparative psychology.

And they were brought here by that excessive love of sunlight which characterizes most faddists of any sort and that urge to find an unsettled, unorganized land in which utopias might take root and burgeon, untroubled by urbane ridicule and tradition-bred opposition—the same urge that led the Mormons to desert-guarded Salt Lake City, their paradise of Deseret.

This seems an adequate explanation, even without bringing in the fact that Los Angeles, a city of retired farmers and small merchants, a city made hectic by the presence of the uncouth motion-picture industry, would naturally attract charlatans of all varieties. Yes, that explanation is still sufficient to me, and I am rather pleased, for even now I should hate to think that those hideously alluring voices a-mutter with secrets from beyond the rim of the cosmos *necessarily* have some dim, continent-wide *range.*

("The carven rim," they are saying now here in my study. "The proto-shoggoths, the diagramed corridor, the elder Pharos, the dreams of Cutlu . . .")

Settling my mother and myself at a comfortable Hollywood boarding-house, where the activities of the infant film industry provided us with colorful distraction, my father tramped the hills in search of a suitable property, bringing to bear his formidable talent for locating underground water and desirable rock formations. During this period, it occurs to me now, he almost certainly pioneered those trails which it is my own invariable and ever more compulsive wont to walk. Within three months he had found and purchased the property he sought near a predominantly Alsatian and French settlement (a scatter of bungalows, no more) bearing the perhaps exaggeratedly picturesque name Vultures Roost, redolent of the Old West.

Clearing and excavation of the property revealed an upthrust stratum of fine-grained solid metamorphic rock, while a little boring provided an excellent well, to the incredulous astonishment of his initially hostile neighbors. My father kept his counsel and began, mostly with his own hands alone, to erect a brick structure of moderate size that by its layout and plans promised a dwelling of surpassing beauty. This occasioned more head-shaking and lectures on the unwisdom of building brick structures in a region where earthquakes were not unknown. They called it Fischer's Folly, I learned later. Little did they realize my father's skill and the tenacity of his masonry!

He bought a small truck and scoured the area as far south as Laguna Beach and as far north as Malibu, searching for the kilns that would provide him with bricks and tiles of requisite quality. In the end he sheathed the roof partly with copper, which has turned a beautiful green with the years. During these searches he became closely acquainted with the visionary and remarkably progressive Abbott Kinney, who was building the resort of Venice on the coast ten miles away, and with the swarthy, bright-eyed, unknown master builder Simon Rodia, self-educated like himself. All three men shared a rich vein of the poetry of stone, ceramics, and metals.

There must have been prodigious reserves of strength in the old man (for my father was that now, his hair whitely grizzled) to enable him to accomplish so much hard labor, for within two years my mother and I were able to move into our new home at Vultures Roost and take up our lives there.

I was delighted with my new surroundings and to be rejoined with my father, and only resentful of the time I must spend at school, to which my father drove me and from which he fetched me each day. I especially enjoyed rambling, occasionally with my father but chiefly by myself, through the wild, dry, rock-crowned hills, spry despite my twisted foot. My mother was fearful for me, especially because of the hairy brown and black tarantulas one sometimes encountered and the snakes, including venomous rattlers, but I was not to be restrained.

My father was happy, but also like a man in a dream as he worked unceasingly at the innumerable tasks, chiefly artistic, involved in finishing our home. It was a structure of rich beauty, though our neighbors continued to shake their heads and cluck dubiously at its hexagonal shape, partly rounded roof, thick walls of tightly mortared (though unreinforced) brick, and the area of brightly colored tile and floridly engraved stone. "Fischer's Folly," they'd whisper, and chuckle. But swarthy Simon Rodia nodded approvingly when he visited and once Abbott Kinney came to admire, driven in an expensive car by a black chauffeur with whom he seemed on terms of easy friendship.

My father's stone engravings were indeed quite fanciful and even a little disconcerting in their subject matter and location. One was in the basement's floor of natural rock, which he had smoothed. From time to time I'd watch him work on it. Desert plants and serpents seemed to be its subject matter, but as one studied it one became aware that there was much marine stuff too: serrated looping seaweeds, coiling eels, fishes that trailed tentacles, suckered octopus arms, and two giant squid eyes peering from a coral-crusted castle. And in its midst he boldly hewed in a flowery stone script, "The Gate of Dreams." My childish imagination was fired, but I was a little frightened too.

It was about this time—1921 or thereabouts—that my sleepwalking began, or at any rate showed signs of becoming disturbingly persistent. Several times my father found me at varying distances from the house along one of the paths I favored in my limping rambles and carried me tenderly back, chilled and shivering, for unlike Kentucky in summer, Southern California nights are surprisingly cold. And more than once I was found huddled and still asleep in our cellar alongside the grotesquely floor-set "Gate of Dreams" bas-relief—to which, incidentally, my mother had taken a dislike which she tried to conceal from my father.

At that time too my sleeping habits began to show other abnormalities, some of them contradictory. Although an active and apparently healthy boy of ten, I was still sleeping infancy's twelve hours or more a night. Yet despite this unusual length of slumber coupled with the restlessness my sleepwalking would seem to have indicated, I never dreamed or at any rate remembered dreams upon awakening. And with one notable exception this has been true for my entire life.

The exception occurred a little later on, when I was eleven or twelve—in 1923 or thereabouts. I remember those few dreams (there were no more than eight or nine of them) with matchless vividness. How else?—since they were my life's only ones and since . . . but I must not anticipate. At the time I was secretive about them, telling neither my father nor my mother, as if for fear my parents might worry or (children are odd!) disapprove, until one final night.

In my dream I would find myself making my way through low passages and tunnels, all crudely cut or perhaps *gnawed* from solid rock. Often I felt I was at a great distance under the earth, though why I thought this in my dream I cannot say, except that there was often a sensation of heat and an indescribable feeling of pressure from above. This last sensation was diminished almost to nothing at times, though. And sometimes I felt there were vast amounts of water far above me, though why I suspected this I cannot say, for the strange tunnels were always very dry. Yet in my dreams I came to assume that the burrows extended limitlessly under the Pacific.

There was no obvious source of illumination in the passages. My dream explanation of how I then managed to see them was fantastic, though rather ingenious. The floor of the tunnels was colored a strange purplish-green. This I explained in my dream as being the reflection of cosmic rays (which were much in the newspapers then, firing my boyish imagination) that came down through the thick rock above from distantmost outer space. The rounded ceiling of the tunnels, on the other hand, had a weird orange-blue glow. This, I seemed to know, was caused by the reflection of certain rays unknown to science that came up through the solid rock from the Earth's incandescent, constricted core.

The eerie mixed light revealed to me the strange engravings or ridgy pictures everywhere covering the tunnels' walls. They had a strong suggestion of the marine to them and also of the monstrous, yet they were strangely *generalized,* as if they were the mathematical diagrams of oceans and their denizens and of whole universes of alien life. If *the dreams* of a monster of supernatural mentality could be given visual shape, then they would be like those endless forms I saw on the tunnels' walls. Or if *the dreams* of such a monster were half materialized and able to move through such tunnels, *they would shape the walls in such fashion.*

At first in my dreams I was not conscious of having a body. I seemed to be a viewpoint floating along the tunnels at a definitely *rhythmic* rate, now faster, now slower.

And at first I never saw anything in those tormenting tunnels, though I was continually conscious of a fear that I might—a fear mixed with a desire. This was a most disturbing and exhausting feeling, which I could hardly have concealed upon awakening save that (with one exception) I never woke until my dream had played itself out, as it were, and my feelings were temporarily exhausted.

And then in my next dream I did begin to see things—creatures—in the tunnels, floating through them in the same general rhythmic fashion as I (or my viewpoint) progressed. They were worms about as long as a man and as thick as a man's thigh, cylindrical and untapering. From end to end, as many as a centipede's legs, were pairs of tiny wings, translucent like a fly's, which vibrated unceasingly, producing an unforgettably sinister low-pitched *hum.*

They had no eyes—their heads were one circular mouth lined with rows of triangular teeth like a shark's. Although blind, they seemed able to sense each other at short distances and their sudden lurching swerves then to avoid colliding with each other held a particular horror for me. (It was a little like my lurching limp.)

In my very next dream I became aware of my own dream body. In brief. I was myself one of those same winged worms. The horror I felt was extreme, yet once more the dream lasted until its intensity was damped out and I could awaken with only the memory of terror, still able (I thought) to keep my dreams a secret.

The next time I had my dream it was to see three of the winged worms writhing in a wider section of tunnel where the sensation of pressure from above was minimal. I was still observer rather than participant, floating in my worm body in a narrower side passageway. How I was able to see while in one of the blind worm bodies, my dream logic did not explain.

They were worrying a rather small human victim. Their three snouts converged upon and covered his face. Their sinister buzzing had a hungry note and there were sucking sounds.

Blond hair, white pajamas, and (projecting from the right leg of those) a foot slightly shrunken and *twisted sharply inward* told me the victim was myself.

At that instant I was shaken violently, the scene swam, and through it my mother's huge terrorized face peered down at me with my father's anxious visage close behind.

I went into convulsions of terror, flailing my limbs, and I screamed and screamed. It was hours literally before I could be quieted down, and days before my father let me tell them my nightmare.

Thereafter he made a strict rule: that no one ever try to shake me awake, no matter how bad a nightmare I seemed to be having. Later I learned he'd watch me at such times with knitted brow, suppressing the impulse to rouse me and seeing to it that no one else tried to do so.

For several nights thereafter I fought sleep, but when my nightmare was never repeated and once more I could never remember having dreamed at all when I wakened, I quieted down and my life, both sleeping and waking, became very tranquil again. In fact, even my sleepwalking became less frequent, although I continued to sleep for abnormally long hours, a practice now encouraged by my father's injunction that I never be wakened unnaturally.

But I have since come to wonder whether this apparent diminishment of my unconscious night-wandering were not because I, or some fraction of me, had become more cunningly deceitful. *Habits* have in any case a way of slipping slowly from the serious notice of those around.

At times, though, I would catch my father looking at me speculatively, as though he would have dearly liked to talk with me of various deep matters, but in the end he would always restrain this impulse (if I had divined it rightly) and content himself with encouraging me in my school studies and rambling exercise despite the latter's dangers: there *were* more rattlesnakes about my favorite paths, perhaps because opossums and raccoons were being exterminated; he made me wear high laced shoes of stout leather.

And once or twice I got the impression that he and Simon Rodia were talking secretly about me when the latter visited.

On the whole my life was a lonely one and has remained so to this day. We had no neighbors who were friends, no friends who were neighbors. At first this was because of the relative isolation of our residence and the suspicion that Germanic names uniformly called forth in the years following the World War. But it continued even after we began to have more neighbors, tolerant newcomers. Perhaps things would have been different if my father had lived longer. (His health was good save for a touch of eyestrain—dancing colors he'd see briefly.)

But that was not to be. On that fatal Sunday in 1925 he had joined me on one of my customary walks and we had just reached one of my favorite spots when the ground gave way under his feet and he vanished from beside me, his startled exclamation dropped in pitch as he fell rapidly. For once his instinct for underground conditions had deserted him. There was a little scraping rumble as a few rocks and some gravel landslided, then silence. I approached the weed-fringed black hole on my belly and peered down fearfully.

From very far below (it sounded) I heard my father call faintly, "Georg! Get help!" His voice now had a strained, higher-pitched sound, as if his chest were being constricted.

"Father! I'm coming down," I cried, cupping my hands about my mouth, and I had thrust my twisted foot into the hole searching for support, when his frantic yet clearly enunciated words came up, his voice still higher-pitched and even more strained, as if he had to make a great effort to get sufficient breath for them: "Do *not* come down, Georg—you'll start an avalanche. Get help . . . a rope!"

After a moment's hesitation I withdrew my leg and set off for home at a hobbling gallop. My horror was heightened (or perhaps a little relieved) by a sense of the dramatic—early that year we had listened for weeks on the little crystal set I'd built to the radioed reports of the long protracted, exciting efforts (ultimately unsuccessful) to rescue Floyd Collins from where he'd got himself trapped in Sand Cave near Cave City, Kentucky. I suppose I anticipated some such drama for my father.

Most fortunately a young doctor was making a call in our neighborhood and he was foremost in the party of men I soon guided back to where my father had disappeared. No sounds at all came from the black hole, although we called and called, and I remember that a couple of men had begun to look at me dubiously, as if I'd invented the whole thing, when the courageous young doctor insisted against the advice of most on being lowered into the hole—they'd brought a strong rope *and* an electric flashlight.

He was a long time going down, descending about fifty feet in all while calls went back and forth, and almost as long being drawn up. When he emerged all smeared with sandy dirt—great orange smudges—it was to tell us (he made a point of laying his hand on my shoulder; I could see my mother hurrying up between two other women) that my father was inextricably wedged in down there with little more than his head exposed and that he was, to an absolute certainty, dead.

At that moment there was another grating rumble, and the black hole collapsed upon itself. One of the men standing on its edge was barely jerked to safety. My mother shrieked, threw herself down on the shaking brown weeds, and was drawn back too.

In the subsequent weeks it was decided that my father's body could not be recovered. Some bags of concrete and sand were dumped into what was left of the hole to seal it. My mother was forbidden to erect a monument at the spot, but in some sort of compensation—I didn't understand the logic of it—Los Angeles County presented her with a cemetery plot elsewhere. (It now holds her own body.) An unofficial funeral service conducted by a Latin-American priest was eventually held at the spot, and Simon Rodia, defying the injunction, put up a small, nonsectarian ovoid monument of his own matchlessly tough white concrete bearing my father's name and beautifully inset with a vaguely aquatic or naval design in fragmented blue and green glass. It is still there.

After my father's death I became more withdrawn and brooding than ever, and my mother, a shy consumptive woman full of hysterical fears, hardly encouraged me to become sociable. In fact, almost as long as I can remember and certainly ever since Anton Fischer's tragic and abrupt demise, nothing has ever bulked large with me save my own brooding and this brick house set in the hills with its strange, queerly set stone carvings and the hills themselves, those sandy, spongy, salt-soaked, sun-baked hills. There has been altogether too much of them in my background: I have limped too long along their crumbling rims, under their cracked and treacherous overhanging sandstones, and through the months-dry streams that thread their separating canyons. I have thought a great deal about the old days when, some Indians are said to have believed, the Strangers came down from the stars with the great meteor shower and the lizard men perished in the course of their frantic digging for water and the scaly sea men came tunneling in from their encampments beneath the vast Pacific which constituted a whole world to the west, extensive as that of the stars. I early developed too great a love for such savage fancies. Too much of my physical landscape has become the core of my mental landscape. And during the nights of my long, long sleepings, I hobbled through them both, I am somehow sure. While by day I had horrible fugitive visions of my father, underground, dead-alive, companied by the winged worms of my nightmare. Moreover, I developed the notion or fantasy that there was a network of *tunnels* underlying the paths I limped along and corresponding to them exactly, but at varying depths and coming closest to the surface at my "favorite spots."

("The legend of Yig," the voices are droning. "The violet wisps, the globular nebulas, Canis Tindalos and their foul essence, the nature of the

Doels, the tinted chaos, great Cutlu's minions . . ." I have made breakfast but I cannot eat. I thirstily gulp hot coffee.)

I would hardly keep harping on my sleepwalking and on the unnaturally long hours I spent so deeply asleep that my mother would vow that my mind was elsewhere, were it not associated with a lapse in the intellectual promise I was said to have shown in earlier years. True, I got along well enough in the semi-rural grade school I trudged to and later in the suburban high school to which a bus took me; true too that I early showed interest in many subjects and flashes of excellent logic and imaginative reasoning. The trouble was that I did not seem ever able to pursue any of those flashes and make a steady and persistent effort. There would be times when my teachers would worry my mother with reports of my unpreparedness and my disregard of assignments, though when examination time came I almost invariably managed to make a creditable showing. My interests in more personal directions, too, seemed to peter out very quickly. I was certainly peculiarly deficient in the power of attention. I remember often sitting down with a favorite book or text and then finding myself, minutes or hours later, turning over pages far ahead of anything I could remember reading. Sometimes only the memory of my father's injunctions to study, to study *deeply*, would keep me prodding on.

You may not think this matter worth mentioning. There is nothing strange in a lonely sheltered child failing to show great willpower and mental energy. There is nothing strange in such a child becoming slothful, weak, and indecisive. Nothing strange—only much to pity and reproach. The powers that be know I reproached myself often enough, for as my father had encouraged me to, I felt a power and a capability somewhere in myself, but somehow inhibited. But there are only too many people with power they cannot loose. It is only *later* events that have made me see something significant in my lapsings.

My mother followed to the letter my father's directions for my higher education, which I only learned of now. Upon my graduation from high school I was sent to a venerable Eastern institution of learning not as well known as those of the Ivy League, but of equally high standing—Miskatonic University, which lies on the serpentine river of that name within the antique town of Arkham with its gambrel roofs and elm-shaded avenues quiet as the footsteps of a witch's familiar. My father had first heard of the school from an Eastern employer of his talents, a Harley Warren for whom he had done some unusual dowsing in a cemetery within a swamp of cypresses, and that man's high praise of Miskatonic had imprinted itself indelibly upon his memory. My previous school record did not permit of this (I lacked certain prerequisites) but I just barely managed—much to the surprise of all my previous teachers—to pass a stiff entrance examination which required, like that of Dartmouth, some knowledge of Greek as well as Latin. Only I knew how much furious, imagination-invoking guessing that took. I could not bear to fall utterly short of my father's hopes for me.

Unfortunately, my efforts were in vain. Before the first term ended I was back in Southern California, physically and mentally depleted by a series of attacks of nervousness, homesickness, actual ailment (anemia), an increase in the hours I devoted to sleep, and an almost incredible recurrence of my sleepwalking, which more than once carried me deep into the wild hills west of Arkham. I tried for what seemed to me a long time to stick it out, but was advised by the college doctors to give it up after some particularly bad attacks. I believe that they thought I was not cut out to be even a moderately strong individual and that they pitied me more than they sympathized with me. It is not a good thing to see a youth racked by sentiments and longings proper to a fearful child.

And they appeared to be right in this (although I know now that they were wrong), for my malady turned out (*apparently*) to be simple homesickness and nothing more. It was with a feeling of immense relief that I returned to my mother and our brick home in the hills, and with each room I reentered I gained more assurance—even, or perhaps especially, the cellar with its well-swept floor of solid rock, my father's tools and chemicals (acids, etc.), and the marinely decorated, floor-set rock inscription "The Gate of Dreams." It was as though all the time I had been at Miskatonic there had been an invisible leash dragging me back, and only now had its pressure slackened completely.

(Those voices *are* continent-wide, of course: "The essential salts, the fane of Dagon, the gray twisted brittle monstrosity, the flute-tormented pandemonium, the coral-encrusted towers of Rulay . . .")

And the hills helped me as much as my home. For a month I roamed them daily and walked the old familiar paths between the parched and browning undergrowth, my mind full of old tales and scraps of childhood brooding. I think it was only then, only with my returning, that I first came fully to realize how much (and a little of *what*) those hills meant to me. From Mount Waterman and steep Mount Wilson with its great observatory and hundred-inch reflector down through cavernous Tujunga Canyon with its many sinuous offshoots to the flat lands and then across the squat Verdugo Hills and the closer ones with Griffith Observatory and its lesser 'scopes, to sinister, almost inaccessible Potrero and great twisting Topanga Canyons that open with the abruptness of catastrophe upon the monstrous, primeval Pacific—all of them (the hills) with few exceptions sandy, cracked, and treacherous, the earth like rock and the rock like dried earth, rotten, crumbling, and porous: all this had such a hold on me (the limper, the fearful listener) as to be obsessive. And indeed there were more and more symptoms of obsession now: I favored certain paths over others for ill-defined reasons and there were places I could not pass without stopping for a little. My fantasy or notion became stronger than ever that there were *tunnels* under the paths, traveled by beings which attracted the venomous snakes of the outer world because they were akin to them. Could some eerie reality have underlaid my childhood nightmare?—I shied away from that thought.

All this, as I say, I realized during the month after my defeated return from the East. And at the end of that month I resolved to conquer my obsession and my revolting homesickness and all the subtle weaknesses and inner hindrances that kept me from being the man my father had dreamed of. I had found that a complete break such as my father had planned for me (Miskatonic) would not work; so I determined to work out my troubles without running away: I would take courses at nearby UCLA (the University of California at Los Angeles). I would study and exercise, build up both body and mind. I remember that my determination was intense. There is something very ironic about that, for my plan, logical as it seemed, was the one sure course to further psychological entrapment.

For quite some time, however, I seemed to be getting on successfully. With systematic exercise and better-controlled diet and rest (still my twelve hours a night), I became healthier than I ever had been before. All the troubles that had beset me in the East vanished completely away. No longer did I wake shuddering from my dreamless sleepwalking; in fact, as far as I could determine at the time, that habit had gone for good. And at college, from which I returned home nightly, I made steady progress. It was then that I first began to write those imaginative and pessimistic poems tinged with metaphysical speculation that have won me some little attention from a small circle of readers. Oddly, they were sparked by the one significant item I had brought back with me from shadow-beset Arkham, a little book of verse I'd bought at a dusty secondhand store there, *Azathoth and Other Horrors* by Edward Pickman Derby, a local poet.

Now I know that my spurt of new effort during my college years was largely deceptive. Because I had decided upon a new course of life that brought me into a few new situations (though keeping me at home), I thought I was progressing vastly. I managed to keep on believing that for all my college years. That I could never study any subject profoundly, that I could never create anything that took a protracted effort, I explained by telling myself that what I was doing was "preparation" and "intellectual orientation" for some great future effort. For several years I managed to conceal from myself the fact that I could only call a tithe of my energy my own, while the residuum was being shunted down only the powers that be know what inner channels.

(I thought I knew what books I was studying, but the voices now are telling me, "The runes of Nug-Soth, the clavicle of Nyarlathotep, the litanies of Lomar, the secular meditations of Pierre-Louis Montagny, the *Necronomicon,* the chants of Crom-Ya, the overviews of Yiang-Li . . .")

(It is midday or later outside, but the house is cool. I have managed to eat a little and made more coffee. I have been down to the basement, checking my father's tools and things, his sledge, carboys of acid, et cetera, and looking at "The Gate of Dreams" and treading softly. The voices are strongest there.)

Suffice it that during my six college and "poetic" years (I couldn't carry a full load of courses) I lived not as a man, but as a fraction of a man. I had gradually given up all grand ambitions and become content to lead a life in miniature. I spent my time going to easy classes, writing fragments of prose and an occasional poem, caring for my mother (who except for her worries about me was undemanding) and for my father's house (so well built it needed hardly any care), rambling almost absentmindedly in the hills, and sleeping prodigiously. I had no friends. In fact, we had no friends. Abbott Kinney had died and Los Angeles had stolen his Venice. Simon Rodia gave up his visits, for he was now totally preoccupied with his great single-handed building project. Once on my mother's urging I went to Watts, a settlement of flower-decked humble bungalows dwarfed by his fabulous backyard towers that were rising like a blue-green Persian dream. He had trouble recalling who I was and then he watched me strangely as he worked. The money my father had left (in silver dollars) was ample for my mother and myself. In short, I had become, not unpleasantly, *resigned.*

This was all the easier for me because of my growing absorption in the doctrines of such men as Oswald Spengler who believe that culture and civilization go by cycles and that our own Faustian Western world, with all its grandiose dream of scientific progress, is headed toward a barbarism that will engulf it as surely as the Goths, Vandals, Scythians, and Huns engulfed mighty Rome and her longer-lived sister, dwindling Byzantium. As I looked from my hilltops down on bustling Los Angeles always a-building, I placidly thought of the future days when little bands of blustering, ill-kempt barbarians will walk the streets of humped and pitted asphalt and look on each of its ruined, many-purposed buildings as just another "hut"; when high-set Griffith Park Planetarium, romantically rock-built, high-walled, and firmly bastioned, will be the stronghold of some petty dictator; when industry and science will be gone and all their machines and instruments rusted and broken and their use forgotten . . . and *all* our works forgotten as completely as those of the sunken civilization of Mu in the Pacific, of the fragments of whose cities only remain Nan Matol and Rapa Nui, or Easter Island.

But *whence* did these thoughts really come? Not entirely or even principally from Spengler, I'll be bound. No, they had a *deeper* source, I greatly fear.

Yet thus I thought, thus I believed, and thus I was wooed away from the pursuits and tempting goals of our commercial world. I saw everything in terms of transciency, decadence, and decline—as if the times were as rotten and crumbling as the hills which obsessed me.

It was that I was *convinced,* not that I was morbid. No, my health was better than ever and I was neither bored nor dissatisfied. Oh, I occasionally berated myself for failure to manifest the promise my father had seen in me, but on the whole I was strangely content. I had a weird sense of power and self-satisfaction, as if I were a man in the midst of some engrossing pursuit. You know the pleasant relief and bone-deep satisfaction that comes after a day of successful hard work? Well, *that was the way I felt almost all the time, day in and day out.* And I took my happiness as a gift of the gods. It did not occur to me to ask, *"Which* gods? Are they from heaven . . . or from *the underworld?"*

Even my mother was happier, her disease arrested, her son devoted to her and leading a busy life (on a very small scale) and doing nothing to worry her beyond his occasional rambles in the snake-infested hills.

Fortune smiled on us. Our brick dwelling rode out the severe Long Beach earthquake of March 10, 1933, without sustaining the least damage. Those who still called it Fischer's Folly were nonplussed.

Last year (1936) I duly received from UCLA my bachelor's diploma in English literature, with a minor in history, my mother proudly attending the ceremony. And a month or so later she seemed as childishly delighted as I at the arrival of the first bound copies of my little book of verse, *The Tunneler Below,* printed at my own expense, and in my hubristic mood of auctorial conceit I not only sent out several copies for review but also donated two to the UCLA library and two more to that at Miskatonic. In my covering letter to the erudite Dr. Henry Armitage, librarian at the latter institution, I mentioned not only my brief attendance there, but also my inspiration by an Arkham poet. I also told him a little about the circumstances of my composition of the poems.

I joked deprecatingly to my mother about this last expansive gesture of mine, but she knew how deeply I had been hurt by my failure at Miskatonic and how strongly I desired to repair my reputation there, so when only a few weeks later a letter came addressed to me and bearing the Arkham postmark, she hurried out into the hills quite against her usual wont, to bring it to me, I having just gone out on one of my rambles.

From where I was, I barely heard, yet also recognized her mortal screams. I rushed back at my most desperate limping speed. At the very spot where my father had perished, I found her writhing on the hard, dry ground and screaming still—and near to her and whipping about, the large young rattlesnake that had bitten her on the calf, which was already swelling.

I killed the horrid thing with the stick I carry, then slashed the bite with my sharp pocketknife and sucked it out and injected antivenin from the kit I have always with me on my walks.

All to no avail. She died two days later in the hospital. Once more there was not only shock and depression, but also the dismal business of a funeral to get through (at least we already owned a grave lot), this time a more conventional ceremony, but this time I was wholly alone.

It was a week before I could bring myself to look at the letter she'd been bringing me. After all, it had been the cause of her death. I almost tore it up unread. But after I had got into it, I became more and more interested and then incredulously amazed . . . and frightened. Here it is, in its entirety:

118 Saltonstall St.,
Arkham, Mass.,
Aug. 12, 1936.

Georg Reuter Fischer, Esq.,
Vultures Roost,
Hollywood, Calif.

My dear Sir:—
Dr. Henry Armitage took the liberty of letting me peruse your *The Tunneler Below* before it was placed on general circulation in the university library. May one who serves only in the outer court of the muses' temple, and particularly outside Polyhymnia's and Erato's shrines, be permitted to express his deep appreciation of your creative achievement? And to tender respectfully the like admirations of Professor Wingate Peaslee of our psychology department and of Dr. Francis Morgan of medicine and comparative anatomy, who share my special interests, and of Dr. Armitage himself? "The Green Deeps" is in particular a remarkably well-sustained and deeply moving lyric poem.

I am an assistant professor of literature at Miskatonic and an enthusiastic amateur student of New England and other folklore. If memory serves, you were in my freshman English section six years ago. I was sorry then that the state of your health forced you to curtail your studies, and I am happy now to have before me conclusive evidence that you have completely surmounted all such difficulties. Congratulations!

And now will you allow me to pass on to another and very different matter, which is nonetheless peripherally related to your poetic work? Miskatonic is currently engaged in a broad interdepartmental research in the general area of folklore, language, and dreams, an investigation of the vocabulary of the collective unconscious, particularly as it expresses itself in poetry. The three scholars I have alluded to are among those active in this work, along with persons in Brown University, Providence, Rhode Island, who are carrying on the pioneering work of the late Professor George Gammell Angell, and from time to time I am honored to render them assistance. They have empowered me to ask you for your own help in this matter, which could be of signal importance. It is a matter of answering a few questions only, relating to the accidents of your writing and in no way impinging on its essence, and should not cut seriously into your time. Naturally any information you choose to supply will be treated as strictly confidential.

I call your attention to the following two lines in "The Green Deeps":

Intelligence doth grow itself within
The coral-palled, squat towers of Rulay.

Did you in composing this poem ever consider a more eccentric spelling of the last (and presumably invented?) word? "R'lyeh," say. And going back three lines, did you consider spelling "Nath" (invented?) with an initial "p"—i.e., "Pnath"?

Also in the same poem:

The rampant dragon dreams in far Cathay
While snake-limbed Cutlu sleeps in deep Rulay.

The name "Cutlu" (once more, invented?) is of considerable interest to us. Did you have phonetic difficulty in choosing the letters to represent the sound you had in mind? Did you perhaps simplify in the interests of poetic clarity? At any time did "Cthulhu" ever occur to you?

(As you can see, we are discovering that the language of the collective unconscious is almost unpleasantly guttural and sibilant! All hawking and spitting, like German.)

Also, there is this quatrain in your impressive lyric, "Sea Tombs":

Their spires underlie our deepest graves;
Lit are they by a light that man has seen.
Only the wingless worm can go between
Our daylight and their vault beneath the waves.

Were there some proofreading errors here?—or the equivalent. Specifically, in the second line should "that" be "no"? (And was the light you had in mind what you might call orange-blue or purple-green, or both?) And, in the next line, how does "winged" rather than "wingless" strike you?

Finally, in regard to "Sea Tombs" and also the title poem of your book, Professor Peaslee has a question which he calls a "long shot" about the subterranean and submarine tunnels which you evoke. Did you ever have fantasies of such tunnels really existing in the area where you composed the poem?—the Hollywood Hills and Santa Monica Mountains, presumably, the Pacific Ocean being nearby. Did you perhaps try actually to trace the paths overlying these fancied tunnels? And did you happen to notice (excuse the strangeness of this question) an unusual number of venomous serpents along such routes?—rattlers, I would presume (in our area it would be copperheads, and in the South water moccasins and coral snakes). If so, do take care!

If such tunnels should by some strange coincidence actually exist, it would be scientifically possible to confirm the fact without any digging or drilling (or by discovering an existent opening), it may interest you to know. Even vacuity—i.e., nothing—leaves its traces, it appears! Two Miskatonic science professors, who are part of the interdepartmental program I mentioned, have devised a highly portable apparatus for the purpose, which they call a magneto-optic geoscanner. (That last hybrid word must sound a most clumsy and barbarous coinage to a poet, I'm sure, but you know scientists!) It is strange, is it not, to think of an investigation of dreams having geological repercussions? The clever though infelicitously named instrument is a simplified adaptation of one which has already discovered two new elements.

I shall be making a trip west early next year, to confer with a man in San Diego who happens to be the son of the scholarly recluse whose researches led to our interdepartmental program— Henry Wentworth Akeley. (The local poet—alas, deceased—to whom you pay such generous tribute, was another such pioneer, it happens oddly.) I shall be driving my own British sports car, a diminutive Austin. I am something of an automobile maniac, I must confess, even a speed demon!—however inappropriate that may be for an assistant English professor. I would be very pleased to make your further acquaintance at that time, if entirely agreeable to you. I might even bring along a geo-scanner and we could check out those hypothetical tunnels!

But I perhaps anticipate and presume too far. Pardon me. I will be very grateful for any attention you are able to give this letter and its necessarily impertinent questions.

Once more, congratulations on *The Tunneler!*

Yrs. very truly,

Albert N. Wilmarth.

It is quite impossible to describe all at once my state of mind when I finished reading this letter. I can only do so by stages. To begin with, I was flattered and gratified, even acutely embarrassed, by his apparently sincere praise of my verses—as what young poet wouldn't be? And that a psychologist and an old librarian (even an anatomist!) should admire them too—it was almost too much.

As soon as the man mentioned freshman English I realized that I had a vivid memory of him. Although I'd forgotten his name in the course of years, it came back to me like a shot when I glanced ahead at the end of the letter and saw it. He had been only an instructor then, a tall young man, cadaverously thin, always moving about with nervous rapidity, his shoulders hunched. He'd had a long jaw and a pale complexion, with dark-circled eyes which gave him a haunted look, as if he were constantly under some great strain to which he never alluded. He had the habit of jerking out a little note-book and making jottings without ceasing for a moment to discourse fluently, even brilliantly. He'd seemed incredibly well read and had had a lot to do with stimulating and deepening my interest in poetry. I even remembered his car—the other students used to joke about it with an undercurrent of envy. It had been a Model T Ford then, which he'd always driven at a brisk clip around the fringes of the Miskatonic campus, taking turns very sharply.

The program of interdepartmental research he described sounded very impressive, even exciting, but eminently plausible—I was just discovering Jung then and also semantics. And to be invited so graciously to take part in it—once again I was flattered. If I hadn't been alone while I read it, I might have blushed.

One notion I got then did stop me briefly and for a moment almost turned me angrily against the whole thing—the sudden suspicion that the purpose of the program might not be the avowed one, that (the presence in it of a psychologist and a medical doctor influenced me in this) it was some sort of investigation of the delusions of crankish, imaginative people—not so much the incidental insights as the psychopathology of poets.

But he was so very gracious and reasonable—no, I was being paranoid, I told myself. Besides, as soon as I got a ways into his detailed questions it was an altogether different reaction that filled me—one of utter amazement . . . and *fear.*

For starters, he was so incredibly accurate in his guesses (for what else could they possibly be? I asked myself uneasily) about those invented names, that he had me gasping. I *had* first thought of spelling them "R'lyeh" and "Pnath"—exactly those letters, though of course memory can be tricky about such things.

And then that *Cthulhu*—seeing it spelled that way actually made me shiver, it so precisely conveyed the deep-pitched, harsh, inhuman cry or chant I'd imagined coming up from profound black abysses, and only finally rendered as "Cutlu" rather dubiously, but fearing anything more complex would seem affectation. (And, really, you can't fit the inner rhythms of a sound like "Cthulhu" into English poetry.)

And then to find that he'd spotted those two proofreader's errors, for they'd been just that. The first I'd missed. The second ("wingless" for "winged") I'd caught, but then rather spinelessly let stand, feeling all of a sudden that I'd perpetuated something overly fantastic when I'd put a figure from my life's one nightmare (a worm with wings) into a poem.

And topping even that, how in the name of all that's wonderful could he have described unearthly colors I'd only dreamed of and never put into my poems at all? Using exactly the same color-words I'd used! I began to think that Miskatonic's interdepartmental research project must have made some epochal discoveries about dreams and dreaming and the human imagination in general, enough to turn their scholars into wizards and dumbfound Adler, Freud, and even Jung.

At that point in my reading of the letter I thought he'd hit me with every-thing he possibly could, but the next section managed to mine a still deeper source of horror and one most disturbingly close to everyday reality. That he should know, somehow deduce, all about my paths in the hills and my odd daydreams about them and about tunnels I'd fancied underlying them—that was truly staggering. And that he should ask *and even warn me* about venom-ous snakes, so that the very letter my mother was carrying unopened when she got her death sting contained a vital reference to it—really, for a mo-ment and more then, I did wonder if I were going insane.

And finally when despite all his jaunty "fancied's" and "long shot's" and "hypothetical's" and English-professor witticisms, he began to talk as if he assumed my imaginary tunnels were real and to refer lightly to a scientific instrument that would prove it . . . well, by the time I'd finished his letter, I fully expected him to turn up the next minute—turn in sharply at our drive with a flourish of wheels and brakes in his Model T (no, Austin) and draw up in a cloud of dust at our door, the geo-scanner sitting on the front seat be-side him like a fat black telescope directed downward!

And yet he'd been so damnably *breezy* about it all! simply didn't know what to think.

(I've been down in the basement again, checking things out. This writing stirs me up and makes me frightfully restless. I went out front, and there was a rattlesnake crossing the path in the hot slanting sunlight from the west. More evidence, if any were needed, that what I fear is true. Or do I hope for it? At all events, I killed the brute. The voices vibrate with, "The half-born worlds, the alien orbs, the stirrings in blackness, the hooded forms, the nighted depths, the shimmering vortices, the purple haze . . .")

When I'd calmed down somewhat next day, I wrote Wilmarth a long let-ter, confirming all his hints, confessing my utter astonishment at them, and begging him to explain how he'd made them. I volunteered to assist the in-terdepartmental project in any way I could and invited him to be my guest when he came west. I gave him a brief history of my life and my sleep anomalies, mentioning my mother's death. I had a strange feeling of unreal-ity as I posted the letter and waited with mixed feelings of impatience and lingering (and also regathering) incredulity for his reply.

When it came, quite a fat one, it rekindled all my first excitement, though without satisfying all my curiosity by any means. Wilmarth was still inclined to write off his and his colleagues' deductions about my word choices, dreams, and fantasies as lucky guesses, though he told me enough about the project to keep my curiosity in a fever—especially about its dis-coveries of obscure linkages between the life of the imagination and ar-chaeological discoveries in far-off places. He seemed particularly interested in the fact that I generally never dreamed and that I slept for very long hours. He overflowed with thanks for my cooperation and my invitation, promising to include me on his itinerary when he drove west. And he had a lot more questions for me.

The next months were strange ones. I lived my normal life, if it can be called that, keeping up my reading and studies and library visits, even writing a little new poetry from time to time. I continued my hill-ramblings, though with a new wariness. Sometimes during them I'd stop and stare at the dry earth beneath my feet, as if expecting to trace the outlines of a trapdoor in it. And sometimes I'd be consumed by sudden, wildly passionate feelings of grief and guilt at the thought of my father locked down there and at my mother's horrible death too; I'd feel I must somehow go to them at all costs.

And yet at the same time I was living only for Wilmarth's letters and the moods of wonder, fantastic speculation, and panic—yet almost delicious terror—they evoked in me. He'd write about all sorts of things besides the project—my poetry and new readings and my ideas (he'd play the professorial mentor here from time to time), world events, the weather, astronomy, submarines, his pet cats, faculty politics at Miskatonic, town meetings at Arkham, his lectures, and the local trips he'd make. He made it all extremely interesting. Clearly he was an inveterate letter-writer and under his influence I became one too.

But most of all, of course, I was fascinated by what he'd write from time to time about the project. He told me some very interesting things about the Miskatonic Antarctic expedition of 1930–31, with its five great Dornier airplanes, and last year's somewhat abortive Australian one in which the psychologist Peaslee and his father, a one-time economist, had been involved. I remembered having read about them both in the newspapers, though the reports there had been curiously fragmentary and unsatisfying, almost as if the press were prejudiced against Miskatonic.

I got the strong impression that Wilmarth would have liked very much to have accompanied both expeditions and was very much put out at not having been able (or allowed) to, though most of the time bravely concealing his disappointment. More than once he referred to his "unfortunate nervousness," sensitivity to cold, fierce migraine attacks, and "bouts of ill health" which would put him to bed for a few days. And sometimes he'd speak with wistful admiration of the prodigious energy and stalwart constitutions of several of his colleagues, such as Professors Atwood and Pabodie, the geoscanner's inventors, Dr. Morgan, who was a big-game hunter, and even the octogenarian Armitage.

There were occasional delays in his replies, which always filled me with anxiety and restlessness, sometimes because of these attacks of his and sometimes because he'd been away longer than he'd expected on some visit. One of the latter was to Providence to confer with colleagues and help investigate the death under mysterious circumstances involving a lightning bolt of Robert Blake, a poet like myself, short-story writer, and painter whose work had provided much material for the project.

It was just after his visit to Providence that with a curious sort of guardedness and reluctance he mentioned visiting another colleague of sorts there (who was in poor health), a Howard Phillips Lovecraft, who had fictionalized (but quite sensationally, Wilmarth warned me) some Arkham scandals and some of Miskatonic's researches and project activities. These stories had been published (when at all) in cheap pulp magazines, especially in a lurid journal called *Weird Tales* (you'll want to tear the cover off, if ever you should dare to buy a copy, he assured me). I recalled having seen the magazine on downtown newsstands in Hollywood and Westwood. I hadn't found the covers offensive. Most of their nude female figures, by some sentimental woman artist, were decorously sleek pastels and their activities only playfully perverse. Others, by one Senf, were a rather florid folk art quite reminiscent of my father's floral chiselings.

But after that, of course, I haunted secondhand bookstores, hunting down copies of *Weird Tales* (mostly) with Lovecraft stories in them, until I'd found a few and read them—one, "The Call of Cthulhu," no less. It cost me the strangest shudders, let me tell you, to see *that* name again, spelled out in cheapest print, under such very outlandish circumstances. Truly, my sense of reality was set all askew and if the tale that Lovecraft told with a strange dignity and power was anything like the truth, then Cthulhu was *real,* an otherdimensional extraterrestrial monster dreaming in an insane, Pacific-sunken metropolis which sent out mental messages (and—who knows?—tunnels) to the world at large. In another tale, "The Whisperer in Darkness," *Albert N. Wilmarth* was a leading character, and that Akeley too he'd mentioned.

It was all fearfully unsettling and confounding. If I hadn't attended Miskatonic myself and lived in Arkham, I'd have thought surely they were a writer's projections.

As you can imagine, I continued to haunt the dusty bookstores and I *bombarded* Wilmarth with frantic questions. His replies were of a most pacifying and temporizing sort. Yes, he'd been afraid of my getting too excited, but hadn't been able to resist telling me about the stories. Lovecraft often laid on things *very* thickly indeed. I'd understand everything much better when we could really talk together and he could explain in person. Really, Lovecraft had an extremely powerful imagination and sometimes it got out of hand. No, Miskatonic had never tried to suppress the stories or take legal action, for fear of even less desirable publicity—and because the project members thought the stories might be a good preparation for the world if some of their more frightening hypotheses were verified. Really, Lovecraft was a very charming and well-intentioned person, but sometimes he went too far. And so on and so on.

Really, I don't think I could have contained myself except that, it now being 1937, Wilmarth sent me word that he was at last driving west. The Austin had been given a thorough overhaul and was "packed to the gills" with the geo-scanner, endless books and papers, and other instruments and materials, including a drug Morgan had just refined, "which induces dreaming and may, conceivably, he says, facilitate clairvoyance and clairaudience. It might make even you dream—should you consent to ingest an experimental dose."

While he was gone from 118 Saltonstall his rooms would be occupied and his cats, including his beloved Blackfellow, cared for by a close friend named Danforth, who'd spent the last five years in a mental hospital recovering from his ghastly Antarctic experience at the Mountains of Madness.

Wilmarth hated to leave at this time, he wrote, in particular he was worried about Lovecraft's failing health, but nevertheless he was on his way!

The next weeks (which dragged out to two months) were a time of particular tension, anxiety, and anticipatory excitement for me. Wilmarth had many more people and places to visit and investigations to make (including readings with the geo-scanner) than I'd ever imagined. Now he sent mostly postcards, some of them scenic, but they came thick and fast (except for a couple of worrisome hiatuses) and with his minuscule handwriting he got so much on them (even the scenic ones) that at times I almost felt I was with him on his trip, worrying about the innards of his Austin, which he called the Tin Hind after Sir Francis Drake's golden one. I on my part had only a few addresses he'd listed for me where I could write him in advance—Baltimore; Winchester, Virginia; Bowling Green, Kentucky; Memphis; Carlsbad, New Mexico; Tucson; and San Diego.

First he had to stop in Hunterdon County, New Jersey, with its quaintly backward farm communities, to investigate some possibly pre-Colonial ruins and hunt for a rumored cave, using the geo-scanner. Next, after Baltimore, there were extensive limestone caverns to check out in both Virginias. He crossed the Appalachians Winchester to Clarksburg, a stretch with enough sharp turns to satisfy even him. Approaching Louisville, the Tin Hind was almost swallowed up in the Great Ohio Flood (which preoccupied the radio news for days; I hung over my superheterodyne set) and he was unable to visit a new correspondent of Lovecraft's there. Then there was more work for the geo-scanner near Mammoth Cave. In fact, caves seemed to dominate his journey, for after a side trip to New Orleans to confer with some occult scholar of French extraction, there were the Carlsbad Caverns and nearby but less well-known subterranean vacuities. I wondered more and more about my tunnels.

The Tin Hind held up very well, except she blew out a piston head crossing Texas ("I held her at high speed a little too long") and he lost three days getting her mended.

Meanwhile, I was finding and reading new Lovecraft stories. One, which turned up in a secondhand but quite recent science-fiction pulp, fictionalized the Australian expedition most impressively—especially the dreams old Peaslee had that led to it. In them, he'd exchanged personalities with a cone-shaped monster and was forever wandering through long stone passageways haunted by invisible whistlers. It reminded me so much of my nightmares in which I'd done the same thing with a winged worm that buzzed, that I airmailed a rather desperate letter to Tucson, telling Wilmarth all about it. I got a reply from San Diego, full of reassurances and more temporizings, and referring to old Akeley's son and some sea caverns they were looking into, and (at last!) setting a date (it would be soon!) for his arrival.

The day before that last, I made a rare find in my favorite Hollywood hunting-ground. It was a little, strikingly illustrated book by Lovecraft called *The Shadow Over Innsmouth* and issued by Visionary Press, whoever they were. I was up half the night reading it. The narrator found some sinister, scaly human beings living in a deep submarine city off New England, realized he was himself turning into one of them, and at the end had decided (for better or worse) to dive down and join them. It made me think of crazy fantasies I'd had of somehow going down into the earth beneath the Hollywood Hills and rescuing or joining my dead father.

Meanwhile mail addressed to Wilmarth care of me had begun to arrive. He'd asked my permission to include my address on the itinerary he'd sent other correspondents. There were letters and cards from (by their postmarks) Arkham and places along his route, some from abroad (mostly England and Europe, but one from Argentina), and a small package from New Orleans. The return address on most of them was his own—118 Saltonstall, so he'd eventually get them even if he missed them along his route. (He'd asked me to do the same with my own notes.) The effect was odd, as though Wilmarth were the author of everything—it almost re-aroused my first suspicions of him and the project. (One letter, though among the last to come, a thick one bearing extravagantly a six-cent airmail stamp and a ten-cent special delivery, had been addressed to George Goodenough Akeley, 176 Pleasant St., San Diego, Cal., and then forwarded care of my own address in the upper left-hand corner.)

Late the next afternoon (Sunday, April 14—the eve of my twenty-fifth birthday, as it happened) Wilmarth arrived very much as I'd imagined it occurring when I'd finished reading his first letter, except the Tin Hind was even smaller than I'd pictured—and enameled a bright blue, though now most dusty. There *was* an odd black case on the seat beside him, though there were a lot of other things on it too—maps, mostly.

He greeted me very warmly and began to talk a blue streak almost at once, with many a jest and frequent little laughs.

The thing that really shocked me was that although I knew he was only in his thirties, his hair was white and the haunted (or hunted) look I'd remembered was monstrously intensified. And he was extremely nervous—at first he couldn't stay still a moment. It wasn't long before I became certain of something I'd never once suspected before—that his breeziness and jauntiness, his jokes and laughs, were a mask for fear, no, for sheer terror, that otherwise might have mastered him entirely.

His actual first words were, "Mr. Fischer, I presume? So glad to meet you in the flesh!—and share your most salubrious sunlight. I look as if I need it, do I not?—a horrid sight! This landscape hath a distinctly cavish, tunnely aspect—I'm getting to be an old hand at making such geological judgements. Danforth writes that Blackfellow has quite recovered from his indisposition. But Lovecraft is in the hospital—I do not like it. Did you observe last night's brilliant conjunction?—I *like* your clear, clear skies. No, I will carry the geo-scanner (yes, it is that); it's somewhat crankish. But you might take the small valise. Really, so very glad!"

He did not comment on or even seem to notice my twisted right foot (something I hadn't mentioned in my letters, though he may have recalled it from six years back) or imply its or my limp's existence in any way, as by insisting on carrying the valise also. That warmed me toward him.

And before going into the house with me, he paused to praise its unusual architecture (another thing I hadn't told him about) and seemed genuinely impressed when I admitted that my father had built it by himself. (I'd feared he'd find it overly eccentric and also question whether someone could work with his hands and be a gentleman.) He also commented favorably on my father's stone carvings wherever they turned up and insisted on pausing to study them, whipping out his notebook to make some quick jottings. Nothing would do, but I must take him on a full tour of the house before he'd consent to rest or take refreshments. I left his valise in the bedroom I'd assigned him (my parents', of course), but he kept lugging the black geo-scanner around with him. It was an odd case, taller than it was wide or long, and it had three adjustable stubby legs, so that it could be set up vertically anywhere.

Emboldened by his approval of my father's carvings, I told him about Simon Rodia and the strangely beautiful towers he was building in Watts, whereupon the notebook came out again and there were more jottings. He seemed particularly impressed by the *marine* quality I found in Rodia's work.

Down in the basement (he had to go there too) he was very much struck by my father's floor-set "Gate of Dreams" stone carving and studied it longer than any of the others. (I'd been feeling embarrassed about its bold motto and odd placement.) Finally he indicated the octopus eyes staring over the castle and observed, "Cutlu, perchance?"

It was the first reference of any sort to the research project that either of us had made since our meeting and it shook me strangely, but he appeared not to notice and continued with, "You know, Mr. Fischer, I'm tempted to get a reading with Atwood and Pabodie's infernal black box right here. Would you object?"

I told him certainly not and to go right ahead, but warned him there was only solid rock under the house (I had told him about my father's dowsing and even had mentioned Harley Warren, whom it turned out Wilmarth had heard of through a Randolph Carter).

He nodded, but said, "I'll take a shot at it nonetheless. We must start somewhere, you know," and he proceeded to set up the geo-scanner carefully so it was standing vertically on its three stubby legs right in the middle of the carving. He took off his shoes first so as not to risk damaging the rather fine stonework.

Then he opened the top of the geo-scanner. I glimpsed two dials and a large eyepiece. He knelt and applied his eye to it, drawing out a black hood and draping it over his head, very much like an old-fashioned photographer focusing for a picture. "Pardon me, but the indications I must look for are difficult to see," he said muffledly. "Hello, what's this?"

There was a longish pause during which nothing happened except his shoulders shifted a bit and there were a few faint clicks. Then he emerged from under the hood, tucked it back in the black box, closed the latter, and began to put on and relace his shoes.

"The scanner's gone crankish," he explained in answer to my inquiry, "and is seeing ghost vacuities. But not to worry—it only needs new warm-up cells, I fancy, which I have with me, and will be right as rain for tomorrow's expedition! That is, if—?" He rolled his eyes up at me in smiling inquiry.

"Of course I'll be able to show you my pet trails in the hills," I assured him. "In fact, I'm bursting to."

"Capital!" he said heartily.

But as we left the basement, its rock floor rang out a bit hollowly, it sounded to me, under his high-laced leather-soled and -heeled shoes (I was wearing sneakers).

It was getting dark, so I started dinner after giving him some iced tea, which he took with lots of lemon and sugar. I cooked eggs and small beef-steaks, figuring from his haggard looks he needed the most restorative sort of food. I also built a fire in the big fireplace against the almost invariable chill of evening.

As we ate by its dancing, crackling flames, he regaled me with brief impressions of his trip west—the cold, primeval pine woods of southern New Jersey with their somberly clad inhabitants speaking an almost Elizabethan English; the very narrow dark roads of West Virginia; the freezing waters of the Ohio flooding unruffled, silent, battleship gray, and ineffably menacing under lowering skies; the profound silence of Mammoth Cave; the southern Midwest with its Depression-spawned, but already legendary, bank robbers; the nervous Creole charms of New Orleans's restored French Quarter; the lonely, incredibly long stretches of road in Texas and Arizona that made one believe one was *seeing* infinity; the great, long, blue, mystery-freighted Pacific rollers ("so different from the Atlantic's choppier, shorter-spaced waves") which he'd watched with George Goodenough Akeley, who'd turned out to be a very solid chap and knowing more about his father's frightening Vermont researches than Wilmarth had expected.

When I mentioned finding *The Shadow Over Innsmouth* he nodded and murmured, "The original of its youthful hero has disappeared *and* his cousin from the Canton asylum. Down to Y'ha-nthlei? Who knows?" But when I remembered his accumulated mail he merely nodded his thanks, wincing a little, as though reluctant to face it. He really did look shockingly tired.

When we'd finished dinner, however, and he'd taken his black coffee (also with lots of sugar) and the fire was dancing flickeringly, both yellow and blue now, he turned to me with a little, venturesomely friendly smile and a big, wonderingly wide lifting of his eyebrows, and said quietly, "And now you'll quite rightly be expecting me to tell you, my dear Fischer, all the things about the projeet that I've been hesitant to write, the answers I've been reluctant to give to your cogent questions, the revelations I've been putting off making until we should meet in person. Really, you have been very patient, and I thank you."

Then he shook his head thoughtfully, his eyes growing distant, as he slowly and rather sinuously and somehow unwillingly shrugged his shoulders, which paradoxically were both frail and wide, and grimaced slightly, as if tasting something strangely bitter, and said even more quietly, "If only I had more to tell you that's been *definitely proved*. Somehow we always stop just short of that. Oh, the artifacts are real enough and certain—the Innsmouth jewelry, the Antarctic soapstones, Blake's Shining Trapezohedron, though that's lost in Narragansett Bay, the spiky baluster knob Walter Gilman brought back from his witchy dreamland (or the nontemporal fourth dimension, if you prefer), even the unknown elements, meteoric and otherwise, which defy all analysis, even the new magneto-optic probe which has given us virginium and alabamine. And it's almost equally certain that all, or almost all, those weird extraterrestrial and extra-cosmic creatures *have* existed—that's why I wanted you to read the Lovecraft stories, despite their lurid extravagances, so you'd have some picture of the entities that I'd be talking to you about. Except that they and the evidence for them *do* have a maddening way of vanishing upon extinction and from all records—Wilbur Whateley's mangled remains, his brother's vast invisible cadaver, the Plutonian old Akeley killed *and couldn't photograph,* the June 1882 meteor itself which struck Nahum Gardner's farm and which set old Armitage (young then) studying the *Necronomicon* (the start of everything at Miskatonic) and which Atwood's father saw with his own eyes and tried to analyze, or what Danforth saw down in Antarctica when he looked back at the horrible higher mountains beyond the Mountains of Madness—he's got amnesia for that now that he has regained his sanity . . . all, all gone!

"But whether any of those creatures exist *today*—there, there's the rub! The overwhelming question we can't answer, though always on the edge of doing so. The thing is," he went on with gathering urgency, "that *if they do exist,* they are so unimaginably powerful and resourceful, they might be"— and he looked around sharply—"anywhere at the moment!

"Take *Cthulhu,*" he began.

I couldn't help starting as I heard that word pronounced for the first time in my life; the harsh, dark, abysmal *monosyllabic* growl it came to was so very like the sound that had originally come to me from my imagination, or my subconscious, or my otherwise unremembered dreams, or . . .

He continued, "If Cthulhu exists, then he (or she, or it) can go anywhere he wants through space, or air, or sea, or earth itself. We know from Johansen's account (it turned his hair white) that Cthulhu can exist as a gas, be torn to atoms, and then recombine. He wouldn't need tunnels to go through solid rock, he could *seep* through it—'not in the spaces we know, but between them.' And yet in his inscrutability he might choose tunnels—there's that to be reckoned with. Or—still another possibility—perhaps he neither exists nor does not exist but is in some half state—'waits dreaming,' as Angell's old chant has it. Perhaps his dreams, incarnated as your winged worms, Fischer, dig tunnels.

"It is those monstrous underground cavern-and-tunnel worlds, not all from Cthulhu by any means, that I have been assigned to investigate with the geo-scanner, partly because I was the first to hear of them from old Akeley and also—Merciful Creator!—from the Plutonian who masked as him—'great worlds of unknown life down there; blue-litten K'n-yan, red-litten Yoth, and black, lightless N'kai,' which was Tsathoggua's home, and even stranger inner spaces litten by colors from space and from Earth's nighted core. That's how I guessed the colors in your childhood dreams or nightmares (or personality exchanges), my dear Fischer. I've glimpsed them also in the geo-scanner, where they are, however, most fugitive and difficult to discern. . . ."

His voice trailed off tiredly, just as my own concern became most feverishly intense with his mention of "personality exchanges."

He really did look shockingly fatigued. Nevertheless I felt impelled to nerve myself to say, "Perhaps those dreams can be repeated, if I take Dr. Morgan's drug. Why not tonight?"

"Out of the question," he replied, shaking his head slowly. "In the first place, I wrote too hopefully there. At the last minute Morgan was unable to supply me with the drug. He promised to send it along by mail, but hasn't yet. In the second place, I'm inclined to think now that it would be much too dangerous an experiment."

"But at least you'll be able to check those dream colors *and* the tunnels with your geo-scanner?" I pressed on, somewhat crestfallen.

"If I can repair it . . ." he said, his head nodding and slumping to one side. The dying flames were all blue now as he whispered mumblingly, ". . . if I am *permitted* to repair it. . . ."

I had to help him to bed and then retire to my own, shaken and unsatisfied, my mind a whirl. Wilmarth's alternating moods of breezy optimism and a seemingly *frightened* dejection were hard to adjust to. But now I realized that I was very tired myself—after all, I'd been up most of the previous night reading *Innsmouth*—and soon I slumbered.

(The voices stridently groan, "The pit of primal life, the Yellow Sign, Azathoth, the Magnum Innominandum, the shimmering violet and emerald wings, the cerulean and vermilion claws, Great Cthulhu's wasps . . ." Night has fallen. I have limpingly paced the house from the low attic with its circular portholes to the basement, where I touched my father's sledge and eyed "The Gate of Dreams." The moment draws nigh. I must write rapidly.)

I awoke to bright sunlight, feeling totally refreshed by my customary twelve hours of sleep. I found Wilmarth busily writing at the table that faced the north window of his bedroom. His smiling face looked positively youthful in the cool light, despite its neatly brushed thatch of white hair—I hardly recognized him. All his accumulated mail except for one item lay open and face downward on the far left-hand corner of the table, while on the far right-hand corner was an impressive pile of newly written and addressed postcards, each with its neatly affixed, fresh, one-cent stamp.

"Good morrow, Georg," he greeted me (properly pronouncing it GAY-org), "if I may so address you. And good news!—the scanner is recharged and behaving perfectly, ready for the day's downward surveying, while that letter George Goodenough forwarded is from Francis Morgan and contains a supply of the drug against tonight's inward researches! Two dosages exactly—Georg, I'll dream with you!" He waved a small paper packet.

"That's wonderful, Albert," I told him, meaning it utterly. "By the way, it's my birthday," I added.

"Congratulations!" he said joyfully. "We'll celebrate it tonight with our drafts of Morgan's drug."

And our expedition did turn out to be a glorious one, at least until almost its very end. The Hollywood Hills put on their most youthfully winning face; even the underlying crumbling, worm-eaten corruptions seemed fresh. The sun was hot, the sky bright blue, but there was a steady cool breeze from the west and occasional great high white clouds casting enormous shadows. Amazingly, Albert seemed to know the territory almost as well as I did—he'd studied his maps prodigiously and brought them along, including the penciled ones I'd sent him. And he instantly named correctly the manzanita, sumac, scrub oak, and other encroaching vegetation through which we wended our way.

Every so often and especially at my favorite pausing places, he would take readings with the geo-scanner, which he carried handily, while I had two canteens and a small backpack. While his head was under the black hood, I would stand guard, my stick ready. Once I surprised a dark and pinkly pale, fat, large serpent, which went slithering into the underbrush. Before I could tell him, he said correctly, "A king snake, foe of the crotaloids—a good omen."

And . . . on every reading, Albert's black box showed vacuities of some sort—tunnels or caves—immediately below us, at depths varying from a few to a few score meters. Somehow this did not trouble us by bright outdoor day. I think it was what we'd both been expecting. Coming out from under the hood, he'd merely nod and say, "Fifteen meters" (or the like) and note it down in his little book, and we'd tramp on. Once he let me try my luck under the hood, but all I could see through the eyepiece was what seemed like an intensification of the dancing points of colored light one sees in the dark with the eyes closed. He told me it took considerable training to learn to recognize the significant indications.

High in the Santa Monicas we lunched on beef sandwiches and the tea-flavored lemonade with which I'd filled both canteens. Sun and breeze bathed us. Hills were all around and beyond them to the west the blue Pacific. We talked of Sir Francis Drake and Magellan and of Captain Cook and his great circumpolar voyagings, and of the fabulous lands they'd all heard legends of—and of how the tunnels we were tracing were really no more strange. We spoke of Lovecraft's stories almost as if they were no more than that. Daytime viewpoints can be strangely unworrying and unconcerned.

Halfway back or so, Albert began looking very haggard once more—frighteningly so. I got him to let me carry the black box. To do that I had to abandon my flat backpack and empty canteens—he didn't seem to notice.

Almost home, we paused at my father's memorial. The sun had westered most of this way, and there were dark shadows and also shafts of ruddy light almost parallel to the ground. Albert, very weary now, was fumbling for phrases to praise Rodia's work, when there swiftly glided out of the undergrowth behind him what I first took to be a large rattlesnake. But as I lunged lurchingly toward it, lashing at it with my stick, and as it slid back into thick cover with preternatural rapidity, and as Albert whirled around, the sinuous, vanishing thing looked for an instant to me as if it were all shimmering violet-green above with beating wings and bluish-scarlet below with claws while its minatory rattle was more a skirling hum.

We raced home, not speaking of it at all, each of us concerned only that his comrade not fall behind. Somewhere mine found the strength.

His postcards had been collected from the box by the road and there were a half dozen new letters for him—and a notification of a registered package for me.

Nothing must do then but Albert must drive me down to Hollywood to pick up the package before the post office closed. His face was fearfully haggard, but he seemed suddenly flooded with a fantastic nervous energy and (when I protested that it could hardly be anything of great importance) a tremendous willpower that would brook no opposition.

He drove like a veritable demon and as though the fate of worlds depended on his speed—Hollywood must have thought it was Wallace Reid come back from the dead for another of his transcontinental racing pictures. The Tin Hind fled like a frightened one indeed, as he worked the gear lever smartly, shifting up and down. The wonders were that we weren't arrested and didn't crash. But I got to the proper window just before it closed and I signed for the package—a stoutly wrapped, tightly sealed, and heavily corded parcel from (it really startled me) Simon Rodia.

Then back again, just as fast despite my protests, the Tin Hind screeching on the corners and curves, my companion's face an implacable, watchful death's-mask, up into the crumbling and desiccated hills as the last streaks of the day faded to violet in the west and the first stars came out.

I forced Albert to rest then and drink hot black coffee freighted with sugar while I got dinner—when he'd stepped out of the car into the chilly night he'd almost fainted. I grilled steaks again—if he'd needed restorative food last night, he needed it doubly now after our exhausting hike and our Dance of Death along the dry, twisting roads, I told him roughly. ("Or Grim Reaper's Tarantella, eh, Georg?" he responded with a feeble but unvanquishable little grin.)

Soon he was prowling around again—he wouldn't stay still—and peering out the windows and then lugging the geo-scanner down into the basement, "to round out our readings," he informed me. I had just finished building and lighting a big fire in the fireplace when he came hurrying back up. Its first white flare of flame as the kindling caught showed me his ashen face and white-circled blue eyes. He was shaking all over, literally.

"I'm sorry, Georg, to be such a troublesome and seemingly ungrateful guest," he said, forcing himself with a great effort to speak coherently and calmly (though most imperatively), "but really you and I must get out of here at once. There's no place safe for us this side of Arkham—which is not safe either, but there at least we'll have the counsel and support of salted veterans of the Miskatonic project whose nerves are steadier than mine. Last night I got (and concealed from you—I was sure it had to be wrong) a reading of fifteen down there under the carving—*centimeters*, Georg, not meters. Tonight I have confirmed that reading beyond any question of a doubt, only it's shrunk to *five* under the carving. The floor there is the merest shell—it rings as hollow as a crypt in New Orleans's St. Louis One or Two—*they* have been eating at it from below and are feasting still. No, no arguments! You have time to pack one small bag—limit yourself to necessities, but bring that registered parcel from Rodia, I'm curious about it."

And with that he strode to his bedroom, whence he emerged in a short while with his packed valise and carried it and the black box out to the car.

Meanwhile I'd nerved myself to go down in the basement. The floor did ring much more hollowly than it had last night—it made me hesitate to tread upon it—but otherwise nothing appeared changed. Nevertheless it gave me a curious feeling of unreality, as if there were no real objects left in the world, only flimsy scenery, a few stage properties including a balsa sledgehammer, a registered parcel with nothing in it, and a cyclorama of nighted hills, and two actors.

I hurried back upstairs, took the steaks off the grill and set them on the table in front of the softly roaring fire (for they were done), and headed after Albert.

But he anticipated me, stepping back inside the door, looking at me sharply—his eyes were still wide and staring—and demanding, "Why aren't you packed?"

I said to him steadily, "Now look here, Albert, I thought last night the cellar floor sounded hollow, so that is not entirely a surprise. And any way you look at it, we can't drive to Arkham on nervous energy. In fact, we can't get even decently started driving east without some food inside us. You say yourself it's dangerous everywhere, even at Miskatonic, and from what we (or at least I) saw at my father's grave there may be at least one of the things loose already. So let's eat dinner—I have a hunch terror hasn't taken away your appetite entirely—and have a look inside Rodia's package, and then leave if we must."

There was a rather long pause. Then his expression relaxed into a somewhat wan smile and he said, "Very well, Georg, that does make sense. I'm frightened all right, make no mistake of that, in fact I've walked in terror for the past ten years. But in this case, to speak as honestly as I'm able, I have been even more concerned for you—it suddenly seemed such a pity, such a disservice, that I should have dragged you into this dreadful business. But as you say, one must bow to necessity, bodily and otherwise . . . and try to show a little style about it," he added with a rather doleful chuckle.

So we sat down before the dancing, golden fire and ate our steaks and fixings (I had some burgundy, he stayed with his sweet black coffee) and talked of this and that—chiefly of Hollywood, as it turned out. He'd glimpsed a bookstore on our headlong drive, and now he asked about it and that led to other things.

Our dinner done, I refilled his cup and my glass, then cleared a space and opened Rodia's parcel, using the carving knife to cut its cords and slit its seals. It contained, carefully packed in excelsior, the casket of embossed copper and German silver which sits before me now. I recognized my father's handiwork at once, which reproduced quite closely in beaten metal his stone carving in the basement, though without the "Gate of Dreams" inscription. Albert's finger indicated the Cutlu eyes, though he did not speak the name. I opened the casket. It contained several sheets of heavy bond paper. This time it was my father's handwriting I recognized. Standing side by side, Albert and I read the document, which I append here:

15 Mar 1925

My dear Son:

Today you are 13 but I write to you and wish you well when you are 25. Why I do so you will learn as you read this. The box is yours—*Leb' wohl!* I leave it with a friend to send to you if I should go in the 12 years between—Nature has given me signs that that may be: jagged flashes of rare earth colors in my eyes from time to time. Now read with care, for I am telling secrets.

When I was a boy in Louisville I had dreams by day and could not remember them. They were black times in my mind that were minutes long, the longest half an hour. Sometimes I came to in another place and doing something different, but never harmful. I thought my black daydreams were a weakness or a judgement, but Nature was wise. I was not strong and did not know enough to bear them yet. Under my father's rule I learned my craft and made my body strong and always studied when and as I could.

When I was 25 I was deep in love—this was before your mother—with a beautiful girl who died of consumption. Pining upon her grave I had a daydream, but this time by the strength of my desire I kept my mind white. I swam down through the loam and I was joined with her in full bodily union. She said this coupling must be our last, but that I now would have the power to move at will under and through the earth from time to time. We kissed farewell forever, *Lorchen* and I, and I swam down and on, her knight of dreams, exulting in my strength like some old kobold breasting the rock. It is not black down there, my son, as one would think. There are glorious colors. Water is blue, metals bright red and yellow, rocks green and brown, *undsoweiter*. After a time I swam back and up into my body, standing on the new-made grave. I was no longer pining, but profoundly grateful.

So I learned how to divine, my son, to be a fish of earth when there is need and Nature wills, to dive into the Hall of the Mountain King dancing with light. Always the finest colors and the strangest hues lay west. Rare earths they are named by scientists, who are wise, though blind. That's why I brought us here. Under the greatest of oceans, earth is a rainbow web and Nature is a spider spinning and walking it.

And now you have shown you have my power, *mein Sohn*, but in a greater form. You have black nightdreams. I know, for I have sat by you as you slept and heard you talk and seen your terror, which would soon destroy you if you could recall it, as one night showed. But Nature in her wisdom blindfolds you until you have the needed strength and learning. As you know by now, I have provided for your education at a good Eastern school praised by Harley Warren, the finest employer that I ever had, who knew a lot about the nether realms.

And now you're strong enough, *mein Sohn*, to act—and wise, I hope, as Nature's acolyte. You've studied deep and made your body strong. You have the power and the hour has come. The triton blows his horn. Rise up, *mein lieber Georg*, and follow me. Now is the time. Build upon what I've built, but build more greatly. Yours is the wider and the greater realm. Make your mind white. With or without some lovely woman's help, now burst the gate of dreams!

Your loving Father

At any other time that document would have moved and shaken me profoundly. Truth to tell, it did so move and shake me, but I had been already so moved and shaken by today's climactic events that my first thought was of how the letter applied to them.

I echoed from the letter, "Now burst the gate of dreams," and then added, suppressing another interpretation, "That means I should take Morgan's drug tonight. Let's do it, Albert, as you proposed this morning."

"Your father's last command," he said heavily, clearly much impressed by that aspect of the letter. Then, "Georg, this is a most fantastic, shattering missive! That sign he got—sounds like migraine. And his references to the rare-earth elements—that could be crucial. And colors in the earth perceived perhaps by extrasensory perceptionl The Miskatonic project should have started investigating dowsing years ago. We've been blind—" He broke off. "You're right, Georg, and I am strongly tempted. But the danger! How to choose? On the one hand a supreme parental injunction and our raging curiosities—for mine's a-boil. On the other hand Great Cthulhu and his minions. Oh, for an indication of how to decide!"

There was a sharp knocking at the door. We both started. After a moment's pause I moved rapidly, Albert following. With my hand on the latch I paused again. I had not heard a car stop outside. Through the stout oak came the cry, "Telegram!" I opened it.

There was revealed a skinny, somewhat jaunty-looking youth of pale complexion scattered with big freckles and with carrot red hair under his visored cap. His trousers were wrapped tightly around his legs by bicycle clips.

"Either of you Albert N. Wilmarth?" he inquired coolly.

"I am he," Albert said, stepping forward.

"Then sign for this, please."

Albert did so and tipped him, substituting a dime for a nickel at the last instant.

The youth grinned widely, said, "G'night," and sauntered off. I closed the door and turned quickly back.

Albert had torn open the flimsy envelope and drawn out and spread the missive. He was pale already, but as his eyes flashed across it, he grew paler still. It was as if he were two-thirds of a ghost already and its message had made him a full one. He held the yellow sheet out to me wordlessly:

LOVECRAFT IS DEAD STOP THE WHIPPOORWILLS DID NOT SING STOP TAKE COURAGE STOP DANFORTH

I looked up. Albert's face was still as ghostly white, but its expression had changed from uncertainty and dread to decision and challenge.

"That tips the balance," he said. "What have I more to lose? By George, Georg, we'll have a look down into the abyss on whose edge we totter. Are you game?"

"I proposed it," I said. "Shall I fetch your valise from the car?"

"No need," he said, whipping from his inside breast pocket the small paper packet from Dr. Morgan he'd shown me that morning. "I had the hunch that we were going to use it, until that apparition at your father's tomb shattered my nerves."

I fetched small glasses. He split evenly between them the small supply of white powder, which dissolved readily in the water I added under his direction. Then he looked at me quizzically, holding his glass as if for a toast.

"No question of to whom we drink this," I said, indicating the telegram he was still holding in his other hand.

He winced slightly. "No, don't speak his name. Let's rather drink to *all* our brave comrades who have perished or suffered greatly in the Miskatonic project."

That "our" really warmed me. We touched glasses and drained them. The draft was faintly bitter.

"Morgan writes that the effects are quite rapid," he said. "First drowsiness, then sleep, and then hopefully dreams. He's tried it twice himself with Rice and doughty old Armitage, who laid the Dunwich Horror with him. The first time they visited in dream Gilman's Walpurgis hyperspace; the second, the inner city at the two magnetic poles—an area topologically unique."

Meanwhile I'd hurriedly poured a little more wine and lukewarm coffee and we'd settled ourselves comfortably in our easy chairs before the fire, the dancing flames of which became both a little blurred and a little dazzling as the drug began to take effect.

"Really, that was a most amazing missive from your father," he chatted on rapidly. "Spinning a rainbow web under the Pacific, the lines those weirdly litten tunnels—truly most vivid. Would Cthulhu be the spider? No, by Gad, I'd liefer your father's goddess Nature any day. She's kindlier at least."

"Albert," I said somewhat drowsily, thinking of personality exchanges, "could those creatures possibly be benign, or at least less malevolent than we infer?—as my father's subterranean visionings might indicate. My winged worms, even?"

"Most of our comrades did not find them so," he replied judiciously, "though of course there's our *Innsmouth* hero. What has he really found in Y'ha-nthlei? Wonder and glory? Who knows? Who can say he knows? Or old Akeley out in the stars—is his brain suffering the tortures of the damned in its shining metal cylinder? Or is it perpetually exalted by ever-changing true visions of infinity? And what did poor shoggoth-stampeded Danforth really think he saw beyond the two horrific mountain chains down there before he got amnesia? And is that last a blessing or a curse? Gad, he and I are suited to each other . . . the mind-smitten helping the nerve-shattered . . . fit nurses for felines. . . ."

"That was surely heavy news he sent you," I observed with a little yawn, indicating the telegram about Lovecraft, which he still held tightly between finger and thumb. "You know, before that wire came, I had the craziest idea—that somehow you and he were the same person. I don't mean Danforth but—"

"Don't say it!" he said sharply. Then his voice went immediately drowsy as he continued, "But the roster of the perished is longer far . . . poor Lake and poor, poor Gedney and all those others under their Southern Cross and Magellanic shroud . . . the mathematical genius Walter Gilman who lost heart most terribly . . . the nonagenarian street-slain Angell and lightning-frozen Blake in Providence . . . Edward Pickman Derby, Arkham's plump Shelley deliquescing in his witch-wife's corpse. . . . Gad, this is hardly the cheerfulest topic. . . . You know, Georg, down in San Diego young Akeley (G. G.) showed me a hidden sea-cave bluer than Capri and on its black beach of magnetite the webbed footprint of a merman . . . one of the Gnorri? . . . and then . . . oh yes, of course . . . there's Wilbur Whateley, who was almost nine feet tall . . . though he hardly counts as a Miskatonic researcher . . . but the whippoorwills didn't get him either . . . or his big brother. . . ."

I was still looking at the fire, and the dancing points of light in and around it had become the stars, thick as the Pleiades and Hyades, through which old Akeley journeyed eternally, when unconsciousness closed on me too, black as the wind-stirred. infinite gulf of darkness which Robert Blake saw in the Shining Trapezohedron, black as N'kai.

I awoke stiff and chilled. The fire at which I'd been staring was white ashes only. I felt a sharp pang of disappointment that I had not dreamed at all. Then I became aware of the low, irregular, inflected humming or buzzing that filled my ears.

I stood up with difficulty. My companion slumbered still, but his shut-eyed, death-pale face had a hideously tormented look and he writhed slowly and agonizedly from time to time as if in the grip of foulest nightmare. The yellow telegram had fallen from his fingers and lay on the floor. As I approached him I realized that the sound filling my ears was coming from between his lips, which were unceasingly a-twitch, and as I leaned my head close to them, the horridly articulate droning became recognizable words and phrases:

"The pulpy, tentacled head," I heard in horror, "*Cthulhu fhtagn,* the wrong geometry, the polarizing miasma, the prismatic distortion, *Cthulhu R'lyeh,* the positive blackness, the living nothingness . . ."

I could not bear to watch his dreadful agony or listen to those poisonous, *twangy* words an instant longer, so I seized him by the shoulders and shook him violently, though even as I did so there sprang into my mind my father's stern injunction never to do so.

His eyes came open wide in his white face and his mouth clamped shut as he came up with a powerful shove of his bent arms against the chair's arms which his hands had been clutching. It was as if it were happening in slow motion, though paradoxically it also seemed to be happening quite swiftly. He gave me a last mute look of utter horror and then he turned and ran, taking fantastically long strides, out through the door, which his outstretched hand threw wide ahead of him, and disappeared into the night.

I hobbled after him as swiftly as I could. I heard the motor catch at the starter's second prod. I screamed, "Wait, Albert, wait!" As I neared the Tin Hind, its lights flashed on and its motor roared and I was engulfed in acrid exhaust fumes as it screeched out the drive with a spattering of gravel and down the first curve.

I waited there then in the cold until all sight and sound of it had vanished in the night, which was already paling a little with the dawn.

And then I realized that I was still hearing those malignant, gloating, evilly resonant voices.

"*Cthulhu fhtagn,*" they were saying (and have been saying and are saying now and will forever), "the spider tunnels, the black infinities, the colors in pitch-darkness, the tiered towers of Yuggoth, the glittering centipedes, the winged worms. . . ."

Somewhere not far off I heard a low, half-articulate whirring sound.

I went back into the house and wrote this manuscript.

And now I shall place the last with its interleafed communications and also the two books of poetry that led to all this in the copper and German silver casket, and I shall carry that with me down into the basement, where I shall take up my father's sledge (wondering in which body I shall survive, if at all) and literally carry out his last letter's last injunction.

Very early on the morning of Tuesday, March 16, 1937, the householders of Paradise Crest (then Vultures Roost) were disturbed by a clashing rumble and a sharp earth-shock which they attributed to an earthquake, and indeed very small tremors were registered at Griffith Observatory, UCLA, and USC, though on no other seismographs. Daylight revealed that the brick house locally known as Fischer's Folly had fallen in so completely that not one brick remained joined to another. Moreover, there appeared to be fewer bricks in view than the house would have accounted for, as if half of them had been trucked away during the night, or else fallen into some great space beneath the basement. In fact, the appearance of the ruin was of a gigantic ant lion's-pit lined by bricks instead of sand grains. The place was deemed, and actually was, dangerous, and was shortly filled in and in part cemented over, and apparently not long afterward rebuilt upon.

The body of the owner, a quietly spoken, crippled young man named Georg Reuter Fischer, was discovered flat on its face in the edge of the rubble with hands thrown out (the metal casket by one of them) as though he had been trying to flee outdoors when caught by the collapse. His death, however, was attributed to a slightly earlier accident or insane act of self-destruction involving acid, of which his eccentric father was once known to have kept a supply. It was well that easy identification was made possible by his conspicuously twisted right foot, for when the body was turned over it was discovered that something had eaten away the entire front of his face and also those portions of his skull and jaw and the entire forebrain.

[*The Disciples of Cthulhu,* ed. Edward Paul Berglund
(DAW Books, 1976)]

ESSAYS BY FRITZ LEIBER

THE WORKS OF H. P. LOVECRAFT:
SUGGESTIONS FOR A CRITICAL APPRAISAL

In his *Appreciation of H. P. Lovecraft*, W. Paul Cook wrote: "He was quite alone in the dreams which he spread on paper. . . . His work owes not even an atmosphere to anyone save himself. Since his advent weird fiction has owed more to Lovecraft than Lovecraft owes to all the body of preceding writers."

Few will disagree with this evaluation of Lovecraft as an innovator. But it naturally brings up the question: Just what, *specifically,* does weird fiction owe to Lovecraft? What new materials and methods did he contribute to the literature of supernatural terror? Thoughtful and scholarly attempts to answer this question are in order, not as much to honor Lovecraft as to provide weird fiction with the critical and realistic comments that are essential for the healthy growth of any branch of art.

The following paragraphs are a modest attempt to point the way for such answers, to single out some of the phases of Lovecraft's work and style worthy of much more extended treatment. They may contain errors of emphasis and omission. But if they give rise to more careful planned efforts, their purpose will have been accomplished.

Perhaps Lovecraft's most important single contribution was the adaptation of science-fiction material for the purpose of supernatural terror. The decline of at least naïve belief in Christian theology, resulting in an immense loss of prestige for Satan and his hosts, left the emotion of supernatural fear swinging around loose, without any well-recognized object. Lovecraft took up this loose end and tied it to the unknown but possible denizens of other planets and regions beyond the space-time continuum. This adaptation was subtly gradual. At first he mingled science-fiction material with traditional sorcery. For example, in "The Dunwich Horror," the hybrid other-dimensional entity is exorcised by recitation of a magical formula, and magical rituals plays a considerable part in the story. But in "The Whisperer in Darkness," "The Shadow out of Time," and *At the Mountains of Madness*, supernatural terror is evoked almost entirely by recital of the doings of alien cosmic entities, and the books of sorcererous ritual have become merely the distorted, but realistic, histories of such entities, especially with regard to their past and future sojourns on Earth. There are, of course, exceptions to this trend of development. In "The Dreams in the Witch House," for instance, he tries a somewhat different tack: the combining of traditional witchcraft with modern multi-dimensional geometry. But as a general trend it seems to hold good.

It would be interesting to see this trend traced in detail, to know the degree to which other writers pointed out the way for Lovecraft, and to have some well-documented opinions as to the extent to which Lovecraft succeeded in his purpose.

The Cthulhu Mythology and the Arkham-Alhazred background constitute a very interesting problem. In this sense: Lovecraft asks us to accept, for the purpose of most of his stories, a world in which there is not only an Innsmouth and an Arkham and a Miskatonic University, but also a great body of forbidden knowledge well-known to a considerable number of sober and reputable scholars. In other words, he does not set his stories in the real world, but in the slightly, but significantly, different Arkham-Alhazred world; and since his characters know of this forbidden knowledge, they are somewhat more susceptible to cosmic terror than ordinary individuals.

Most weird authors have occasionally fabricated occult books and authorities to quote from. But few if any have done it to the degree that Lovecraft did (so that mention of the *Necronomicon* became a kind of interior signature of his stories) and with such consistency that a definite alternate real-world is created. Arthur Machen, for example, though inventing, I believe, a few quotations from classical authors, did not postulate a set of closely-guarded books in the British Museum dealing with the history of "the little people."

This device gives Lovecraft's stories a potent kind of authenticity and—paradoxically!—puts them at a further remove from the real world. A detailed study of the growth of the Mythology and the background, and also an appraisal of the extent to which it helped or hampered Lovecraft's writings, would be very worth while.

Closely related to the Mythology and the background is Lovecraft's intensive use of the document-story. That is, the story that purports, à la Poe's "Ms. Found in a Bottle," to be a real document rather than a mere tale. This device is common in weird literature, but again few if any authors have taken it quite as seriously as did Lovecraft. He set great store by the narrator having some vitally pressing motive for recounting all his past experiences, and was ingenious at devising such motives: justificatory confession in "The Thing on the Doorstep" and "The Statement of Randolph Carter"; warning in "The Whisperer in Darkness" and *At the Mountains of Madness;* attempt by the narrator to clarify his own ideas and come to a decision, in the "The Shadow over Innsmouth"; scholarly summing up of a weird series of events, in *The Case of Charles Dexter Ward* and "The Haunter of the Dark," to name but a few.

Use of the document-story had a progressive effect on Lovecraft's style, favoring the employment of a matter-of-fact, uncolored prose and a dispassionate, scholarly viewpoint. Certainly there seems to be more witchery of words in an early tale like "The Dunwich Horror" than in a later one like "The Shadow out of Time," though the later story has a greater unity and technical perfection. There is much to be said both for and against the objective style of his later stories as contrasted with the more subjective style of his earlier ones.

Regarding Lovecraft's style—that is, the way he told a story rather than the materials he used—the most noteworthy feature is perhaps his dependence on confirmation rather than revelation. (I am indebted to Henry Kuttner for ths neat phrase.) In other words, the story-ending—"The Outsider" and a few other excepted—does not come as a surprise but as a final, long-anticipated "convincer." The reader knows, and is supposed to know, what is coming, but this only prepares and adds to his shivers when the narrator supplies the last and incontrovertible piece of evidence. In *The Case of Charles Dexter Ward* the reader knows from almost the first page that Ward has been supplanted by Joseph Curwen, yet the narrator does not state this unequivocally until the last sentence of the book.

So closely related to his use of confirmation as to be only another aspect of it, is Lovecraft's employment of the *terminal* climax—that is, the story in which the high point and the final sentence coincide. Who can forget the supreme chill of: "But by God, Eliot, *it was a photograph from life*" or "*It was his twin brother, but it looked more like the father than he did*" or "They were, instead, the letters of our familiar alphabet, spelling out the words of the English language in my own handwriting" or ". . . the face and hands of Henry Wentworth Akeley." Use of the terminal climax made it necessary for Lovecraft to develop a special type of story-telling, in which the explanatory and return-to-equilibrium material is all deftly inserted before the finish and while the tension is still mounting. It also necessitated a very careful structure, with everything building from the first word to the last.

Lovecraft's reinforced this structure with what may be called symphonic prose—sentences that are repeated with a constant addition of more potent adjectives, adverbs, and phrases, just as in a symphony a melody introduced by a single woodwind is at last thundered by the whole orchestra. "The Statement of Randolph Carter" provides one of the simplest examples. In it, in order, the following phrases occur concerning the moonlight: ". . . waning crescent moon was high in the vaporous heavens . . . wan, waning crescent moon peered through the noisome vapours . . . pallid, peering crescent moon . . . amorphous, necrophagous shadows dance beneath an accursed waning moon . . ." Subtler and more complex examples can undoubtedly be found in the longer stories.

In a letter reprinted in *The Acolyte* (Summer 1944) Anthony Boucher states that Lovecraft, like Poe, achieved horror by overstatement rather than understatement. This points the way for another interesting critical study. Or for several—at least, it suggests several things: 1) Lovecraft's use of a detailed description and history of feared entities, as in *At the Mountains of Madness*, as opposed to the more sketchy and shadowy demoniac entities M. R. James and others; this of course involves the difference in their subject-matter, particularly Lovecraft's use of science-fictional material. 2) Lovecraft's Machen-esque mentioning of pieces of forbidden knowledge known to the narrator but too terrible to be revealed to the reader, involving references to the unmentionable, the nameless and so on. 3) (and in this regard

Lovecraft employs anything but overstatement) His practice in some stories of having no actual visible horror, but letting everything rest on inference. For example, he begins "The Whisperer in Darkness" with the statement, "Bear in mind closely that I did not see any actual visible horror at the end." And he sticks to it, for what has the narrator Wilmarth seen at the end? Photographs of odd stones and footprints—and even those might have been doctored. A bizarre dictaphone record—which could have been faked. The written and verbal statements of Akeley—all of them possibly lies. Some queer machines, some actual footprints, some confused alien voices—all susceptible to faking. And finally a head and hands that might have been wax models. None of these things are horrible in themselves, none of the evidence is incontrovertible—everything depends on the inference that the narrator and reader make. In this story, in one sense, Lovecraft makes a greater use of understatement than James, whose narrators generally physically sense, at least for a moment, something monstrous and supernaturally horrible.

This brief essay omits many phases of Lovecraft's work worth study. For example, the use of several balancing sources of horror (see especially "The Dreams in the Witch House") and a shifting of the focus of horror, so that the feared entities gradually become the fearing entities, as in "The Shadow out of Time" and *At the Mountains of Madness* (where the reader, at first dreading the Old Ones, comes to sympathize with them in their dread of the Shoggoths).

But if it calls out additions, disagreements, and corrections—and especially if it stimulates the present enthusiasm for Lovecraft into crystalizing in definite appraisals and summings-up, as in the Derleth-Wandrei prefaces and the Laney glossary—so much the better.

[*Acolyte,* Fall 1944]

SOME RANDOM THOUGHTS ABOUT LOVECRAFT'S WRITINGS

I believe that the entities of the Cthulhu Mythology, as employed by Lovecraft, are predominately malevolent, or, at best, cruelly indifferent to mankind. They are a reflection of Lovecraft's oft-avowed scientific materialism—his belief in a soul-less and goal-less cosmos, whose only meaning is that dreamed into it by frail organisms which are themselves the sport of blind chance.

Any attempt to analyze the Cthulhu Mythology, as employed by Lovecraft, into balancing hierarchies of good and evil, à la Zoroastrianism, is highly misleading. The characteristic Lovecraftian flavor is thereby lost: that sense of a universe in which only the most inadequate and arbitrary barriers stand between mankind and ravening, paralyzing horror. Lovecraft's stories are at the antipodes from the traditional Christian tales of the supernatural, in which God defeats Satan off-hand, or with the assistance of a dash of holy water, from those pseudo-oriental yarns in which a Black Magician is conquered by a White, and from others of the ilk. Like James, he believed that in a satisfying horror tale that spectral phenomena should be malevolent.

It is noteworthy that, as Laney points out in his "Glossary," the benevolent Elder Gods, with the exception of Nodens, are never mentioned save by inference. I fancy that they were only brought into the Lovecraftian horror-cosmos to explain why the malevolent entities had not long ago overrun mankind, and to provide a source for incantations by which earthlings could to some degree defend themselves, as in "The Dunwich Horror" and *The Case of Charles Dexter Ward*. However, in the majority of Lovecraft's tales it is the chance indifference of the malevolent entities that allows the hero to survive, and in some ("The Dreams in the Witch House," "Dagon") they plainly triumph.

Furthermore, the benevolence of the Elder Gods is dubious. In *The Dream-Quest of Unknown Kadath* we find the Gods of Earth to be relatively weak and feeble (symbolic of the ultimate weakness of even mankind's traditions and dreams) and the more potent "Other Gods" or "Ultimate Gods" to be "blind, voiceless, tenebrous, mindless . . ."

Undoubtedly Azathoth is the supreme entity and embodiment of the Cthulhu Mythology. There is never any question of his being merely an alien entity from some other planet or dimension (like Cthulhu or Yog-Sothoth or the alien races of the later stories). He is unquestionably and unalterably "god." And he is the blind, idiot god, the god of the ultimate chaos—perfect personification of the purposeless, mindless, cruelly indifferent cosmos of materialistic belief.

And Nyarlathotep, the crawling chaos, is his messenger—not mindless like his master, but evilly intelligent, pictured in *The Dream-Quest* in the form of a suave pharaoh. The Nyarlathotep legend is one of Lovecraft's most interesting creations. It appears in the prose poem of that name and the XXI *Fungi from Yuggoth*. In a time of widespread social upheaval and nervous tension, one looking like a pharaoh appears out of Egypt. He is worshipped by the fellahin, "wild beasts followed him and licked his hands." He visits many lands and gives lectures with queer pseudo-scientific demonstrations, obtaining a great following—rather like Cagliostro or some other similar charlatan. A progressive disintegration of man's mind and world follows. There are purposeless panics and wanderings. Nature breaks loose. There are earthquakes, weedy cities are revealed by receding seas, an ultimate putrescence and disintegration sets in. Earth ends.

Just what does Nyarlathotep "mean"? That is, what meanings can most suitably be read into him, granting that, by him, Lovecraft may not have "meant" anything. Man's self-destructive intellectuality—his knowing too much for his own good? The spirit of the blatantly commercial, advertising, and acquisitive world that Lovecraft loathed? (Nyarlathotep always has that aura of the charlatan, that brash contemptuousness.) The mockery of a universe man can never really understand or master? It is interesting to speculate.

Great natural catastrophes seem to have fascinated Lovecraft, as might by expected in one who chose cosmic horror for his time. It is possible that reports of such catastrophes caused some of his stories to crystalize, or were that nucleus around which they crystalized. The Vermont floods of 1927 and "The Whisperer in Darkness." Reports of oceanic earthquakes and upheavals and "Dagon" and "The Call of Cthulhu." The inundation of acres of woodlands by a manmade reservoir and "The Colour out of Space." Regional degeneration and "The Dunwich Horror," "The Shadow over Innsmouth," and "The Lurking Fear."

It has always seemed to me a particular pity that Lovecraft did not live to experience the terrific and unparalleled New England hurricane of Autumn, 1938. I was in Chicago at the time, when, partly crowded out of the headlines by the Munich conference, the alarming report came in, including word that the downtown heart of Providence had been invaded by the sea, to the accompaniment of terrific wind and downpour. My first thought was, "What a story that would eventually have gotten out of him!"

Lovecraft's *great* poetry—*Fungi from Yuggoth*—was written within a week, December 27, 1929–January 4, 1930. I wonder just why that creative burst came. I note that, of his tales, "The Dunwich Horror" was written in 1928 and "The Whisperer in Darkness" in 1930, with nothing intervening. The poem "Brick Row" is dated December 7, 1929. Perhaps this excellent poem, inspired by a demolition-threat to old warehouses in South Water Street, Providence, was the harbinger of the sonnets. This leaves completely unexplained why he suddenly shifted to the sonnet form after years of heroic couplets and Poe-esque rhyme schemes. Now if it could be proved that "The Messenger," a sonnet form reply to a newspaper challenge, had been written at about the same time . . .

At any rate, the peaks of his prose and poetic creativity coincided.

I disagree with many, including Lovecraft himself, who rate "The Music of Erich Zann" as one of his two or three most excellent tales. Of course, this business of choosing "bests" is just a literary pastime, but it strikes me that "Zann" is uncharacteristic—an experiment in the genre of E. T. Hoffmann. The same applies to "The Outsider," the most Poe-like tale. I would look for his best among those stories that are, in style and subject matter, most wholly his own, in the main current of his creativity. They include "Dagon," "The Statement of Randolph Carter," "The Temple," "The Festival," "The Shunned House," "Pickman's Model," "The Haunter of the Dark," "The Dreams in the Witch House," "The Thing on the Doorstep," "The Call of Cthulhu," "The Colour out of Space" (a good choice for his "best," as many agree), "The Dunwich Horror," "The Shadow over Innsmouth," "The Shadow out of Time," and *At the Mountains of Madness*. My personal favorites are "The Shadow out of Time" and, especially, "The Whisperer in Darkness."

The last story is remarkable for the way in which the horror of the alien and the fascination of the alien are equally maintained until almost the very end. Machen is the only other writer I can think of who could do this as well.

[*Acolyte*, Winter 1945]

LEIBER ON ONDERDONK

[*Editors' Note:* The following is a letter of comment on Matthew H. Onderdonk's important article on Lovecraft, "The Lord of R'lyeh," published in *Fantasy Commentator* in Spring 1945. It is here reprinted by permission of A. Langley Searles, editor of *Fantasy Commentator.*]

Ondordonk hits the nail on the head in pointing out how Lovecraft effected a transition from the supernatural to the supernormal. He himself put it nicely in the introductory section of his "Supernatural Horror in Literature": ". . . men with minds sensitive to hereditary impulse will always tremble at the thought of the hidden and fathomless worlds of strange life which may pulsate in the gulfs beyond the stars, or press hideously upon cur own globe in unholy dimensions which only the dead and the moonstruck can glimpse." (The only thing questionable in that statement is the "hereditary impulse" angle—modern science has certainly been as responsible as tradition for o-pening the eerie vistas he mentions.)

But right there Lovecraft tells us that he is not looking to religion or folklore for the main source or rationale of his horrors—he is taking them out of the realms of the *possible.*

The transition shows plainly in his own tales. The relatively earlier ones tend to depend on black magic, incantations, spells, etc., as major factors, while the later ones do not. Compare, for instance, "The Dunwich Horror" with "The Shadow out of Time." (Come to think of it, there may be chronological exceptions to this, but at any rate the transition is there, whether neatly chronologic or not.)

In an interesting backhand sort of way, the *Necronomicon* mythology (Arkham-Al Hazred set-up) illustrates this transition. In "The Dunwich Horror," the *Necronomicon* is a vital factor; incantations from it are used in the story to effect important ends; it could not be eliminated. But by the time he was writing *At the Mountains of Madness* and "The Shadow out of Time," the *Necronomicon* mythology was merely a source of local color, so to speak, and could have been eliminated without harming (perhaps even *helping*) the tales.

The fascinatiom of the *Necronomicon* mythology is so great that one is apt to mistake the shadow for the substance. Personally, I think it eventually became a minor millstone around Lovecraft's neck. For instance, Wilmarth of "The Whisperer in Darkness" might just as well have been an instructor at Brown or Harvard, and no references made to forbiddon.books at all—they weren't necessary to the tale. (This criticism is of course a casual and minor one; I just make it because admirers of Lovecraft, writers and readers both, are apt to think that the mythos was the important thing about Lovecraft instead of his vastly more important achievement in working out the transition from the supernatural to the supernormal that Onderdonk describes.)

[*Fantasy Commentator,* Summer 1945]

A LITERARY COPERNICUS

I

Howard Phillips Lovecraft was the Copernicus of the horror story. He shifted the focus of supernatural dread from man and his little world and his gods, to the stars and the black and unplumbed gulfs of intergalactic space. To do this effectively, he created a new kind of horror story and new methods for telling it.

During the Middle Ages and long afterwards, the object of man's supernatural fear was the Devil, together with the legions of the damned and the hosts of the lead, earthbound and anthropomorphic creatures all. Writers as diverse as Dante and Charles Maturin, author of *Melmoth the Wanderer,* were able to rouse terror in their readers by exploiting this fear.

With the rise of scientific materialism and the decline of at least naive belief in Christian theology, the Devil's dreadfulness quickly paled. Man's supernatural fear was left without a definite object. Writers seeking to awaken supernatural fear restlessly turned to other objects, some old, some new.

Horror of the dead proved to be a somewhat hardier feeling than dread of the Devil and the damned. This provided the necessary ground for the genre of the ghost story, ably exploited by Montague Rhodes James and others.

Arthur Machen briefly directed man's supernatural dread toward Pan, the satyrs, and other strange races and divinities who symbolized for him the Darwinian-Freudian "beast" in man.

Earlier, Edgar Allan Poe had focused supernatural dread on the monstrous in man and in nature. Abnormal mental and physiological states fascinated him, as did the awesome might of the elements, natural catastrophes, and the geographic unknown.

Algernon Blackwood sought an object for horror especially in the new cults of occultism and spiritualism, with their assertion of the preternatural power of thoughts and feelings.

Meanwhile, however, a new source of literary material had come into being: the terrifyingly vast and mysterious universe revealed by the swiftly developing sciences, in particular astronomy. A universe consisting of light-years and light-millennia of black emptiness. A universe containing billions of suns, many of them presumably attended by planets housing forms of life shockingly alien to man and, likely enough in some instances, infinitely more powerful. A universe shot through with invisible forces, hitherto unsuspected by man, such as the ultraviolet ray, the X-ray—and who can say how many more? In short, a universe in which the unknown had vastly greater scope than in the little crystal-sphered globe of Aristotle and Ptolemy. And yet a real universe, attested by scientifically weighed facts, no mere nightmare of mystics.

Writers such as H. G. Wells and Jules Verne found a potent source of literary inspiration in the simple presentation of man against the background of this new universe. From their efforts arose the genre of science-fiction.

Howard Phillips Lovecraft was not the first author to see in this new universe a highly suitable object for man's supernatural fear. W. H. Hodgson, Poe, Fitz-James O'Brien, and Wells too had glimpses of that possibility and made use of it in a few of their tales. But the main and systematic achievement was Lovecraft's. When he completed the body of his writings, he had firmly attached the emotion of spectral dread to such concepts as outer space, the rim of the cosmos, alien beings, unsuspected dimensions, and the conceivable universes lying outside our own space-time continuum.

Lovecraft's achievement did not come overnight. The new concept of the horror story did not spring full-grown from his mind. In his earlier tales he experimented with the Dunsanian strain and also wrote a number of effective stories in the vein of Poe, such as "The Statement of Randolph Carter," "The Outsider," "Cool Air," and "The Hound." He shared Machen's horror of the human beast and expressed it in "The Lurking Fear," "The Rats in the Walls," "The Horror at Red Hook," and "Arthur Jermyn." Though even in these briefer tales we find broad hints of the new concept: vast life-forms from earth's past in "Dagon" and a linkage of a human being's insanity with the appearance of a new star in "Beyond the Wall of Sleep." But with "The Call of Cthulhu" the line of development becomes clearly marked, as shown by the opening sentences: "The most merciful thing in the world, I think, is the inability of the human mind to correlate all its contents. We live on a placid island of ignorance in the midst of black seas of infinity, and it was not meant that we should voyage far. The sciences, each straining in its own direction, have hitherto harmed us little; but some day the piecing together of dissociated knowledge will open up such terrifying vistas of reality, and of our frightful position therein, that we shall either go mad from the revelation or flee from the deadly light into the peace and safety of a new dark age."

For a while Lovecraft tended to mix black magic and other traditional sources of dread with the horrors stemming purely from science's new universe. In "The Dunwich Horror" the other-dimensional creatures are thwarted by the proper incantations, while witchcraft and the new Einsteinian universe appear cheek-by-jowl in "The Dreams in the Witch House." But when we arrive at "The Whisperer in Darkness," *At the Mountains of Madness,* and "The Shadow out of Time," we find that the extra-terrestrial entities are quite enough in themselves to awaken all our supernatural dread, without any medieval trappings whatsoever. White magic and the sign of the

cross are powerless against them and only the accidents of space and time—
in short, sheer chance—save humanity.

In passing, it is to be noted that Lovecraft, like Poe, was fascinated by
great natural catastrophes and new scientific discoveries and explorations,
as is understandable in one who chose cosmic horror for his theme. It is
likely that reports of such events engendered many of his stories. "The
Whisperer in Darkness" begins with the Vermont floods of 1927 and one
notes other possible linkages: reports of oceanic earthquakes and upheavals
and "Dagon" and "The Call of Cthulhu"; the inundation of acres of woodland
by a man-made reservoir and "The Colour out of Space"; threat of demolition
of some old warehouses on South Water Street, Providence, and the poem
"Brick Row," which is dated December 7, 1929, and may have been the germ
of Lovecraft's great sonnet cycle *Fungi from Yuggoth,* written between December 27, 1929, and January 4, 1930; regional decay and degeneration and
"The Lurking Fear" and "The Shadow over Innsmouth"; ravages of German
submarine warfare and "The Temple"; polar exploration and *At the Mountains
of Madness;* discovery of the planet Pluto by C. W. Tombaugh in 1930 and
"The Whisperer in Darkness," featuring that discovery and written in the
same year.

It is a great pity that Lovecraft did not live to experience the unparalleled New England hurricane of 1938, when the downtown heart of his own
Providence was invaded by the sea, to the accompaniment of terrific wind
and downpour. What a story that would eventually have got out of him!

II

The universe of modern science engendered a profounder horror in
Lovecraft's writings than that stemming solely from its tremendous distances
and its highly probable alien and powerful non-human inhabitants. For the
chief reason that man fears the universe revealed by materialistic science is
that it is a purposeless, soulless place. To quote Lovecraft's "The Silver Key,"
man can hardly bear the realization that "the blind cosmos grinds aimlessly
on from nothing to something and from something back to nothing again,
neither heeding nor knowing the wishes or existence of the minds that
flicker for a second now and then in the darkness."

In his personal life Lovecraft met the challenge of this hideous realization by taking refuge in traditionalism, in the cultivation of mankind's time-
honored manners and myths, not because they are true, but because man's
mind is habituated to them and therefore finds in them some comfort and
support. Recognizing that the only meaning in the cosmos is that which man
dreams into it, Lovecraft treasured beautiful human dreams, all age-worn
things, and the untainted memories of childhood. This is set forth clearly in
"The Silver Key," the story in which Lovecraft presents his personal philosophy of life.

In the main current of Lovecraft's supernatural tales, horror of the mechanistic universe gave shape to that impressive hierarchy of alien creatures and gods generally referred to as "the Cthulhu mythos," an assemblage of beings whose weird attributes reflect the universe's multitudinous environments and whose fantastic names are suggestive renderings of nonhuman words and sounds. They include the Elder Gods or Gods of Earth, the Other Gods or Ultimate Gods, and a variety of entities from distant times, planets, and dimensions.

Although they stem from that period in which Lovecraft mixed black magic in his tales and was attracted to Dunsanian pantheons, I believe it is a mistake to regard the beings of the Cthulhu mythos as sophisticated equivalents of the entities of Christian demonology, or to attempt to divide them into balancing Zoroastrian hierarchies of good and evil.

Most of the entities in the Cthulhu mythos are malevolent or, at best, cruelly indifferent to mankind. The perhaps benevolent Gods of Earth are never mentioned directly, except for Nodens, and gradually fade from the tales. In *The Dream-Quest of Unknown Kadath* they are pictured as relatively weak and feeble, symbols of the ultimate weakness of even mankind's traditions and dreams. It is likely that Lovecraft employed them only to explain why the more numerous malevolent entities had not long ago overrun mankind, and to provide a source of incantations whereby earthlings could to some degree defend themselves, as in "The Dunwich Horror" and *The Case of Charles Dexter Ward*. In the later tales, as we have mentioned, Lovecraft permitted mankind no defense, except luck, against the unknown.

In contrast to the Elder Gods, the Other Gods are presented as powerful and terrible, yet also—strange paradox!—"blind, voiceless, tenebrous, mindless . . ." (*The Dream-Quest*).

Of the Other Gods, Azathoth is the supreme deity, occupying the topmost throne in the Cthulhu hierarchy. There is never any question of his being merely an alien entity from some distant planet or dimension, like Cthulhu or Yog-Sothoth. He is unquestionably "god," and also the greatest god. Yet when we ask what sort of god, we discover that he is the blind, idiot god, ". . . the mindless daemon-sultan . . .," ". . . the monstrous nuclear chaos. . . ."

Such a pantheon and such a chief deity can symbolize only one thing: the purposeless, mindless, yet all-powerful universe of materialistic belief.

And Nyarlathotep, the crawling chaos, is his messenger—not mindless like his master, but evilly intelligent, pictured in *The Dream-Quest* in the form of a suave pharaoh. The Nyarlathotep legend is one of Lovecraft's most interesting creations. It appears both in the prose poem and in the sonnet of that name. In a time of widespread social upheaval and nervous tension, one looking like a pharaoh appears out of Egypt. He is worshipped by the fellahin, "wild beasts followed him and licked his hands." He visits many lands and gives lectures with queer pseudo-scientific demonstrations, obtaining a great following—rather like Cagliostro or some similar charlatan. A progressive disintegration of man's mind and world follows. There are purposeless panics and wanderings. Nature breaks loose. There are earthquakes, weedy cities are revealed by receding seas, an ultimate putrescence and disintegration sets in. Earth ends.

Just what does Nyarlathotep "mean"? That is, what meanings can most suitably be read into him, granting that, by him, Lovecraft may not consciously have "meant" anything. One possibility is that the pharaoh-charlatan expresses the mockery of a universe man can never understand or master. Another is that he symbolizes the blatantly commercial, self-advertising, acquisitive world that Lovecraft loathed (Nyarlathotep always has that aura of the salesman, that brash contemptuousness). Yet a third possibility is that Nyarlathotep stands for man's self-destructive intellectuality, his awful ability to see the universe for what it is and thereby kill in himself all naive and beautiful dreams.

In this connection it is to be noted that Lovecraft, to his last month a tireless scholar and questioner, was the embodiment of the one noble feeling scientific materialism grants man: intellectual curiosity. He also expressed this passion in his supernatural tales. His protagonists are often drawn to the unknown as much as they dread it. Quaking at the horrors that may lurk there, they yet cannot resist the urge to peer beyond the rim of space. "The Whisperer in Darkness," perhaps his greatest story, is remarkable for the way in which the horror and fascination of the alien are equally maintained until almost the very end.

This alchemist-like yearning for "hidden knowledge" was one of the forces which led Lovecraft to create that remarkable series of imaginary but deceptively realistic "secret books," chief among them the *Necronomicon,* which are featuted prominently in his later stories.

III

Lovecraft's matured method of telling a horror story was a natural consequence of the importance of the new universe of science in his writings, for it was the method of scientific realism, approaching in some of his last tales (*At the Mountains of Madness* and "The Shadow out of Time") the precision, objectivity, and attention to detail of a report in a scientific journal. Most of his stories are purported documents and necessarily written in the first person. This device is common in weird literature, as witness Poe's "Ms. Found in a Bottle," Haggard's *She,* Stoker's *Dracula,* and many others, but few writers have taken it quite as seriously as did Lovecraft.

He set great store by the narrator having some vitally pressing motive for recounting his experiences, and was ingenious at devising such motives: justificatory confession in "The Thing on the Doorstep" and "The Statement of Randolph Carter"; warning, in "The Whisperer in Darkness" and *At the Mountains of Madness;* attempt by the narrator to clarify his own ideas and come to a decision, in "The Shadow over Innsmouth"; scholarly summing up a weird series of events, in *The Case of Charles Dexter Ward* and "The Haunter of the Dark."

The scientifically realistic element in Lovecraft's style was a thing of slow growth in a writer early inclined to a sonorous and poetic prose with an almost Byzantine use of adjectives. The transition was never wholly completed, and like all advances, it was attended by losses and limitations. Disappointingly to some readers, who may also experience impatience at the growing length of the stories (inevitable in scientific reports), there is notably less witchery of words in, say, "The Shadow out of Time" than in "The Dunwich Horror," though the former story has greater unity and technical perfection. And Lovecraft's own restricted and scholarly life hardly fitted him to be an all-over realist. He always observed a gentlemanly reserve in his writings and depicted best those types of characters which he understood and respected, such as scholars, New England farmers and townsmen, and sincere and lonely artists; while showing less sympathy (consider "He") and penetration in the presentation of business men, intellectuals, factory workers, "toughs," and other admittedly brash, uninhibited, and often crude denizens of our modern cities.

There were three important elements in Lovecraft's style which he was able to use effectively in both his earlier poetic period and later, more objective style.

The first is the device of *confirmation* rather than revelation. (I am indebted to Henry Kuttner for this neat phrase.) In other words, the story-ending does not come as a surprise but as a final, long-anticipated "convincer." The reader knows, and is supposed to know, what is coming, but this only prepares and adds to his shivers when the narrator supplies the last and incontrovertible piece of evidence. In *The Case of Charles Dexter Ward* the reader knows from almost the first page that Ward has been supplanted by Joseph Curwen, yet the narrator does not state this unequivocally until the last sentence of the book. This does not mean that Lovecraft never wrote the revelatory type of story, with its surprise ending. On the contrary, he used it in "The Lurking Fear" and handled it most effectively in "The Outsider." But he did come more and more to favor the less startling but sometimes more impressive confirmatory type.

So closely related to his use of confirmation as to be only another aspect of it, is Lovecraft's employment of the terminal climax—that is, the story in which the high point and the final sentence coincide. Who can forget the supreme chill of: "But by God, Eliot, *it was a photograph from life,*" or "*It was his twin brother, but it looked more like the father than he did,*" or "They were, instead, the letters of our familiar alphabet, spelling out the words of the English language in my own handwriting," or ". . . the face and hands of Henry Wentworth Akeley." Use of the terminal climax made it necessary for Lovecraft to develop a special type of story-telling, in which the explanatory and return-to-equilibrium material is all deftly inserted before the finish and while the tension is still mounting. It also necessitated a very careful structure, with everything building from the first word to the last.

Lovecraft reinforced this structure with what may be called *orchestrated prose*—sentences that are repeated with a constant addition of more potent adjectives, adverbs, and phrases, just as in a symphony a melody introduced by a single woodwind is at last thundered by the whole orchestra. "The Statement of Randolph Carter" provides one of the simplest examples. In it, in order, the following phrases occur concerning the moon: ". . . waning crescent moon . . . wan, waning crescent moon . . . pallid, peering crescent moon . . . accursed waning moon. . . ." Subtler and more complex examples can be found in the longer stories.

Not only sentences, but whole sections, are sometimes repeated, with a growing cloud of atmosphere and detail. The story may first be briefly sketched, then told in part with some reservations, then related more fully as the narrator finally conquers his disinclination or repugnance toward stating the exact details of the horror he experienced.

All these stylistic elements naturally worked to make Lovecraft's stories longer and longer, with a growing complexity in the sources of horror. In "The Dreams in the Witch House" the sources of horror are multiple: ". . . Fever—wild dreams—somnambulism—illusions of sounds—a pull toward a point in the sky—and now a suspicion of insane sleep-talking. . . ." While in *At the Mountains of Madness* there is a transition whereby the feared entities become the fearing; the author shows us horrors and then pulls back the curtain a little farther, letting us glimpse the horrors of which even the horrors are afraid!

An urge to increase the length and complexity of tales is not uncommon among the writers of horror stories. It can be compared to the drug addict's craving for larger and larger doses—and this comparison is not fanciful, since the chief purpose of the supernatural tale is to arouse the single feeling of spectral terror in the reader rather than to delineate character or comment on life. Devotees of this genre of literature are at times able to take doses which might exhaust or sicken the average person. Each reader must decide for himself just how long a story he can stand without his sense of terror flagging. For me, all of Lovecraft, including the lengthy *At the Mountains of Madness,* can be read with ever-mounting excitement.

For it must be kept in mind that no matter how greatly Lovecraft increased the length, scope, complexity, and power of his tales, he never once lost control or gave way to the impulse to write wildly and pile one bloodcurdling incident on another without the proper preparation and attention to mood. Rather, he tended to write with greater restraint, to perfect the internal coherence and logic of his stories, and often to provide alternate everyday explanations for the supernatural terrors he invoked, letting the reader infer the horror rather than see it face to face, so that most of his stories fulfill the conditions set down by the narrator of "The Whisperer in Darkness": "Bear in mind closely that I did not see any actual visual horror at the end . . . I cannot prove even now whether I was right or wrong in my hideous inference," or by the narrator of "The Shadow out of Time": "There is reason to hope that my experience was wholly or partly an hallucination—for which, indeed, abundant causes existed."

IV

Strangely paralleling the development of Lovecraft's scientific realism was an apparently conflicting trend: the development of an imaginary background for his stories, including New England cities such as Arkham and Innsmouth, institutions such as Miskatonic University in Arkham, semi-secret and monstrous cults, and a growing library of "forbidden" books, such as the *Necronomicon*, containing monstrous secrets about the present, future, and past of earth and the universe.

Any writer, even a thoroughgoing realist, may invent the names of persons and places, either to avoid libel or because his creations are hybrid ones, combining the qualities of many persons or places. Some of Lovecraft's inventions are of a more serious sort altogether, definitely distorting the "real" world that forms the background for many of his later supernatural tales. Not only are the *Necronomicon*, the *Unaussprechlichen Kulten* of von Junzt and other volumes presumed to have a real existence (in few copies and under lock and key, rather closely guarded secrets), but the astounding and somewhat theosophical tale they have to tell of non-human civilizations in earth's past and of the frightful denizens of other planets and dimensions, is taken seriously by the scholars and scientists who people Lovecraft's stories. These individuals are in all other ways very realistically minded indeed, but having glimpsed the forbidden knowledge, they are generally more susceptible to cosmic terror than ordinary people. Sober and staid realists, they yet know that they live on the brink of a horrid and ravening abyss unsuspected by ordinary folk. This knowledge does not come to them solely as the result of the weird experiences in which the stories involve them, but is part of their intellectual background.

These "awakened" scholars are chiefly on the faculty of imaginary Miskatonic University. Indeed, the fabulous history of that institution, insofar as it can be traced from Lovecraft's stories, throws an interesting light on the development of this trend in his writing.

In June 1882 a peculiar meteor fell near Arkham. Three professors from Miskatonic came to investigate and found it composed of an evanescent substance defying analysis. Despite this experience, they were highly skeptical when later on they heard of eerie changes occurring on the farm where the meteor fell and, contemptuous of what they considered folk superstitions, they stayed away during the year-long period in which a hideous decay gradually wiped out the farm and its inhabitants. In other words, they behaved as professors are conventionally supposed to behave, intolerant of ghostly events and occult theories—and certainly showing no signs of having read the *Necronomicon*, if there was a copy at Miskatonic at that date, with any sympathy. It is significant that the story in which these events occur, "The Colour out of Space," is praised by Edmund Wilson, a generally adverse critic.

But in the course of the next twenty-five years, perhaps as an insidious result of the strange meteor fall, a change took place in Miskatonic University and in the intellectual equipment of at least some of its faculty members. For when the child prodigy Edward Pickman Derby entered Miskatonic he was able to gain access for a time to the copy of the *Necronomicon* in the library; and Nathaniel Wingate Peaslee, the political economist, during his five-year amnesia which began May 14, 1908, made indecipherable marginal notes in the same volume. Still later, a stranger who was picked up near-dead in Kingsport harbor on Christmas (in 1920, I think) was allowed to view the dread book in St. Mary's Hospital at Arkham.

During the 'twenties there was a wild, decadent set among the students (Miskatonic's lost generation, apparently), who were of dubious morality and were reputed to practice black magic. And in 1925 the *Necronomicon* was consulted yet again, this time by the uncouth and precocious giant Wilbur Whateley. He sought to borrow it, but Henry Armitage, the librarian, wisely refused.

In 1927 (the year they were surveying for the new reservoir for Arkham) the talented young mathematician Walter Gilman also obtained temporary access to the volume. He came to a hideous end in a haunted rooming house, but not before he had presented to Miskatonic a queer, spiky image formed of unknown elements and later placed on display in the Miskatonic museum. It was not, however, the first unearthly accession to the museum, which also boasted some strangely alloyed and fantastically piscine gold jewelry from Innsmouth.

In the late 'twenties Asenath Waite, fascinating daughter of a reputed Innsmouth sorcerer, took a course in medieval metaphysics at Miskatonic, and we can be sure she did not lose the opportunity of prying into even more dubious branches of knowledge.

On the whole, the late 'twenties were a period particularly productive of spectral occurrences in and around Arkham; in particular the year 1928, which can in this connection be termed "The Great Year," and in even greater particular September 1928, which may be titled "The Great Month."

We can presume that the unfortunate Gilman perished that year and that Asenath Waite was one of the student body, but those presumptions are only a beginning. Consultation of the *Journal of the American Psychological Society* shows N. W. Peaslee then began to publish a series of articles describing his strange dreams of earth's non-human past. And on May sixth Albert N. Wilmarth, an instructor in literature, received a disquieting letter from the Vermont scholar Henry W. Akeley about extra-terrestrial creatures lurking in his native woodlands. In August Wilbur Whateley died horrifyingly while attempting to burglarize the Miskatonic library and steal the *Necro-*

nomicon. On September ninth Wilbur's twin brother, who took after his non-human father to an even greater extent, broke loose near Dunwich, Massachusetts.

On September twelfth, Wilmarth, lured by a forged letter, set out to visit Akeley in Vermont. On the same day Dr. Armitage learned of the eruption of Wilbur's twin brother.

That night Wilmarth fled in horror from Akeley's farm. On the fourteenth Armitage set out for Dunwich with two of his colleagues, and next day managed to destroy the Dunwich horror.

It is startling indeed to think of two such tremendous sequences of supernatural events reaching their crisis at almost precisely the same time. One likes to think of the frantic Armitage passing the apprehensive Wilmarth as the latter hurried to catch his train. (The most obvious explanation is that Lovecraft prepared a rather elaborate chronology for "The Dunwich Horror," written in 1928, and then made use of the same chart in laying out the plot of "The Whisperer in Darkness," written in 1930 with no other tales intervening.)

After the excitement of The Great Month, almost any events seem anticlimactic. However, one should mention the Miskatonic Antarctic Expedition of 1930–31; the discovery of the secrets of the Witch House in March 1931, with further accessions to the museum; and the Australian expedition of 1935. Both expeditions included Professor William Dyer of the geology department, who also knew something of Wilmarth's dreadful experience and who can perhaps therefore lay claim to having been involved in more preternatural events than anyone else on the faculty.

One can only speculate as to why Lovecraft created and made such intensive use of Miskatonic University and the *Necronomicon.* Certainly the Miskatonic faculty constitutes a kind of Lovecraftian utopia of highly intelligent, aesthetically sensitive, yet tradition-minded scholars.

As for the *Necronomicon,* it appears that Lovecraft used it as a back door or postern gate to realms of wonder and myth, the main approaches to which had been blocked off by his acceptance of the new universe of materialistic science. It permitted him to maintain in his stories at least occasional sections of the poetic, resonant, and colorful prose which he loved, but which hardly suited his later, scientifically realistic style. It provided him with a cloud of sinister atmosphere which would otherwise have had to be built afresh with each story. It pictured vividly his Copernican conception of the vastness, strangeness, and infinite eerie possibilities of the new universe of science. And finally, it was the key to a more frightening, yet more fascinating "real" world than the blind and purposeless cosmos in which he had to live his life.

[*Something about Cats and Other Pieces,* by H. P. Lovecraft
and Divers Hands (Arkham House, 1949)]

MY CORRESPONDENCE WITH LOVECRAFT

I read "The Colour out of Space" when it first appeared in *Amazing Stories* and its dismal gray horror chilled my dreams for weeks. Some years later I gulped down in two nights most of Lovecraft's published stories, preserved in magazine tearsheets by a college acquaintance. I read "The Shadow out of Time" and *At the Mountains of Madness* when they came out in *Astounding Stories*.

These tales gave me a wonder, mystery, and delightful terror I found in no other writing. They were sensational yet studious, weird as a theosophist's cosmos yet with no touch of charlatanry. It was the dream come true of meeting the mysterious scholar who tells one, yes, there are forbidden books, secret cults, undreamed eras of history, non-human intelligences, and all the rest of it. I imagine this acute effect was due to the channeling, both in me and the stories, of several powers: discounted mystical aspects of a hampered sexual urge, the wonder of science beyond all dull textbooks and elementary laboratory courses, the culturally deep-rooted love and dread of secret societies, the intoxication of metaphysics, the simple joy of excitement and surprise which Lovecraft himself referred to as "adventurous expectancy."

In 1936 these stories had maintained their spell over me to such a degree that I was searching second-hand magazine stores for them, chiefly to have them for rereading and permanent possession, though there were a few I had missed. I remember purchasing from Forrest J. Ackerman tearsheets of "The Silver Key" and "The Whisperer in Darkness."

Then in the late summer my wife, with a bold directness I had been unable to conceive for myself, wrote a letter to Lovecraft care of *Weird Tales*. A few days later the great man replied with what we thought was a long letter, until we had received some of his average-sized communications. That was the beginning of an orgy of letter-writing which lasted the few short months until his death. My wife wrote more letters herself and shortly we were joined by my friend and fellow enthusiast for the fantastic, Harry O. Fischer, then of Louisville, Kentucky. Our letters were returned to us by Mrs. Gamwell afterwards. The entire correspondence was excerpted by Derleth for the volume of letters and later borrowed and retained, permanently as yet, by another individual who shall remain nameless here.

The first things that struck me about Lovecraft from his letters were the wide range of his interests and his courteousness and great helpfulness, always tactful yet always ready. In his first letter he recalled at length my father's spirited Philip Faulconbridge in a performance of *King John* early in the century and quoted in full the speech that begins, "This England never did, nor never shall, lie at the proud foot of a conqueror. . . ." When I merely mentioned to him my intention of writing a novel set in Roman times, he sent me several thousand words of highly pertinent advice, including a longer and shorter bibliography for researching the period. Now, setting to work on such a novel twenty years later, I am helped by his remembered instructions. Ancient Rome, I discovered then, was the historical period with which Lovecraft identified himself most intensely, next to Restoration England.

Lovecraft's famous handwriting, which packed so very many words on a page or card, yearning toward all four edges sometimes by way of interlineations and balloons, was only superficially crabbed and difficult. Every tiny graceful hieroglyph for the simpler words was abbreviated and shaped exactly the same each time. With a bit of practice his handwriting made for fast easy reading. Lovecraft was a writer in many senses, not all of them current; in particular, the production of many pages of fine impromptu prose each day (chiefly in letters) was to him the breath of life.

He asked to see my own writing, none of it published, as soon as I told him about it. I sent him a long fantasy and a set of poems, "The Demons of the Upper Air." He praised and criticized both in detail, correcting each spelling error and infelicity, and carefully debating each dubious word-choice. He was particularly hard on such ponderous affectations as "activate" for "move." The fantasy was afterwards published by Arkham House as "Adept's Gambit" in my collection *Night's Black Agents*. This action on his part, crazily generous by hard-headed standards, influenced me permanently toward greater care in the polishing and final preparation of manuscripts.

His criticisms were not solely literary. When I praised Charles Fort for poking holes in scientific theories, he replied at once with a carefully reasoned, convincing defense of the dogmatism of the professional scientist. Fort's books, he said, were not to be taken seriously, though amusing enough and a great source of materials for the writer of fantasy and science fiction.

And he was unsparingly and I think excessively critical of his own writings, quite as harsh in fact as Edmund Wilson. He thought most of his stories were labored, unhumorous, wanting in lively human portraits, and heavy with a sort of pseudo-realism and with intentional partial repetitions designed to build atmosphere. He told me of his practice of disavowing from time to time stories which he found aesthetically wanting and he sent me a list, of which I still have a copy, of stories not disavowed as yet; "Herbert West—Reanimator" was still on the list but, he said, it was about to get the ax.

For my part, I think that Lovecraft, besides writing some excellent short stories somewhat in the manners of Poe, Dunsany, Machen, Hoffmann, and Bulwer-Lytton, and in addition to giving fiction with solid New England background a unique spectral note, did more than any other author to establish the science-fiction story as a vehicle for supernatural horror—a clear-cut and valid story form. Occasionally overshadowed by timelier, catchier, more chameleon-like fantasy and science fiction, such tales as "The Whisperer in Darkness," "The Dunwich Horror," "The Colour out of Space," "The Shadow out of Time," and "The Dreams in the Witch House" will live.

Besides setting me in his letters an enduring example of honest scholarly criticism, Lovecraft did something of equal importance for my future. He circulated the fantasy and poems I sent him among several other congenial correspondents. As a result I met Robert Bloch, Henry Kuttner, and later several other writers in the fantasy field. I came to think of myself as at least potentially a professional author.

Lovecraft is sometimes thought of as having been a lonely man. He made my life far less lonely, not only during the brief half year of our correspondence but during the twenty years after.

Yet those six precious months did have a special magic. Here are some examples. Inspired by Lovecraft's stories I produced several pictures in a medium I called splatter-stencil: star-fields splattered on black paper silhouette monstrous forms and structures. I sent a set to Lovecraft and he liked them. And I recall I was going to play Scipio Africanus in a drama about Hannibal that had a short life on the stages of San Francisco and Los Angeles. In the end I did not get the part, but we had a fine time commenting in our letters on this unexpected intrusion of old Rome. And there was talk of a volume of Lovecraft's short stories being published in hard covers, though he discounted the possibility since it had more than once occurred and failed to materialize before.

There seemed no reason why our stimulating and fruitful relationship would not go on indefinitely. Although he sometimes referred to himself as the Old Gentleman, Lovecraft had only become 46 years old on August 20th—"in my 47th year" was his way of putting it. His letters proved that his reserves of energy were prodigious, his interest fresh, his attitudes youthful—how many middle-aged men make friendships of the temperamental, unreserved, impractical sort by mail? To us, there was every indication that a long life remained to Lovecraft.

Yet there were disturbing hints that the situation was not quite like that. With more of her directness, my wife asked Lovecraft about his diet. The Old Gentleman obliged us with his College Street menu: chiefly coffee and a doughnut for breakfast, coffee and bread and cheese or a small can of beans for supper.

In the winter there was a brief hiatus in his replies. Then he wrote that he had been in a hospital for a few days, but was out again and taking his regular walks, though in slippers or in shoes that had been cut out to accommodate his swollen feet.

Again his replies ceased. In Los Angeles my wife and I hid our fears from each other. In a Louisville attic, where his family had been driven by the Great Ohio Flood that opened 1937 (and destroyed a set of my splatter-stencils), Harry Fischer noted down, in a letter he had no way of sending me at the time, that something must be done to provide Lovecraft with fresh vegetables.

It was a little late for vitamins. Shortly afterwards Mrs. Gamwell informed us of her nephew's death. Only then did we realize that his letters to us newcomers were, beyond their other values, an example of truly smiling fortitude, of the enjoyment of life in the face of the greatest adversity.

[*Fresco,* Spring 1958]

LOVECRAFT: A SYMPOSIUM

[*Editors' Note:* The following excerpts have been taken from a panel discussion on the works and life of H. P. Lovecraft, involving Fritz Leiber, Arthur Jean Cox, Robert Bloch, Leland Sapiro, and Sam Russell at the Los Angeles Science Fantasy Society, on October 24, 1963. It was first published as a pamphlet, *H. P. Lovecraft: A Symposium* (Riverside Quarterly/Los Angeles Science Fantasy Society, 1963). We have used the following source: "H. P. Lovecraft: A Symposium," *Crypt of Cthulhu* No. 97 (Hallowmas 1997). We have decided to omit almost all of the other authors' comments regarding Lovecraft, as this is a collection dealing primarily with Lovecraft and Leiber and we also feel that much of what Leiber said can stand alone as solid piece of commentary. However, there are a few occasions in which Leiber continues a discussion begun by one of the other authors, and in these cases we have included the author's commentary. We also left out certain phases of commentary by Leiber that we found to be irrelevant to the general topic at hand.]

Fritz Leiber: I think that in this question of displaced identity—or exchanges of souls, as it would have been called by most writers of that time—we come very close to the deepest sort of metaphysical problem: how our consciousness, how our vivid picture of reality in my mind that seems to extend out into space—and into time, by way of memory—how this picture of reality can exist in the material world, the world we know about through bumps and knocks, the world that has been described by science as the bumps and knocks that a number of people have agree upon. What consciousness is and how it exists in the world is eternally a puzzle, and I think that Lovecraft tended to go to these ultimate points for basing his stories and typing them down.

And the very fact that he avoided the Christian cosmology made his points even more acute, because he didn't take the easy out, [utilized by] so many writers of ghost stories and supernatural fiction, of setting the story against an all-religious background that provides an easy explanation.

Fritz Leiber: In some of his stories, particularly the later stories, the so-called monsters, actually highly intelligent members of other species, became—to me, at least—the sympathetic characters. The Old Ones at *The Mountains of Madness*—who, having been in suspended animation for millions of years, awake in a howling blizzard [only to be] attacked by savage dogs, with one of them being vivisected by a human scientist—the way they face this situation and fight their way out—Lovecraft himself in that story has one of the scientists say, "By God, whatever they were, they were men!"

So without making the old suggestion that the author feels himself to be the monster, I would suggest that there is the possibility, at least, that Lovecraft's sympathy went out to them. The monsters at the end turn out to be scholars above everything else, who spend their lives doing things like carrying the brains of other scholars around the universe with them in metal canisters in order that these brains could see and talk about and hear explanations of everything there was in the universe.

Fritz Leiber: I can't but help but feel that the brains in the cylinders in "The Whisperer in Darkness" represent to some extent a scholar's utopia, and yet the brain of the one earthly scholar, Henry Akeley, that does speak from these cylinders speaks in a frightened and horrified way. There is a conflict there, and it runs through the story.

Fritz Leiber: He wrote many of his stories in a vivid first person: generally the narrator was explaining himself or writing a document explaining himself or writing a document explaining what had happened to him or making one of those pleas that a certain area not be investigated for fear of what would be discovered. With this sort of first person I don't think we can take the remarks and interjections as belonging to the author. In any case, an atheist scholar or scientist will use expressions like "Great God" and so on, and "Gad" that runs through "Pickman's Model." He'll use them as emotional expressions without meaning any belief in them.

In my short correspondence with him, one of the first things that came up, I remember, was that I made some rather complimentary remarks about Charles Fort's books, saying something to the effect that these books showed that scientists didn't know everything and that there was lots of information that scientists were deliberately disregarding because they couldn't figure out any good explanation. He came back on a rather hot defense of the scientist: he pointed out that he was a materialist himself and that the scientist had to demand that recorded events be confirmed in the most detailed way, that if a thing be seen, that you describe how an experiment could be set up to produce the same effect again. He assured me that although Fort's books, his collections of newspaper and magazine clippings, were very interesting and great background material for the writer, they weren't to [be] taken seriously in the way of a refutation of scientific theory. I just cite that as an example of his thoroughgoing scientific approach to life outside stories.

Leland Sapiro: I'd like to read a quotation from [Lovecraft] which to me has always been rather puzzling:

Modern science has in the end proved an enemy to art and pleasure; for by revealing to use the whole sordid and prosaic basis of our thoughts, motives, and acts, it has stripped the world of glamour, wonder, and all those illusions of heroism, nobility, and sacrifice which used to sound impressive when romantically treated. ["Lord Dunsany and His Work," *Marginalia*, p. 139]

So it seems that Lovecraft's attitude would be that science was a detriment to fiction.

Fritz Leiber: A detriment to fiction? I understand him to say it's a detriment to art and pleasure simply by taking away illusions, revealing that the universe is a machine, and that the actions that we feel are noble or idealistic are, after all, the actions of a machine that is run by psychics and chemistry, I mean psychological chemistry of the human body. Illusions like the idea of indwelling spirits, the sort of thing that would add charm to mythology and the earlier religions, that there were beings, some perhaps frightening and some benign in the objects around us, in sticks and stones and trees—well, science takes this away—and it says that any idealistic impulse is still based on chemical reactions in the nerves, in the glands; and this is a difficult thing to face up to.

Fritz Leiber: In the majority of his stories, especially his later and longer stories involving what has come to be called the "Cthulhu Mythos," he invented an alternate world superficially like or own world but different in that there was evidence, available to certain scholars, that there were other forces, other beings, operating in the world by various secret methods, that this proved that witchcraft had a real material background, and so on. I don't think that any one but a seriously realistic writer would have made such a point in inventing this alternate world.

Arthur Jean Cox: It seems to me that [Loveraft's] stories express this theme [which Leland Sapiro describes as an "obsession with heredity and racial degeneracy" and Robert Bloch as a "fear of decay—physical decay and decadence ascribable to hereditary traits"] so predominately that is must have had some personal relevance to him.

Fritz Leiber: It had a relevance, yet, but the theme—the theme of decay—is the theme of death, and it is universal. Although Lovecraft used that particular theme often—the theme of a degenerate population, in "The Shadow over Innsmouth," "The Lurking Fear," "He," and to a lesser extent, in "The Dunwich Horror"—I don't feel that Lovecraft was obsessed in the sense that his judgement as a realist and as a creative artist was impaired.

After all, we could make the same statement about Arthur Machen. Machen wrote "The Novel of the Black Seal" about degenerate Pictish cave-dwelling beings in the Welsh hills, "The Great God Pan" about a woman who was the child of Pan and a mad mother, and who brought to the people she came in contact with an influence that caused them to reverse their evolution. In "The Novel of the White Powder" a powder is developed that is the basis of the wine of the Sabbath; and this does the same thing to the people who drink it: it degenerates them in a matter of weeks; they literally go back through various savage stages to the primal ooze. Now I don't recall hearing any particular influences of a parallel sort in Machen's life.

Leland Sapiro: So could it be that Lovecraft did have some appreciation of the worth of his own stories—that he realized that Farnsworth Wright had limitations himself?

Fritz Leiber: I would say that although he was very doubtful about the worth of his own particular stories—easily shaken by editorial disapproval—he wasn't at all weak as far as what he considered aesthetic judgements in general. A contrived ending on a horror tale, the idea of building up an atmosphere of supernatural horror and then explaining it was just a dream or a mechanism that waves the white sheet, offended his artistic sense.

Fritz Leiber: I guess I must be a bit out of the ordinary, because Lovecraft did frighten me when I first read him. The first story I ever read by Lovecraft was "The Colour out of Space" in *Amazing,* and that story really spooked me. It affected me and frightened me as the same time, as a boy of around seventeen.

About this business of using words like "eldritch," "nameless," it has to be remembered that these words were used along with very explicit detailed descriptions; they were an added mist of colour that he put on his story. It's like a painter doing some kind of final spread on top of everything else, sort of filling up the empty spaces in the mosaic. He did get these very general words like "strange" and "weird" and "horrible," but they didn't stand alone: there was always explicit description with them, and I think he used them for a kind of musical quality.

Lovecraft did use overstatement, admittedly. Writers, even quite versatile writers, get wedded to certain ways of telling stories, and it's rarely that they break completely free. It's rare that a man who writes by way of extremes, almost a kind of overstatement, will decided to change and go in for understatement. It would have been extremely strange if someone like Lovecraft had been able to tone down his stories to the point where he was writing things that were only meant half or a quarter seriously, say like John Collier's stories, which had a persistent humorous element. I don't think that writers, even the hard working writers, make changes to that degree. Lovecraft gambled his creativity from the start on the Edgar Allan Poe sort of story and that is why he stuck to it.

Fritz Leiber: "The Shadow out of Time" was the most extended and systematic imaginative effort that Lovecraft made to give body and substance to the idea of mankind being only an incident. He had several stages of recollection there, where the narrator remembers talking with Nug-Soth, magician of the dark conquerors who were to come in 5000 A.D. and then jumps back to the great-headed brown people who ruled Africa in 50,000 B.C. He gives you a feeling of the mutability of the human race—and then goes on with detailed explanations of how, after mankind, a race of beetles, a coleoptroid race, develops on Earth; then there is a migration, I think, to Venus and finally to Mercury of different races, sort of joined together because the Great Race had taken their minds over—and he slips in, just in one sentence, something that is extremely terrifying, and one example of understatement in Lovecraft: He says, "The fate of the human race affected me so much that I won't set it down here."

Fritz Leiber: We [the "Lovecraft Circle"] were moved by his simple generosity. My later memories are of the large amounts of really good advice he gave me. I'd say something in a letter about thinking of writing a novel set in Roman times. Back would come four or five pages of good advice on how to prepare a novel set in the times of Republican Rome, a longer and shorter bibliography of books that I should read for background. Lovecraft was a writer in the old sense of the word, of a man who wrote a great deal and who had taken some sort of oath of Aesculapius suitable for writers rather than doctors, who felt called upon to teach a pupil that came to him. It was something I'm still very grateful for.

Fritz Leiber: I would like to say that I think Lovecraft posthumously became a symbol of something that he wasn't in reality—for science-fiction writers rebelling against the *Weird Tales* influence, and it's an indication of how strong that influence was, that there was such a passionate rebellion. To some of the very young science-fiction writers of the time it was convenient to make Lovecraft stand for the superstitious interpretation of reality, as opposed to the straightforward, scientific sort of sociologically bedded approach. As a result they would point at Lovecraft and criticize or merely shout Nyah!—or satirize, as Phil Stong did. He sort of set the note of using Lovecraft as symbolizing the superstitious old-fashioned horror and science-fiction story.

[*H. P. Lovecraft: A Symposium,* by Fritz Leiber, Robert Bloch,
Sam Russell, Arthur Jean Cox, and Leland Sapiro
(Riverside Quarterly/Los Angeles Science Fantasy Society, 1963)]

THE "WHISPERER" RE-EXAMINED

During the quarter-century since his death, the stories of H. P. Lovecraft have received lavish praise and bitter dispraise, both largely uncritical. While this bickering may satisfy some and amuse others, it isn't enough for me, as I was greatly influenced by both the man and his writings, so for my own sake I must try to keep things as straight and fully analyzed as I can.

In "A Literary Copernicus" (which I could have more pinpointingly titled "The Copernicus of the Modern Horror Story") I analyzed the virtues of Lovecraft's writings and of the literary and creative devices he used. Now I shall try to give briefly the other side of the picture, not to invalidate my earlier analysis, but to round it out, filling in the blacks as well as the whites. I intend to do it largely in terms of "The Whisperer in Darkness," my favorite among Lovecraft's stories, because it is a product of his best mature period (it was written in 1930), is long enough (25,000 words) to make a good sample, strongly arouses both adventurous expectancy and dread, evenly combines his earlier leanings toward black magic and legendry as story background with his later preference for speculative science as the source of eerie atmosphere—and probably chiefly because "The Whisperer" gave me the most excited shivers when I first read it.

First, briefly, the plot (to refresh the memories of those who have read the tale; all others . . . read it first!):

Albert Wilmarth, an amateur folklorist and instructor of literature at Miskatonic University, takes the skeptical side of a scholarly newspaper argument as to whether there are strange beings from another world in the Vermont hills. Henry Akeley, a recluse scholar living on the spot, convinces him by correspondence that there are such beings, come from Pluto, but persuades him also to keep this knowledge secret, since the beings might decide to conquer Earth if disturbed. Akeley becomes convinced that the beings will soon kill or kidnap him as one who knows too much. He begs Wilmarth to keep clear. Next he writes Wilmarth a letter showing a great change in viewpoint and personality: he has contacted the beings, they are benign, he urges Wilmarth to visit him (bringing their correspondence). Wilmarth complies and has several hours' conversation with a strangely stiff-seeming Akeley in a dim room. That night—apparently only because he failed to drink some acrid-tasting drugged coffee—he overhears a conversation indicating that one of the Plutonian beings had been impersonating Akeley and that they intend to kidnap Wilmarth too. He sees evidence of this and successfully escapes from Akeley's house and the Vermont hills.

This outline in no way conveys the atmosphere and power of the story, but it allows me to place my comments—or, rather, my "reader reactions."

First, I have never been convinced that Wilmarth would have been so easily hoodwinked into going to Vermont, since the plot of the Plutonians stands out a mile. I have always had to stop to assure myself that Wilmarth must have been so very fascinated that he lost all sense of caution—though the story never convinced me of this—and then go on with my reading of it. After his arrival in Vermont, Wilmarth continues to be incredibly slow in seeing through the deception, though he is given clue after clue.

Second, there is no real explanation, stated or hinted, as to why the beings play cat-and-mouse with Wilmarth so long—and with Akeley too, for that matter. The assertion that they are clumsy in getting around Earth, after having had an outpost on it for several hundred years, does not seem very convincing. True, this makes the Plutonians no more ineffectual than Dr. Fu Manchu in his cat-and-mousing with Nayland Smith; but one expects a bit more from galaxy-striding extraterrestrials. Also their methods are largely those of melodrama: drugged coffee, faked telegrams, hypnotism, elaborate facial disguises, and secret car trips by night.

Third, the Vermont landscape is described in considerable detail at least four times: in Wilmarth's preliminary remarks in Akeley's letter, during Wilmarth's journey to Akeley's Vermont home, and during his flight from it. This repetition, which I have always found wearing, foreshadows the repeated and rerepeated trudgings through corridors of cyclopean masonry in "The Shadow out of Time" and *At the Mountains of Madness*.

There are superbly effective moments in the story, as when Wilmarth is first shown a small shiny cylinder containing a captive brain left only the senses of sight and hearing and the power of speech. (I used the same concept in my novel *The Silver Eggheads*, writing in an acknowledgment.) But the story is effectively dramatized in only a few spots; the long stretches of generalized description, elaborate hinting, and deliberate repetitions tend to drag.

The reason for this sort of story structure seems to me to be that Lovecraft planned a great climactic scare for Wilmarth (and the reader) and wrote his way relentlessly toward it, resolutely avoiding any side-trails—though the last are often the most fruitful parts of a story, conveying insights, observations of daily life, and subtleties of characterization.

This march toward the climactic scare seems to be the reason for the rarity of fully dramatized moments in the story. There must be a build-up from the generalized opening statements, things seen from a distance, hearsay and hints, to the final blindingly vivid lightning flash; too much close-focus stuff early in the tale might spoil the step-by-step approach to a peak of terror. This is the reason too for the cat-and-mousing of Wilmarth: the Plutonians must spend hours making hintful revelations to him after they have him in their power, simply because this will maximize his scare. Lovecraft must cat-and-mouse with us as well, interminably exploiting the hesitations and reluctances of his narrator to tell us what the basic horror is. Such devices can work quite well as far as generating supernatural dread goes, but they make for a rigid, limited, monorail sort of story. And most of Lovecraft's stories have this rigid narrow pattern. From a short-short like "The Statement of Randolph Carter" to a novel like *At the Mountains of Madness,* there is a sense in which the second of these stories goes no further than the first. Ideas must be hinted at rather than analyzed, the characters can almost never be allowed to interact dramatically, the monsters in particular must not be analyzed or explored inwardly—since any of these things might spoil the mood of terror, break its spell.

In "Notes on the Writing of Weird Fiction" Lovecraft summed up this limitation: "All that a wonder story can ever be is *a vivid picture of a certain type of human mood.*" This aesthetic dictum, while having some technical validity, breathes loneliness and can be very stultifying to the writer's urge to say things about the real world, set down insights into real people, speculate imaginatively, and get closer to his reader than merely sharing "a vague illusion of the strange reality of the unreal."

I guess what I am saying comes down to this: that HPL wrote supernatural horror stories and that such stories, especially when created by a purist, are of limited scope. For instance, analyzing the monsters or exploring them inwardly can well change a story of supernatural terror into one of science-fiction.

There's also this suggestion: that HPL's stories grip the reader like nightmares and were written the same way, the mind unable to get out of its dreadful groove and look around until the end is reached. A drumming, somnambulistic intensity—reader and writer drawn endlessly and will-lessly down some high interminable corridor or through some endless city or dread forest—a progress through a panorama of horrifying arabesques—these episodes seem straight out of nightmare or hypnagogic vision. And specifically with regard to "The Whisperer," which Lovecraft wrote in a week, the reader must, to make the story believable, accept that Wilmarth is in some sort of nightmare hypnagogic mind-state from the moment he receives Akeley's last letter.

I'm sorry this brief article must neglect many grand things about "The Whisperer": the way it springs from fresh topical realities such as the Vermont floods of 1927, the discovery of Pluto, and the growth of cheap summer resorts in New England; the smooth way in which it brings in Machen, Fort, and other literary influences; the several fine short dramatic-dialogue sections; the excellent use of clawprints and other tiny clues; the basically excellent science-fiction; the occasional feelings of boiling adventurous excitement at the thought of the myriad unutterably strange wonders and weirdnesses the universe must hold. These grand things are all as vital and vivid as they are, incidentally, almost completely absent from the stories of Lovecraft's imitators. For despite the cramping limitations of his favorite fictional medium—which at times shackled him dreadfully, I believe—Lovecraft still always tried to use it to express what he knew and felt about life itself, rather than merely create mannered eldritch horror stories.

[*Haunted*, December 1964]

THROUGH HYPERSPACE WITH BROWN JENKIN

LOVECRAFT'S CONTRIBUTION TO SPECULATIVE FICTION

Beginning with "The Call of Cthulhu" and "The Colour out of Space," speculative science played a larger part in Lovecraft's fiction: hibernating races and travel through space, hyperspace, and time. That those two tales were written very soon after *Amazing Stories* was founded in 1926 and the second published in that magazine is at least suggestive.

Amazing Stories began with reprints of Wells and Verne, giving hopes of at least a moderately high literary level—hopes largely dashed, which may account for Lovecraft veering away from that market after his first sale.

In more than half his subsequent fiction, however, monsters raised by black magic and thwarted by white are replaced by extra-terrestrial or even extra-cosmical beings who sojourned on earth in the past and may secretly reside among us today. The *Necronomicon* largely ceases to be used for its spells of exorcism, but remains a sourcebook on the habits and history of these more realistic monsters.

True Lovecraft said in "Some Notes on a Nonentity," "I doubt if I could ever succeed well in the ordinary kind of science fiction," while in "Some Notes on Interplanetary Fiction" he gloriously lambasted "dime-novel theatricalism," "stock romance," and such clichés as "over-facile language learning . . . weddngs with beautiful anthropomorphic princesses . . . stereotyped Armageddons with ray-guns and space-ships . . . court intrigues and jealous magicians . . . hairy ape-men of the polar caps," and advised writers to concentrate on describing realistically, thoughtfully, and with emotional power and proper awe the take-off from earth, the trip through space, and the landing on the strange planet.

Here clearly Lovecraft is excoriating Buck Rogers, the Martian novels of Edgar Rice Burroughs, and similar extravaganzas; the *Weird Tales* stories which Farnsworth Wright described with wonderful precision as pseudo-scientific or weird-scientific (electric space-ships leaping about the cosmos, battles of anthropomorphized angels and devils, carnivorous plants, murderous scientists, gray fungoid plagues, mysterious serums from tropic blooms, giant spiders); and the magazine speculative fiction of what Isaac Asimov called the Gernsback Era (1926–1938)—stories fairly long on science but very short on all literary qualities and further enfeebled by Gernsback's idealistic dictum that "scientifiction" should be sugar-coated science education.

When stories of any literary merit appeared, he was quick to recognize them. He said of the tales of Stanley G. Weinbaum, "I saw with pleasure that someone had at last escaped the sickening hackneyedness in which 99.99% of all pulp interplanetary stuff is engulfed. Here, I rejoiced, was somebody who could think of another planet in terms of something besides anthropomorphic kings and beautiful princesses . . . etc."

Lovecraft also asserted, "Social and political satire are always undesirable." Here perhaps even more clearly he seems to be thinking of the crude anti-religious element in Burroughs and perhaps of such books as Bellamy's *Looking Backward* and Jack London's *The Iron Heel.* He can hardly be referring to *Gulliver's Travels* or to such novels by H. G. Wells as *The First Men in the Moon,* or to Olaf Stapledon's *Last and First Men.*

The fact is that Lovecraft barely but completely missed the beginning in America and the rekindling in Britain of literate speculative fiction. He died in 1937. In that year was published William Sloane's *To Walk the Night,* a novel written in a lively but solid modern style and with almost excessive restraint about the sojourn of an extra-terrestrial being on earth—and which also arouses a quite Lovecraftian mood of awe, puzzlement, and cosmic dread. In the same year Karel Capek's *War with the Newts* was published in an English translation. Still farther in the future lay C. S. Lewis' *Malacandra* (or *Out of the Silent Planet*), an interplanetary novel which reads as if it had been written to satisfy Lovecraft's criteria. Literate writers like Robert Heinlein, Norman Knight, Don Stuart, Isaac Asimov, and Lovecraft's protégé Henry Kuttner were still to appear in *Astounding Stories* and that magazine under the editorship of John Campbell to begin to work toward the research realism in speculative writing which Lovecraft desired. While it would be a decade or two before the publication of such outstanding novels of speculative fiction as Edgar Pangborn's *A Mirror for Observers,* Theodore Sturgeon's *More Than Human,* Arthur Clarke's *Childhood's End,* Philip Dick's *The Man in the High Castle,* Kurt Vonnegut's *Cat's Cradle,* John Hersey's *The Child Buyer,* Philip Wylie's *The Disappearance,* Gore Vidal's *Messiah,* Ward Moore's *Greener Than You Think* and *Bring the Jubilee,* Judith Merril's *Shadow on the Hearth* and *The Tomorrow People,* Ray Bradbury's *Fahrenheit 451,* George Orwell's *1984,* Frederick Pohl's and Cyril Kornbluth's *The Space Merchants,* Frank Herbert's *The Dragon in the Sea,* Herbert Best's *The 25th Hour,* Clifford Simak's *Way Station,* Robert Heinlein's *Beyond This Horizon,* Hal Clement's *Mission of Gravity,* James Blish's *A Case of Conscience,* and Robert Graves' *Watch the North Wind Rise* (in England *Seven Days in New Crete*).

But during the very Gernsback Era he detested, Lovecraft made his own contribution to speculative fiction, in addition to the critical item already noted. Both worked, along a horror-story side track, toward the maturation of the field.

These contributions were largely in the direction of paying proper attention to cosmology, astronomy, and geology and to impressing on the reader the vast size and duration of the cosmos. Lovecraft's extra-terrestrials were never stock humanoid figures (such as the appealing yet ridiculous oviparous princesses of Burrough's Mars), but beings with a wholly non-human morphology and biology, and with languages, architectures, industries, and cultures wholly their own.

Lovecraft did his best to get writers to stop using obvious English roots in devising the names of earth-aliens—"Tarko," say, or "Akor"—and instead try to imagine non-human sounds and then render them phonetically. While some of his biological creations are masterful feats of imagination: the appearance of a specimen of the Old Ones, as described by Lake in *At the Mountaim of Madness*, is chillingly real—if the reader will make the effort to visualize the being as described in dry scientific language. If Lovecraft had been willing to put such a being *into action* in one of his tales, he would doubtless have won many new readers. But for reasons in part aesthetic he never took this step. Perhaps he was tempted to and his hesitation fully to abandon supernatural horror for less restrictive speculative fiction was one of the reasons for his creative slowdown during his last years.

Certainly Lovecraft helped lead the way toward greater realism in subsequent speculative fiction.

It must be admitted, however, that Lovecraft devoted very little attention to novel inventions, to science speculations for their own sake, and to extrapolations from present-day society into the future—aside from a general conviction that human affairs would get worse, at least from the viewpoint of a lover of traditions and of social stability. After all, his chief artistic interest was in creating backgrounds for horror stories; graveyards and homely ghosts were losing interest, while cosmic outsideness was gaining, and in one way he simply followed this trend—to the point of seeing both *At the Mountains of Madness* and "The Shadow out of Time" published in *Astounding Stories*.

However, what science speculations the Old Gentleman did make were very clever indeed and most of them were carefully researched. His scientists and their paraphernalia—their personalities and mannerisms and daily professional work—were convincingly presented; Lovecraft was always good on the scholarly type.

Moreover, in his cosmic speculations Lovecraft was following not only an outward trend, but a deep inward passion, as shown by a statement he makes in a letter to Clark Ashton Smith (Oct. 17, 1930): "The true function of phantasy is to give the imagination a ground for limitless expansion, and to satisfy aesthetically the sincere and burning curiosity and sense of awe which a sensitive minority of mankind feel toward the alluring and provocative abysses of unplumbed space and unguessed entity which press in upon the known world from unknown infinities and in unknown relationships of time, space, matter, force, dimensionality, and consciousness. I *know* that my most poignant emotional experiences are those which concern the lure of unplumbed space, the terror of the encroaching outer void, and the struggle to transcend the known and established order."

Hibernating Races: Cthulhu's "House at R'lyeh" is really a sort of time-capsule—a sunken city whose extra-terrestrial inhabitants are held in suspended animation until the city appears again above the surface of the sea. The full functioning of the beings also depends on, the stars "being right," when they can plunge from planet to planet and exercise other tremendous powers. Cthulhu himself is a shape-changer: he can rearrange his molecules into their original pattern, when they have been disrupted, and surely this would make it easier for him to space-travel. The architecture of R'lyeh suggests that its builders had a knowledge, working rather than the theoretical, of non-Euclidean geometry.

Also in "The Call of Cthulhu" the background of professional archaeology and anthropology is most authentically presented, particularly at an imagined meeting of the American Archaeological Society in 1908.

Space-travel: the Plutonian beings or Mi-Go in "The Whisperer in Darkness" are able to fly through space "on clumsy, powerful wings which have a way of resisting the ether." This notion was good speculative fiction back in the 1920's when the ether was still a fringe-fashionable science concept, and today the notion of sailing or perhaps even winging through space is back in speculative style again, light pressure taking the place of ether. A very patient sailor could even tack in from Pluto on these photonic winds, braving storms in the solar plasma, and perhaps find tail winds in one of the hydrogen bands streaming through the cosmos or in some steady gust of cosmic wavicles. Had he lived, we can be sure that Lovecraft would have made great use of the new astronomy in his fiction; World War Two, culminating in its world-changing discoveries in atomics and rocketry, would have worked at least as powerfully on him as it did on other imaginative writers.

Most of Lovecraft's monsters were equipped to live indefinitely in the thinness of space: by having extremely tough tissues, by suspended animation, or by having shape-changing powers like Cthulhu and perhaps traveling between planets and stars as a cloud of independent molecules, like Stapledon's Martians. If an animal were tough as a spaceship, there's no reason he mightn't be able to travel as efficiently as one—he could carry his fuel like a camel carries his water.

"The Whisperer" also has the charmingly friendly touch of the Mi-Go carrying about with them through space in small canisters—tucked under their wings or clutched in their maternal pincers—the living brains of beings so unfortunate as not to be able to travel space embodied. In the story this is effectively presented as a horror, but on second thought such immortality has great appeal.

The folklore and anthropology background of "The Whisperer" is well handled. The authors Akeley lists to prove his competence in those fields are a nice selection.

The centipedal beings which Lovecraft devised to provide a rationale for the round-robin story "The Challenge from Beyond" broadcast by rocket throughout the galaxy small encapsulated send-receive telepathy stations which enable them to exchange minds with any being who finds one of the stations and starts to listen in. It is noteworthy that it was Lovecraft who provided the scientifically plausible explanation in this story rather than any other of the authors: C. L. Moore. A. Merritt, Robert E. Howard, and Frank Belknap Long. The same method of space-travel by exchange of minds is used in "The Thing on the Doorstep," but for shorter trips.

The beings in "The Colour out of Space"—it is a moot point whether these were intelligent—traveled by meteorite imbedded in an unidentifiable plastic element or compound—". . . a piece of the great outside . . . dowered with outside properties . . ." The beings arrive in the form of or inside small brittle strangely colored spheres about as big as baseballs—a spore or seed is suggested—and take off at the story's end in a more active flamelike corruscating form, as if naturally equipped with antigravity and an ionic drive.

The color itself in this story—the color of the brittle spheres, later that of the corruscations—at first seems impossible, since color is something in the brain's coding system rather than anything inherent in outside objects. But Lovecraft says, "It was only by analogy they called it colour at all." It is possible to think of textures, layered transparencies, and the like that would be completely novel on earth and give novel visual effects. However, the same color turns up in the spectroscope when the unidentifiable material of the meteorite is analyzed—and this is harder to understand.

As Edmund Wilson pointed out in his *New Yorker* article, this remarkably gripping story (which gave me the gloomy creeps for weeks as a kid, when it turned up as a dark intruder in *Amazing*) describes phenomena rather remarkably like the effects of atomic radiation: mutations, morphological peculiarities in the newborn or newly budded, and the deadliest radiation sickness. Also, the corruscations given off by the beings about to depart from earth are very like those given off by the strange radioactive substance in Stewart Edward White's and Samuel Hopkins Adams' gripping early science-adventure novel *The Mystery*. In both cases showers of sparks are mentioned and much is made of the resemblance to St. Elmo's Fire.

Hyperspace-Travel: This may occur *in* "The Dunwich Horror," though that richly textured story is more an extrapolation from black magic and Arthur Machen than from science; at any rate the monsters walk "Not in the spaces we know, but *between* them"—which suggest interpenetrating universes and makes us think with a shiver about the immense amount of empty space in even the solidest substance. Here an extreme form of the impossible hybrid between species is the main subject-matter: the offspring of woman and horrendous, emphatically extra-terrestrial monster. Also the huge extra-terrestrials (or extra-cosmicals!) in "The Dunwich Horror" have a fascinating morphology: they are made of gigantic tissue-ropes that interweave and slide against each other—living knots bigger than barns.

From "The Dunwich Horror" and his other later stories it can be argued that Lovecraft was a transition-writer between horror fiction and speculative fiction and that he did all the hard, thankless work transition-writers do *(cf.*

the transition-writers between the stories observing all sexual taboos and the stories observing none) and that his stories suffered from the same unavoidable defects.

But "The Dreams in the Witch House" is Lovecraft's most carefully worked out story of hyperspace-travel. Here (1) a rational foundation for such travel is set up; (2) hyperspace is visualized; and (3) a trigger for such travel is devised.

(1) Our three-dimensional continuum is embedded in a four-dimensional continuum (another name for hyperspace) in such a freakishly convoluted way that is possible to travel in seconds through hyperspace to points many light-millennia distant in normal space—and also to other continua, in some of which time does not exist, so that one does not age there.

By traveling hyperspace one can escape from any prison, enter and leave all manner of locked rooms.

An old Salem witch, Keziah Mason, and her rat-bodied, man-headed and man-handed familiar Brown Jenkin mastered hyperspace-travel as early as 1692 and used it to keep the Witch Cult alive in Arkham down to 1932, hiding out in a centuries-boarded-up attic in Arkham and in other witch-holes dotted about this cosmos and other universes. They tempt Walter Gilman, a brilliant young student of mathematics at Miskatonic University, to join the Witch Cult and finally doom himself in episodes of hyperspace-travel which he keeps trying to explain rationally as dreams.

These hyperspace trips take Gilman to points as close as the boarded-up attic just above the ceiling of his rented room in the Witch House and as distant as other planets and even "the throne of Azathoth at the centre of the ultimate chaos." One touch is amazingly fine: after one night visiting the planet of a star in the constellation Hydra, Gilman next day finds himself psychologically attracted to that point in Hydra as it moves under the earth, rises in the southeast about midday, and slowly mounts the sky—until the compulsion which had begun as an impulse to stare at a spot on the floor turns into an urge to leap mystically upward, a marvellously realistic linkage between man and cosmos. Certainly the boy who in his early teens hectographed *The Rhode Island Journal of Astronomy* made excellent use in his fiction of the astronomical knowledge he piled up.

(2) Lovecraft makes a bold attempt to describe what hyperspace looks like and how it strikes the other senses as Gilman travels through it with Keziah and Brown Jenkin. It looks, in brief, like the wildest of modernistic art and sounds like pandemonium; everything is "marvellously transmuted and obliquely projected." In hyperspace Keziah Mason appears as a "rather large congeries of iridescent, prolately spheroidal bubbles," while Brown Jenkin takes the form of "a very much smaller polyhedron of unknown colours and rapidly shifting surface angles." There's a resourceful little rat-man for you!

Logical purists and other spoil-sports may object at this point that three-dimensional eyes can't see the fourth dimension and that it's silly to try to visualize hyperspace; all you can do is write mathematical formulas describing it. But what the deuce!—Bohr picturing the atom as a tiny solar system stimulated tens of thousands of imaginations, even if we're now told this attempt was naive. One of the finest things speculative fiction can do is try to picture "the unpicturable"; some analogies are remarkably suggestive and great notions may turn up this way.

(3) The trigger or secret of hyperspace travel in "The Dreams in the Witch House" is advanced mathematical knowledge intuitively applied—you simply think yourself into hyperspace, hyper-travel a bit, and then . . . Hey, Presto! . . . think yourself out again. You see a direction others can't see. Gilman is first helped to see this direction by the strange angles of the walls and ceilings of his rented room; later, on a weird high-gravity planet Keziah and Brown Jenkin point two arms and a forepaw in directions which determine a vector along which Gilman moves to get back into hyperspace. True, three vectors in three-dimensional space add up to only one more vector. Still, there might be another answer—two and two make twenty-two as well as four—and at the least we have here a fine recreation of early twentieth-century reactions to the news that there is a fourth dimension: the wistful desire to be inspired to "see" that direction in three-dimensional space.

This "secret of hyperspace travel" is on first acquaintance something of a whopper—hard to swallow—yet to have used machinery would have weighted down Lovecraft's story unbearably, especially since Keziah had to be flitting in and out of hyperspace back in 1692. Yet the more one considers it, the more one finds something very neat, even elegant, about making hyperspace-travel one more form of psionic power or telekinesis: hyper-levitation! As a matter of fact, Selena, the beautiful mysterious intruder in Sloane's *To Walk the Night,* uses advanced mathematics and extra-sensory perception to time-travel. In the same respect Keziah Mason is the speculative ancestress of Barbara Haggerswell in Moore's *Bring the Jubilee* and Lucy Fisher in Simak's *Way Station.* The romantically minded may think of her as Robert Graves' Triple Goddess in her hag persona.

Time-travel, generally achieved by personality-exchange between beings as much as a billion years apart, is exploited richly and detailedly in "The Shadow out of Time," a work so often reprinted and discussed that anything said about it will tend to cover old ground. But once again—and also in *At the Mountains of Madness*—Lovecraft does the scientists and science-references very well: palaeontology, anthropology, psychology, biology, geology, even engineering.

In both *At the Mountains of Madness* and "The Shadow out of Time" it is clear that Lovecraft has become deeply interested in picturing in detail the careers of galactic races and the future history of mankind; that, although still holding onto the supernatural-horror pattern in his stories, he was trending more and more in the direction of creativity like Olaf Stapledon's. The extra-terrestrials are the real heroes of these long stories. Their unending struggles for survival and to increase their store of knowledge, their wise, rational, enlightened, and even "humane" cultures, are Lovecraft's finest vision of mind embattled against space and time. Between the two stories he devotes at least 10,000 words to such matters, apart from wordage spent on biological descriptions, architectural visionings of their cities, and the adventures of the human protagonists in those eldritch metropolises.

By collating these two short novels, one can discover an imagined history of the earth, not altogether unlike Robert Heinlein's "future history," though on a much vaster scale and concerned mostly with the past. Lovecraft appeared to set some store by it, as he worked into it both the octopoid Cthulhu creatures and the Mi-Go of "The Whisperer in Darkness," though neither of these races figure actively in the two tales.

A little after the material of the moon was wrenched from the South Pacific and before the continents had begun to separate and drift away from their Antarctic area of origin and before there was any life on earth—in short, in Azoic times, perhaps a billion and a half years ago—the star-headed, barrel-bodied Old Ones came flying through the ether, each on his five membranous wings, the fashion of the Mi-Go. They built cities both on and under the sea, being vastly adaptable. They created earth life for food, allowing some to evolve unsupervised—the plants and animals we know. They also created hypnotically controlled protoplasmic masses which were their chief machines. These Shoggoths eventually evolved mental powers which made them extremely dangerous to their creators. (Here we begin to see Lovecraft's own evolving sympathy for his monsters: by and large he is for the Old Ones and against the Shoggoths.)

The continents began their long drifts. New lands rose from the Pacific in time to receive the Cthulhu spawn or cosmic octopi sifting down from infinity. There were wars between them and the Old Ones, ending in stalemate.

Next comers to earth were a race of cone-shaped beings, half animal, half vegetable, as were the Old Ones. They established themselves in and around the land mass which eventually became Australia.

Then about six hundred million years ago, near the beginning of the Palaeozoic Era, there arrived on earth and three other solar planets a half polypous race we may call the Blind Beings. They had traveled through several universes and were constituted only in part of matter as we know it. They flew without wings, used winds as weapons, and built windowless basalt cities. They dominated earth for a time, preying particularly on the cone-shaped beings.

Then the minds of the Great Race migrated from transgalactic Yith into the bodies of the cone-shaped beings. They were a match for the horrifying Blind Beings and managed to drive them underground into great cavern worlds, but were unable to exterminate them. (Here again Lovecraft favors the Great Race against adversaries; in a sense, indeed, the Great Race came to earth as saviors.)

During the Carboniferous Period, rather late in the Palaeozoic, Europe, then conjoined more closely with Africa, supported a serpent people, the Valusians.

Then in the Permian Period, about one hundred and fifty million years ago, there was a great rebellion of the Shoggoths against their masters. The Old Ones won out, though their ability to fly was beginning to fail, while the Shoggoths kept evolving new powers.

The Mesozoic dawned, the era of reptiles. During the Jurassic Period the Mi-Go came flying from Pluto, challenging the Old Ones and winning from them the northern hemisphere. The Mi-Go were mountain dwellers and may today account for some of the tracks attributed to the "Abominable Snowmen."

Somewhat later, the Great Race, menaced by the vast eruption of the Blind Beings, migrated mentally en masse into the bodies of the hardy coleopterous or beetle race which succeeds mankind as the intellectual earth-born lords of earth. The Blind Beings, having had their revenge, retired to their caves and gradually died out.

The glacial ages of the late Cenezoic worked great hardship on the Old Ones, who were driven from their terrestrial cities by the Shoggoths, through perhaps surviving under the sea.

Then the anthropoid races began to appear, perhaps earliest among them "the furry prehuman Hyperborean worshippers of Tsathoggua." The kingdom of Lomar existed in a polar area 100,000 years ago and was wiped out by the yellow Inutos. In 50,000 B.C. a great-headed brown people held South Africa. In 15,000 B.C. the Cimmerians flourished. Then come modern times. By 5,000 A.D. the cruel empire of Tsan-Chan is in existence; in 16,000 A.D. there are "dark conquerors," possibly African.

The human race is followed, as we have seen, by a mighty beetle civilization which comes to hold the era-leaping minds of the Great Race.

The last intelligent denizens of earth are spiders—the first earth-born land dwellers proving to be the last intelligent race to dominate the planet.

As the sun grows cold, Venus becomes the home of intelligent life, then Mercury. The Great Race transfers itself to the bodies of bulbous vegetable entities on that planet and later to cavern-dwelling beings there, which seem to be the last intelligent race of the solar system.

This is certainly, on the whole, a pessimistic view of the destiny of man, created by accident by superior beings, preceded in his brief dominion over earth by vastly superior races, suffering a fate so dreadful that the narrator of "The Shadow out of Time" refuses to set it down, and superseded by the insects. It can be viewed, of course, not so much as a serious speculation by Lovecraft in any of its parts, as an attempt to create a suitably gloomy background for two horror stories. One wonders if the technological achievements of the past quarter century would have caused him to revise it much. Likely not.

One notes in it nods to his friends Robert E. Howard and Clark Ashton Smith: the mention of Cimmeria, Valusia, and Tsathoggua.

Perhaps Lovecraft would have written more about earth's imagined non-human races except for the limitations of his medium. The fiction of supernatural horror can only hint, unlike speculative fiction, which seeks to exhaust imagination, or as Lovecraft put it in his previously quoted letter to Smith, "give the imagination a ground for limitless expansion."

Yet Lovecraft went beyond hinting. He even speculated about the governments of the Old Ones and of the Great Race. Of the former he says, "The prevailing intellectual and aesthetic life was highly evolved, and produced a tenaciously enduring set of customs and institutions. Government was evidently complex and probably socialistic," while of the latter he remarks, "The Great Race seemed to form a single, loosely knit nation or league, with major institutions in common, though there were four definite divisions. The political and economic system of each unit was a sort of fascistic socialism, with major resources rationally distributed, and power delegated to a small governing board elected by the votes of all able to pass certain education and psychological tests. Family organization was not over-stressed, though ties among persons of common descent were recognized and the young were generally reared by their parents. . . .

"Industry, highly mechanized, demanded but little time from each citizen; and the abundant leisure was filled with intellectual and aesthetic activities of various sorts. The sciences were carried to an unbelievable height of development, and art was vital part of life . . .

"Crime was surprisingly scant, and was dealt with through highly efficient policing. Punishments ranged from privilege deprivation and imprisonment to death or major emotion wrenching, and were never administered without a careful study of the criminals motivation."

In these rather conservative speculations, one gets a hint of the sort of utopia Lovecraft may well have favored: an aristocracy of the mind—those with the finest controlled imaginations ranking highest; the most strongly and actively thinking minds ruling the duller, though with some tenderness for all mentality; beings ranked by Imagination Quotient, the "dyspeptic ploughman" subordinate to the poet able to conjure up "the peerless beauty of Narath with its hundred cavern gates and domes of chalcedony."

Through a lifetime of thinking about the monstrous shapes he feared, from the Night-Gaunts of his childhood to the Blind Beings of his last years, Lovecraft came to love them. It is with the deepest and most real feeling that William Dyer, Miskatonic geologist, exclaims of the Antarctic Old Ones, ". . . poor Old Ones! Scientists to the last . . . God, what intelligence and persistence! What a facing of the incredible! Radiates, vegetables, monstrosities, star-spawn—whatever they had been, they were men!"

[*Shangri-L'Affaires,* September 1963; rev. in
The Dark Brotherhood and Other Pieces, by H. P. Lovecraft
and Divers Hands (Arkham House, 1966)]

THE CTHULHU MYTHOS: WONDROUS AND TERRIBLE

Howard Phillips Lovecraft used the superanatural entities, alien races, and occult books of his Cthulhu Mythos as part of the weird, hintful atmosphere of about a dozen of his later stories. Occasionally an entity such as Yog-Sothoth or Cthulhu would be central to one of his stories, but then it would be retired into the hazy, sinister background again. For the very purpose of all of them—entities, races, books—was to be and sound eerie, remote, menacing from afar, mysterious, almost unknown, in line with his dictum in his *Supernatural Horror in Literature* that "The one test of the really weird is simply this—whether or not there be excited in the reader a profound sense of dread, and of contact with unknown spheres and powers; a subtle attitude of awed listening, as if for the beating of black wings or the scratching of out-side shapes and entities on the known universe's utmost rim." Any thorough-going explanation and systemization of the Mythos would have defeated its artistic purpose. True, in *At the Mountains of Madness* and "The Shadow out of Time" Lovecraft did organize the history and relations of some of his alien races in a rather science-fictional fashion. But he did no more than that.

What he *did* do was introduce into the Mythos affectionate little refer-ences to the more congenial of his writer friends. "The Atlantean high-priest Klarkash-Ton" is clearly Clark Ashton Smith; "Crom-Ya, a Cimmerian chieftan of 15,000 B.C." surely Robert E. Howard. And when such writer friends used his *Necronomicon* in their stories and in equally affectionate response in-vented imaginative and appropriate Mythos items, he would give them his seal of approval by using them in his own tales; for example, such shudder-some books as von Junzt's *Unaussprechlichen Kulten* (Howard), *The Book of Ei-bon* (Smith), *Cultes des Goules* by Comte d'Erlette (August Derleth), and Ludvig Prinn's hellish *De Vermis Mysteriis* (Robert Bloch).

These charming little in-jokes (as they'd be called today) went a bit fur-ther. In 1928 Frank Belknap Long (Belknapius) published in *Weird Tales* a quite powerful horror story "The Space-Eaters," wherein an heroic Lovecraft referred to simply as "my friend" and "Howard" is destroyed by supernatural forces. In 1934 Bloch did the same thing in his "The Shambler from the Stars." This time Lovecraft responded with one of his finer tales (and his last) "The Haunter of the Dark," wherein Bloch is depicted (and destroyed—a sort of accolade) as Robert Blake, author of such fantasies as "The Burrower Beneath."

I can personally testify to the siren power of the temptation to get into the Mythos game. I corresponded voluminously with Lovecraft during his last eight months and it had two profound effects on me: I was permanently inculcated with his scientific skepticism toward all branches of the occult and I became convinced that the supernatural horror story and the fantasy (and the sword-and-sorcery story) are as much high art as any other sort of fiction and demand a writer's best efforts—self-and-world-searching honesty, scholarship, and carefulest polishing. In my enthusiasm I not only completed some Lovecraftian poems ("The Demons of the Upper Air") and did a series of dark, starlit illustrations for his tales (splatter-stencils), I also inserted a few Mythos references into my Fafhrd-Mouser novella "Adept's Gambit" (not published until ten years later) and I wrote some 3,000 words of a modern-setting Mythos novelette to be titled "The Burrower Beneath."

Then Lovecraft died. I put away the fragment of novelette and soon wrote the Mythos-references out of "Adept's Gambit"; they clearly had no place there.

Elsewhere, inevitably and in a way quite properly, the Mythos game went on, after a decent period of mourning. In particular, Derleth began to write his many posthumous collaborations with Lovecraft, whose contributions to them were at most a brief entry (sometimes a sentence only) in his *Commonplace Book*. In so doing, Derleth began to systematize the Mythos to its artistic detriment, dividing its entities into good and evil powers, making the latter kindred to some degree to the fallen Satan (*I* believe that if they symbolized anything for the atheistical Lovecraft, it was the inhuman soullessness of the universe) and referring to some of the entities as elementals, although Lovecraft had warned of the vitiating effect of the jargon of occultism on horror stories.

New Lovecraft-smitten writers followed Derleth's lead, adding to the Mythos, further sytematizing but also complicating and recomplicating it. Whatever one thinks of this, it must be admitted that it added to the artistic task. The writer had not only to evoke supernatural terror, a *frisson* of cosmic dread, in the reader—never an easy job—he also had to know the Mythos, keep up with it, and manage it properly, a task which became more difficult with each passing year. While the only effective seal of approval was publication by Derleth's Arkham House.

This culminated in 1969 in Arkham publishing the two-volume *Tales of the Cthulhu Mythos*. By now even Derleth was feeling the strain and looking for an end to it all. He wrote in his introduction: "Certainly the Mythos as an inspiration for new fiction is hardly likely to afford readers with enough that is new and sufficiently different in concept and execution to create a continuing and growing demand."

Two of the five new stories in the book were by a young Britisher, Brian Lumley. "The Sister City" was a rather touching reworking of the theme of Lovecraft's "The Shadow over Innsmouth" with material from "The Doom That Came to Sarnath." A lonely young man's interest in the weird broadens from Scott's *Arabian Nights* to Howard and Lovecraft, until he rejoins his fishy forebears by way of an underground river in England. There is even a quaint charm in such statements as "They did not like the bump low at the rear of my bathing costume" and "The short tail which protrudes from the base of my spine is now not so much an oddity as an addition. . . ."

"Cement Surroundings" is more ambitious and rather less successful. Lumley creates a deep-dwelling fire elemental Shudde-M'ell, filling an empty spot in Derleth's occult pantheon, then relates how this entity burrows its way from Africa to England to destroy an archeologist, Sir Amery Wendy-Smith, who has stolen its eggs, which resemble huge pearls, and also destroy Sir Amery's nephew Paul, who is the narrator.

Well and good. But large-size deep-down high-speed burrowing monsters are extremely difficult to make plausible, and Lumley gives us very little assistance here, save for Sir Amery's dread of the London underground, reminiscent of the fear of subways possessing the narrator of "Pickman's Model."

The only scientific instrument in the story is a seismograph *without a solid base*, because the story requires it to be portable.

Lumley has overly hopeful ideas of the accuracy with which history keeps track of common people. A manuscript coming down from the Roman days of the emperors Commodus, "the Blood Maniac," and "the hag-ridden" Caracalla, describes how the building of Hadrian's Wall was disturbed by earth tremors and mentions a centurion named Sylvanus, "by the signet ring on one of its fingers, has been lately found beneath the ground (deep) where once stood a Vicus Tavern at Housesteads Fort."

Additionally, there is the occasional use of disturbingly grotesque words, especially in figures of speech as in (italics are mine): "I could feel upon my spine the chill, *hopping* feet of some abysmal dread from the beginning of time. My previously wholesome nervous system had already started to *crumble* . . ."

All of which brings us to:

THE BURROWERS BENEATH, by Brian Lumley, DAW, 1974, 95¢, 160 pages.

Building on "Cement Surroundings," Lumley has constructed a full-blown Mythos novel.

The two chief characters:

Titus Crow of London, British occultist, letter-writer, and profound student of the Mythos.

Henri-Laurent de Marigny, French diarist resident in London and profound student of the Mythos.

Most long supernatural horror stories emphasize and slowly build up an eerie landscape or locale: the Vermont woods, the British moors, the fog-bound streets of London, lonely and overgrown islands in the Danube, Transylvania, Wuthering Heights. Not so this novel, which goes directly to more vital matters. Let us examine continuously its first third, to sample its texture:

Nine letters from and to Crow—11 pages. In the longest of these a mine-inspector tells how he finds some "cave pearls" (Shudde-M'ell eggs) and a network of intrusive tunnels in a deep, disused coal mine. It is quite reminiscent of the Horta episode in *Star Trek*, where the deep tunneling is done by burrowing sentient rocks. Its language is curt and colloquial, but over-homely ("In and out of the old workings, lacing them like holes in Gorgonzola, those damned smooth-lined tunnels came and went. . . .") and depending on filmic comparisons ("I found myself thinking of giant moles! I once saw one of these sensational film things about just such animals.")

Crow and Marigny meet and talk Mythos—11 pages.

Crow naps while Marigny reads "Cement Surroundings"—21 pages.

Crow and Marigny talk Mythos—12 pages.

Marigny goes home to bed and thinks and dreams Mythos—9 pages.

And when Peaslee finally turns up twenty pages later, *he* talks Mythos—16 pages.

Now I am belaboring this, I know, but that is exactly what the book does.

To what does all this Mythos talk lead? Simply to a melange of purely science-fictional explanations:

"The 'magic' of the Elder Gods was in fact super-science."

The Shuddle-M'ell turn out to be "octopus things without heads or eyes, creatures capable of organic tunneling through the deepest buried rock with as little effort as hot knives slicing butter!"

"Shub-Niggurath . . . fertility symbol in the cycle."

"Azathoth is nothing more than a nuclear explosion, a destructive device against the CCD (Cthulhu Cycle Deities—F.L.)."

"We might try 'Ludvig Prinn on Azathoth.' . . . Prinn (*Mysteries of the Worm*, recall?—F.L.) had in fact specified a critical mass of highly fissionable material."

Finally, Azathoth is also "nothing less than the Big Bang itself, and to hell with your Steady-State theorists!"

"The magic of the Elder Gods was a sort of psychiatric science. . . . They implanted mental and genetic blocks into the psyches and beings of the forces of evil."

Now I submit that whatever this stuff may achieve, it does not engender in the reader "a profound sense of dread" or "a subtle attitude of awed listening." Instead, our ears are assaulted by crackpot scientists bellowing pseudo-profundities at each other.

This is not just science fiction, it is science fiction of the cosmic-war-of-the-gods sort which Lovecraft most detested. DAW honestly blurbs it as a "science fiction horror novel."

In the last fifty pages of the book there is more action, some of it on a world scale, though only as described in letters and in Marigny's notebooks and diaries. The CCD fight back, England is saved by a special delivery from the United States of a great number of five-pointed star-stones—soapstone-porcelain pentacles manufactured in Miskatonic's kilns and which activate the CCD's mental blocks, etc. However, the Mythos talk keeps on at least half the time.

The total result is certainly not a supernatural horror story. The Mythos was only *one* of Lovecraft's devices for arousing spectral fear, and he used it sparingly. Here it becomes almost the *only* device—in fact, the entire subject matter of the novel. It is on stage at all times, so how can the reader be afraid?

Well, that's enough top-blowing. Even Lovecraft found that the Mythos began to overload his stories; they got longer and longer. And really there's no way to keep something as specific as the Mythos remote and mysterious when you're using it over and over again.

And after all, it was Lovecraft himself who created the Mythos game, no matter in how marginal and trifling a fashion, so it can be interpreted that he gave other writers full leave to trespass. And no one—least of all another writer—can tell writers how to expend their creative energy.

[*Fantastic*, June 1975]

LOVECRAFT IN MY LIFE

I read Lovecraft's "The Colour out of Space" in the summer of 1927 when I was halfway through my senior year at Lake View High School in Chicago. It put me off *Amazing Stories,* which hitherto had pleased me with its tales in which science could solve almost any mystery. Its powerful pessimistic statement of mysteries beyond the ken of science and of the futility of life in the face of the inevitability of death depressed me for weeks. It frightened me as much and more profoundly than *The Cat and the Canary.* (In those days I eschewed *Weird Tales*—its stories were too morbidly uncanny for me. Even Fu Manchu scared me—all those centipedes and spiders!)

In 1932 or thereabouts, when I was rooming at Hitchcock Hall at the University of Chicago, I read in about two days most of Lovecraft's professionally published stories, preserved in magazine tearsheets by an acquaintance whose name I have forgotten. By then I was less afraid of the dark and had a new lifelong friend, Franklin MacKnight, with whom I shared a taste for the eerie. (He loaned me the October 1923 *Weird Tales* with "Dagon" in it and I lost it—even then a crime for which I am still deeply ashamed.)

All of the stories thrilled me. They matchlessly conveyed, I felt, the fascinating and strangely sparkling mysteriousness of the cosmos. My enthusiasm was uncritical; I recall thinking that "The Moon Bog," a trifle, was perhaps the best. I describe my reactions in more detail in "My Correspondence with Lovecraft" in *Fresco: The University of Detroit Quarterly,* Spring 1958.

At the Mountains of Madness surfaced spectacularly in the January, February, March 1936 issues of *Astounding Stories.* During a protracted spell of zero weather I read it aloud to my new-wed wife, Jonquil Stephens, who loved supernatural horror stories, in an apartment on Chicago's South Side which we occupied the first three months of our marriage. Later that spring, when we'd moved in with my parents in Beverly Hills, California, we read "The Shadow out of Time" in the same magazine and also reread "The Silver Key" and "The Whisperer in Darkness," which I bought in tearsheets from a Los Angeles schoolboy, Forrest J. Ackerman.

Then that summer Jonquil wrote Lovecraft care of *Weird Tales* and for the next half-year, until his death, there was much furious corresponding (described in my *Fresco* article). We also read "The Haunter of the Dark" and "The Thing on the Doorstep" as they appeared in *Weird Tales.*

It was an odd period. I was supposed to be humping myself to get publicity and jobs as a movie actor, but all my real interest was focused on an obscure pulp writer and my efforts to write stories more or less like his. In the summer of 1937 we met Lovecraft's young fellow fantasy writers Robert Bloch and Henry Kuttner, who had learned about me from Lovecraft, and later (when we'd returned to editorial work in Chicago) August Derleth, whose Arkham House published *The Outsider and Others* in 1939. I caught up on the Lovecraft I'd missed, especially his almost book-length essay "Supernatural Horror in Literature."

Back in Los Angeles in 1942, living in Santa Monica Canyon near the sea, Jonquil and I met (at the home of our neighbor Craig Rice, the popular mystery writer) Francis T. Laney, publisher of the early Lovecraft fan magazine *The Acolyte,* which had some fine Lovecraft covers by Alva Rogers. For it I wrote two short articles about Lovecraft's fiction. (Later Laney "gafiated" from fandom and wrote about it all in his remarkable, mimeographed, book-length *Ah, Sweet Idiocy!)* By then I had sold supernatural horror stories to *Weird Tales* and *Unknown,* especially my witchcraft novel *Conjure Wife,* inspired by Jonquil and a year teaching dramatics at Occidental College.

In the late 1940s, when I was (1945–1956) associate editor of *Science Digest* in Chicago, I combined my *Acolyte* articles with additional material into "A Literary Copernicus," published in *Something About Cats,* edited by August Derleth, Arkham House, 1949. This essay analyzes Lovecraft's style, interprets the Cthulhu Mythos as symbolizing Lovecraft's atheism and materialism, gives a brief history of Miskatonic University as Lovecraft developed it in his fiction, and argues that Lovecraft's chief original achievement was in shaping science fiction to the ends of supernatural horror. At the time it was my swan song to things Lovecraftian. My own interests then lay chiefly in other directions. I silently disapproved of Derleth's posthumous collaborations with Lovecraft and disagreed with his claim that he could mimic his style perfectly. I saw nothing good in *anyone* writing Lovecraft pastiches.

By that time Derleth had excerpted Lovecraft's letters to myself and Jonquil (for eventual appearance in the last of the *Selected Letters* volumes, still to come) and I loaned them to a seemingly serious scholar, whose name I have truthfully forgotten and who has not yet returned them. I didn't care much then—a measure of my mood.

It was about fourteen years until nostalgia hit me really hard. (The 1958 *Fresco* article was a minor attack.) Jonquil and I were living in the placid, well-to-do city of Santa Barbara with its solid Mexican-American subcommunity and I was, most appropriately, helping care for three cats and cleaning dead wood out of and bringing to new life a fantastically overgrown garden. I decided at long last to write a story in the *style* of Lovecraft, though with no references whatever to the Cthulhu Mythos. I still looked down on writers of *that* sort. The result was "The Black Gondolier," published in *Over the Edge,* edited by Derleth, Arkham House, 1964. The story must have meant a lot to me emotionally, because *after* writing it I explored its "almost impenetrable" Potrero Canyon, finding three easy ways down into it, tramping its entire length alone and in company, and surprising large mule deer there amongst its thickety vegetation. And I ended up living in its Venice (1967–1969).

Having indulged nostalgia once, I continued to do so. I was becoming philosophical about Derleth's Lovecraftian activities. After all, the man was keeping Lovecraft in print, forcing mainstream critics and libraries to pay attention to him, and putting into hardcover books for the first time writers as diverse as Robert Bloch, Ray Bradbury, A. E. Van Vogt, and myself. That he should have a lot of ego and behave very possessively toward Lovecraft and his works were inevitable.

Moreover, I was having to admit the great and continuing influence of Lovecraft on my life. I *was* writing supernatural horror stories from time to time. "The Dreams of Albert Moreland" (1947), "The Girl with the Hungry Eyes" (1949), *You're All Alone* (novel, 1950), "I'm Looking for Jeff" (1952), "The Hatchery of Dreams" (1961), "A Bit of the Dark World" (1962), "The Spider" (1963), "Midnight in the Mirror World" (1964), "Four Ghosts in Hamlet" (1965), etc. (The long gap here from 1952 to 1961 covers four years when I was writing almost nothing and then five when my entire output was science fiction.)

Moreover, during this period Lovecraft was one of the writers I would read just before going to sleep. The stories one reads this private way are one's true favorites, at least in my case, whatever ones one rates "best" publicly. The other writers were Clark Ashton Smith, Robert E. Howard, Montague Rhodes James, Poe, Robert Heinlein, Robert Graves, Eric Ambler, and Nigel Balchin. In this way I read most of Lovecraft's stories over and over again. (Later I came to include Dashiell Hammett, Ian Fleming, and John D. MacDonald.)

Finally, I was trying to heed Lovecraft's injunctions to be skeptical, research and choose words carefully, pay attention to organization and grammar, and polish the final product.

Again I began to write little articles about Lovecraft for the fanzines, culminating in "Through Hyperspace with Brown Jenkin" and "To Arkham and the Stars," both published in *The Dark Brotherhood*, Arkham House, 1966, the first an essay about the science-fiction element in Lovecraft's last stories (especially "The Shadow out of Time," *At the Mountains of Madness,* "The Call of Cthulhu," "The Colour out of Space," and "The Dreams in the Witch House," where Brown Jenkin is the familiar of the witch Keziah Mason), the second a whimsical short story of Arkham and Miskatonic as they might be today along with the professors who were Lovecraft's heroes, now grown old but as resourceful as ever. (It is a Cthulhu Mythos story, if you will, since the *Necronomicon* and the weird denizens of Lovecraft's Vermont, Antarctica, and the Australian desert are mentioned.)

During the same period Walter J. Daugherty, director of the Los Angeles Photography Center, made slides of photographs of Lovecraft and places associated with him and of almost all the illustrations, both published and unpublished, of his stories (including those of Alva Rogers, Rankin, and some of my own). A sound tape was made to be shown with these. I chose and read suitable short selections from the stories to go with the illustrations, while biographic material to go with the photographs was prepared and recorded by Samuel Russell, for the second issue of whose magazine *Haunted* I wrote the article, "The Whisperer Re-examined." After a few successful showings, the slides and tapes were stolen and have not been recreated.

In 1969 Jonquil died and I left Venice for San Francisco. In 1973 I wrote "Midnight by the Morphy Watch" (*Worlds of If,* August 1974), my first supernatural-horror story set in San Francisco.

Then early in 1974 Raymond H. Ramsay, author of the fascinating *No Longer on the Map* (Viking and Ballantine) and columnist and book reviewer for the *Berkeley Barb,* organized the Berkeley H. P. Lovecraft Society, which had several enjoyable informal meetings at the Berkeley home of the actress Jean Hauck, where we read stories by Lovecraft and others. My interest in the man was pleasantly restimulated.

There came simultaneously a spate of new Lovecraftian books, and so I devoted to them the next four Fantasy Books sections I write for the magazine *Fantastic.* The first of these (June 1975) sets down a short history of the Cthulhu Mythos and reviews *The Burrowers Beneath,* a Mythos novel by Brian Lumley. By some proofreader's oversight the short fifth paragraph was omitted from that review, so I give it here:

> Wingate Peaslee of Miskatonic University, American professor and profound student of the Mythos.

The following three sections in *Fantastic* will (1) briefly discuss the horror novel over the past fifty years and review an excellent collection of "best" horror stories; (2) review *The Watchers out of Time* by H. P. Lovecraft and August Derleth, discussing the pros and cons of the latter's very large influence on the Mythos; and (3) review Willis Conover's interesting, lively and off-trail *Lovecraft at Last* and L. Sprague de Camp's big biography of Lovecraft, which I recommend highly.

Coincidentally with Ramsay's activities, Douglas Palmer got me to do some story readings in Berkeley, became more deeply interested in Lovecraft, and launched this journal.

San Francisco is spectrally electrifying—Lovecraft would have loved her! Last summer her TV tower on Sutro Crest and her forgotten nearby hill— Corona Heights—stimulated me to write my first supernatural horror novel in twenty-five years, *The Pale Brown Thing,* just now finished.

And right now I'm in the midst of writing a fullblown Cthulhu Mythos novelette, having finally come around and decided it's permissible for me to do so—at least once.

[*Journal of the H. P. Lovecraft Society,* 1976]

AFTERWORD

Fritz Leiber is the only writer among H. P. Lovecraft's friends and colleagues who can be placed on an equal footing with him in regard to his literary achievement. Robert Bloch, C. L. Moore, and Henry Kuttner variously attained celebrity in the fields of mystery, horror, fantasy, and science fiction, but in the final analysis even the best of their work can only be regarded as high-grade popular literature. August Derleth, although he once was on the verge of attaining a reputation as a mainstream novelist, is now best known as the founder of Arkham House and the publisher of Lovecraft's own writings. But Leiber's prodigally bountiful work, spanning and intermingling the genres of science fiction, fantasy, and horror, is of such depth and substance as to transcend the limitations of genre to become an authentic contribution to American and world literature.

Lovecraft's influence upon Leiber's work is eloquently attested both in the actual stories included in this volume and in Leiber's writings on Lovecraft. It will be observed that the majority of tales that bear a heavily Lovecraftian stamp were written early in Leiber's career; it could well be asserted that Leiber—like Ramsey Campbell a generation later—largely exhausted the Lovecraft influence by the time he assembled his first collection of tales, *Night's Black Agents* (1947), in which several of the tales in this book were first gathered. But whereas Campbell, after he had written the crude Lovecraft pastiches that were included in *The Inhabitant of the Lake and Less Welcome Tenants* (1964), violently repudiated Lovecraft and began writing work of a markedly different sort, Leiber never felt the need to put Lovecraft at a distance. Possibly this is because of that brief but significant six-month correspondence in which he and Lovecraft engaged, a form of personal contact that Leiber remembered and cherished for the whole of his life; possibly it is because Leiber never produced the obvious, superficial Lovecraft imitations that have brought such disrepute to those many well-meaning hacks who have sought to "add" to Lovecraft's myth-cycle. From the very beginning, Leiber saw through the flamboyant externals of Lovecraft's tales to their inner substance; saw that what Lovecraft was really writing about was not a clutch of outlandish monsters but the much more terrifying conception of human beings facing a hostile or indifferent universe—or a universe that was hostile *because* it was indifferent—in which forces of incalculable power could engulf us at any moment, for reasons that we cannot comprehend or for no reason at all. Leiber's early articles, landmarks as they are in the interpretation of Lovecraft's work and thought, show clearly his grasp of the essence of Lovecraft's vision. If nothing else, they are among the earliest works of criticism to challenge what would, for decades, become the standard (but profoundly erroneous) view of Lovecraft's mythos, perpetrated by August Derleth—a view that would absurdly claim a naïve good-vs.-evil dichotomy between one set of cosmic deities (deemed by Derleth the Elder Gods, although they in fact have no existence in Lovecraft) and another (the Great Old Ones—Cthulhu, Yog-Sothoth, etc.). Leiber's quiet statement, uttered as early as 1945, that "Any attempt to analyze the Cthulhu Mythology, as employed by Lovecraft, into balancing hierarchies of good and evil, à la Zoroastrianism, is highly misleading" would by itself have spelled the downfall of the "Derleth Mythos" if it had been given the attention it deserves. But in any event, Leiber embodied that exact principle in his own creative writing.

It would be unfair to state that Lovecraft's impress appears only in Leiber's early work. Can it be denied that, in *Conjure Wife* (1953), the harrowing picture of witchcraft in the modern world owes something to Lovecraft's "The Dreams in the Witch House"? Even Leiber's purely science fictional works, as with those of Arthur C. Clarke, show clearly the influence of Lovecraft's two pioneering ventures into science fantasy, *At the Mountains of Madness* and "The Shadow out of Time." Far more work should be done in tracing the Lovecraftian thread throughout Leiber's voluminous output, just as Leiber's work as a whole deserves a more thoroughgoing analysis and explication, so that he can attain his proper place as a titan of twentieth-century American literature.

—S. T. JOSHI
Seattle, Washington

About the Editors

Ben Szumskyj was born in Australia in 1982 and in the short span of almost three years has become a member of a number of amateur press associations. These include REHUPA (the Robert E. Howard United Press Association) and the E*O*D (Esoteric Order of Dagon—the H. P. Lovecraft equivalent). He is also the founder of S.S.W.F.T, an a.p.a. devoted to the genres of dark fantasy/sword and sorcery and weird fiction. He is also the editor and creator of a forthcoming magazine dedicated to Robert E. Howard titled *Robert E. Howard: The Power of the Writing Mind*. Professionally, he is a qualified Librarian Technician in the Diploma of Library and Information Studies

S. T. Joshi is the editor of the corrected edition of H. P. Lovecraft's fiction, revisions, miscellaneous writings, and poetry and the author of such critical and biographical studies as *The Weird Tale* (1990), *Lord Dunsany: Master of the Anglo-Irish Imagination* (1995), *H. P. Lovecraft: A Life* (1996), and *The Modern Weird Tale* (2001). He has prepared editions of such weird writers as Ambrose Bierce, Arthur Machen, Algernon Blackwood, Robert Hichens, Donald Wandrei, and others. He is the editor of *Lovecraft Studies* and *Studies in Weird Fiction*.

Made in the USA
Monee, IL
30 October 2020